Topsell, Edward.
The fowles of heauen.

Edward.
vles of heauen.

The Fowles of Heauen

or

History of Birdes

By Edward Topsell

a yeare for twentie yeares together, and sometimes
enfeebled to write thorough a paraliticke righte
arme, euen from my birth, yet for the benefitt
of my Nation, and the glorie of him, to whome
the glorie of all works, witts, and natures are due,
did vndertake the taske, and five or six yeares
agoe finished the Histories of Beasts & Serpents
in some fashion, to my great trauaile, & charges
diuulginge them to the world to the Stationers great
proffitt, and my owne empouerishinge. Ffor
(I beseech your Lordship, giue me leaue to say it) they
are the men which are rich by makinge schollers
poore: and schollers are poore by makinge them riche.
And if I had respected either reward from Patron
or Printers, I had vtterly failed, and neuer gone
further. But my first resolution beinge whetted
on, by the daylie verball encouragements of some Lords,
Gentlemen, and men of worth, hath preuailed with
me, to vndertake the third part of liuinge Creatures,
The fowles of Heauen, and this greater then both
the former by a third parte. The first fruicts
whereof I most humblie here offer to your Hon:
viewe not printed, but written, neither soe exactly
written, figured, and compiled, as I could wishe;

But

[The author's hand in the Dedication, page 4]

The Fowles *of* Heauen *or* History *of* Birdes

By EDWARD TOPSELL

Edited by
THOMAS P. HARRISON
Emeritus Professor of English
The University of Texas at Austin
and
F. DAVID HOENIGER
Professor of English
Victoria College, The University of Toronto

Austin : The University of Texas

Library of Congress Catalog Card No. 75–635320

Published for The University of Texas at Austin
by the Humanities Research Center

Distributed by the University of Texas Press
Austin 78712

Manufactured in the United States of America
by the Printing Division of the University of Texas

Contents

Illustrations

Preface

THIS BOOK is an abridgement of an abridgement, which as such was uncompleted and, never published, now exists as a unique manuscript in the Henry E. Huntington Library (El. 1142). Edward Topsell had found Gesner briefer than Aldrovandi so that when, after completing and publishing his histories of quadrupeds and of serpents according to the Swiss naturalist, he turned to the huge new work on birds by the Italian he found himself swamped before actually getting well started. The bird names commencing with the first three letters of the alphabet required 248 leaves, and the copying and coloring of 124 woodcuts was no mean task for his artist. Unfortunately for readers interested in wild birds, the third letter included COCKE, which, involving the whole of Aldrovandi's Book XIV, *De Pvlveratricibus Domesticis,* Topsell condensed into twelve chapters, still almost 100 leaves. But fortunately for readers here these chapters on domestic "dustscatterers" are omitted. For doing so there are two excuses. Despite their possible importance for economic reasons, their exclusion permits concentration upon wild birds alone, affording opportunity to assess the state of ornithology in the early seventeenth century. Besides, Aldrovandi's entire Book XIV has recently been translated with full apparatus by Professor L. R. Lind (*Aldrovandi on Chickens,* University of Oklahoma Press, 1963), who describes it as "the most fascinating single collection of lore ever assembled on the domestic rooster and hen." The headings of Topsell's dozen chapters are quoted in the present Notes, and as it turns out, a handful of birds described by Topsell here are wild birds, which hence are included in the present chronology.

The *Fowles of Heauen* treats the third and last part of living creatures. Topsell's only planned addition to his Latin source was an assembly of English coats of arms bearing figures of birds he had described. Here was a clear bid for sale of the work he initially expected to publish. Quailing at the task yet to be done, he presented this sample of his handiwork with its colored birds pasted onto the proper leaves to Lord Ellesmere. The sequel perhaps we shall never know; a guess is ventured in the Introduction (see pp. xxii, xxiii). One can hope that the parson of Aldersgate would approve of the ultimate realization of his hopes in this fragment which treats the third and last part of living creatures.

For the Renaissance a treatise on birds was more philological than ornithological. In preparing this manuscript for publication, the editors have tried to measure up in both fields. The most time-consuming job has been to run down the quotations—ancient and modern—and to identify their authors, the results to be seen in the Notes and Catalog of Proper Names. As amateur ornithologists, the editors have added to the Notes occasional information in keeping with the bird under discussion, and in the identifications have sought to avoid misstep. If Topsell was puzzled, it would be over the Latin of his original, not over the identity of a bird. Even naturalists like Aldrovandi were forced often to describe "new" species brought to them discolored and dirtied by fowlers or found in poulterers' markets. Passing afterwards through the hands of Topsell and his illustrator, small wonder that many birds were inaccurately described. Sixty-one of the colored drawings are reproduced here and appear at or as near as possible to the places in the MS where they were pasted onto the sheets. Reproduction is not attempted when the subjects are either very badly executed or entirely unidentifiable.

Editorial Procedure

The text of the manuscript has been transcribed with minimal changes. In general the original spellings of Topsell and his scribes were retained. Capitals, however, have been introduced (except for "ff") when lacking at the beginning of a sentence; and contractions have been expanded: "o^{r}" for *our*, "w^{t}" for *with*, "ꝑ" for *per*, "m̄" for *mm*, etc. The minims "u" and "n," which appear indiscriminately throughout have been silently normalized according to usual spellings as have also the frequent variants in proper names: "Kiramides" for Kiranides, "Athaeneus" for Athenaeus and the like. Obvious scribal errors we have attempted to rectify. Unintentionally omitted words have been supplied in brackets. The spellings of foreign bird names we have often corrected by reference to Gesner, from which source they were transmitted via Aldrovandi to Topsell and his scribes. In punctuation, the manuscript was followed as consistently as possible, deliberate changes being introduced only when the original might have obscured the meaning for the modern reader. But as fullstops, commas and mere inkspots are often hard to distinguish in the manuscript, precision was impossible. Virgules in the MS are usually conveyed as fullstops or as colons. Secretary and italic scripts have been exactly reproduced only as far as the top of folio 21v, the end of the Prolegomena, which pages were possibly written by Topsell himself. For the rest, we have confined italics to foreign bird-names and quotations, though in the manuscript most of the proper names and the entire sections devoted to coats of arms are similarly set off.

In transcribing the classical and other quotations out of Aldrovandi, Topsell frequently not only abridged but took liberties with the text, changing the number of nouns and verbs, introducing new words, changing their order, or omitting words which were yet included in his subsequent translations. We have corrected quotations only in those instances where Topsell's text is either grammatically indefensible or so garbled as to destroy the sense of the original. His scribes had small Latin and less Greek. Here as elsewhere, departures from the manuscript text are duly listed among the Variant Readings. In checking the Latin quotations, the editors have relied chiefly upon the Loeb texts but with frequent resort to sixteenth-century editions. All the Greek quotations except the first appear as transliterations. The original Greek has been restored to the text in correct form and Topsell's often confused transliterations transferred to Variant Readings.

A few unfamiliar words are glossed at the foot of the page. The Notes proper provide tentative identifications and other ornithological comment, but are largely devoted to the location of passages quoted from classical, medieval, and Renaissance authorities, with superscribed letters and numbers in the text as guides for the reader. Variant readings (Appendix I) include the more important textual changes, chiefly in spelling and punctuation. Three other Appendices comprise a tentative identification of birds in the author's projected list, D–Y, intended to complete his volume, a short glossary of heraldic terms to clarify the often abbreviated jargon of the College of Arms, and finally a catalog of the proper names of persons and places. A Bibliography of Primary and Secondary sources may be found at the end.

Acknowledgments

Acknowledgment is due first to the Henry E. Huntington Library not only for permission to reproduce *The Fowles of Heauen* but for extending its facilties to the editors in working on the MS and later in providing microfilm and color slides. Of the staff Miss Jean Preston gave expert help in deciphering difficult passages and in identifying the three hands in the manuscript. Other libraries generous in affording their facilities include the William Andrews Clark Memorial, in Los Angeles, the Newberry and John Crerar, in Chicago, the Houghton and Widener at Harvard, the Folger Shakespeare Library, and the university libraries at Toronto, Illinois, and Texas. At the Folger Dr. Louis Wright and Dr. James G. McManaway offered valuable advice concerning editorial method, and Dr. Giles E. Dawson kindly read parts of our manuscript. For assistance in correcting and amending classical quotations the editors are grateful to Mrs. Ernestine F. Leon. Ornithological problems were submitted to two experts, Mr. Edgar Kincaid, of Austin, Texas, and the Reverend Edward A. Armstrong, of Cambridge, England; both have been generous. To Mr. VanCourtright Walton, who saw the book through the press, both editors are grateful for his patience as for his keen eye in detecting errors.

The work of Professor Hoeniger has been facilitated by a Fellowship awarded for 1964–65 by the John Simon Guggenheim Memorial Foundation. His share in the preparation of this book has involved chiefly three areas: Topsell's text, the glosses, and the variant readings. By consulting the manuscript at the Huntington, he solved many textual problems, which included the question of the various hands. Professor Harrison is responsible for the other editorial matters.

Introduction

The Manuscript

The Fowles of Heauen by Edward Topsell (1572–1625) is extant in a unique manuscript (El. 1142) in the Henry E. Huntington Library, which acquired it from the Bridgewater House Library in 1917. This famous collection was begun by the nobleman to whom Edward Topsell addressed the treatise, namely Sir Thomas Egerton, Lord Keeper since 1596, and created Baron Ellesmere and Lord Chancellor in 1603. Bound in vellum, the MS comprises 248 leaves, 8¾ inches by 12⅞ inches, each margin ruled in red ink. One hundred and twenty-four bird figures, executed in ink and water color, ranging in size from about two by three inches to about five inches square, are pasted onto the pages above their respective descriptions.

Three hands can be detected in the manuscript. The first comprises the Dedication and the Prolegomena, that is, up to the top of folio 21v. Despite his complaint in the Dedication about his "sometimes . . . paraliticke righte arme," this hand may well be Topsell's own. The writing is large and neat and shows a predilection for flashy capitals. Except for "printed" heading and quotations, the mode in the Dedication is italic, while in the Prolegomena it is mixed secretary, with quotations and proper names set off in italics (see frontispiece and p. 24). Excepting folios 74r–101v, the rest of the manuscript belongs to "my writer," Topsell's main scribe (see p. 192). Usually employing secretary, he resorted to italics for quotations, proper names and several sections devoted to coats of arms. Though mainly clear, his writing is not evenly legible because of a tendency towards overcrowding, frequent use of long upstrokes, and heavy inking which has sometimes penetrated to the reverse side of the page. The third hand, of the middle folios, is by contrast always clear, the words well spaced, yet distinguished by sparse punctuation, or none at all (see p. 120). Assuming then, that Topsell himself penned his Dedication to Lord Ellesmere together with the Introduction or Prolegomena, the author prepared a rough manuscript to be copied. From inadvertent omissions, repetitions and misreadings, copy from manuscript rather than from dictation can be inferred.

Edward Topsell and His Work

Edward Topsell was born in 1572 at Sevenoaks in Kent. In 1587 he entered Christ's College, Cambridge, where four years later he graduated B.A., and presumably proceeded M.A. in 1595 (J. Peile, *Biog. Register of Christ's College*). After taking his first degree Topsell began preaching in 1592 at Hartfield in Sussex (Byrne, pp. ix–x). Afterwards he held a succession of livings, sometimes in plurality: Framfield and East Hoathly in Sussex, 1593–98; Datchworth in Herts., 1598–1601; Syresham in Northants., 1602–1608; Mayfield in Sussex, 1605–1606; Hartfield, 1609; East Grinstead in Sussex, 1610–15; and finally Little Bytham in Lincolnshire, 1618–24. In 1604 he was appointed perpetual curate of St. Botolph's, Aldersgate, where he was buried in 1625.

Topsell was twice married. By the unknown first wife he had a son, Abel, born in 1602, and a daughter, Mary, who in 1617 married Thomas Grice of Littleton, in Middlesex. In 1612 the father married Mary, widow of Gregory Seaton, a stationer of St. Ann and St. Agnes, Aldersgate; apparently she did not survive her husband. Topsell's will was drawn up in 1624 and the next year proved in the Prerogative Court of Canterbury. To Abel, "he left £300, to come to him at the age of thirty, together with his books and a moiety of his linen and household stuff. Mary and her husband were made his executors, and he left bequests, amongst others, to his brothers Richard and Robert, and his cousin Thomas Topsell" (Byrne, p. xi). Abel, too, became an ordained minister of the Church of England, first at Peterborough and later in Ireland

(Venn), and tried unsuccessfully to get into print a last scientific translation from his father's hand.

Like William Turner before him and Gilbert White, Edward Topsell was both clergyman and naturalist. His numerous livings reflect the man's persistent efforts to win patronage. First he penned religious tracts: *The Reward of Religion*, 1596, 1597, 1601, 1613 (S.T.C. 24127–30), addressed to Margaret Baroness Dacres; *Times Lamentation or an Exposition on the prophet Joel*, 1599 and 1613 (S.T.C. 24131–32), the first edition addressed to Sir Charles Blount, Lord Mountjoy, "the meane of my preferment," the second to Henry Montague, first earl of Manchester, Sir Thomas Fanshawe, and George Alington; *The Historie of Adam* by Henry Holland (S.T.C. 13587), edited and completed by Topsell and dedicated to Richard Neile, Dean of Westminster. *The Householder or Perfect Man*, 1609 and 1610 (S.T.C. 24125–26), dedicated to Richard Sackville, Earl of Dorset, and his wife, Lady Anne Clifford, who had recommended him to the vicarage of East Grinstead, and, listed by Greg (p. 90) and Arber (III, 199), *Two Soliloquies . . . to comfort good Christians*, 1610, are the last of Topsell's comments upon Scripture written "to condemn 'atheisme, paganisme and papisme'—particularly the last-named—and to inculcate a solid and pedestrian virtue" (Raven, p. 219). *Two Soliloquies* is extant only in a single manuscript, the Address to the Reader signed by Edward Topsell, in the William A. Clark Library of the University of California, Los Angeles.

But today Topsell is universally known as the author of *The Historie of Fovr-footed Beastes*, 1607, and *The Historie of Serpents*, 1608. Both, in illustrated folio, were printed by William Jaggard, printer of Shakespeare's First Folio. In 1658 the works were reissued together with a translation of Thomas Moffet's *Insectorum . . . Theatrum* by John Rowland.* By providing English abridgements of Conrad Gesner, Topsell recognized and made accessible in English the most recent authority on two divisions of the animal world. The first two volumes of the *Historiae animalium*, on viviparous and on oviparous quadrupeds, had appeared at Zürich in 1551 and 1554; Gesner's studies of birds and of fish intervening (1555 and 1558), the fifth and last volume, on serpents, was issued posthumously in 1587. For the book on quadrupeds Topsell depended solely upon Gesner; for the second treatise he added

* This edition has recently been reprinted as *The History of Four-Footed Beasts and Serpents and Insects* with a brief introduction by Willy Ley. 3 vols. New York, Da Capo Press, 1967.

to Gesner much matter from Moffet's *Insectorum . . . Theatrum* (1634, a work largely by Thomas Penny), which he consulted either in manuscript or in an earlier printed version now lost, and a few notes from *De Differentiis Animalium*, by Edward Wotton (1552). To Topsell quadrupeds are first in importance because they came "next before the creation of Man, as though they alone were appointed the Ushers, going immediately before the race of Men" (Dedication to Neile, Dean of Westminster). *The Historie of Serpents,* he states, is "to the work [on quadrupeds] an ornament, and to the History a more ample declaration . . . And although I cannot say that I have said all that can be written of these living Creatures, yet I dare say I have wrote more than ever was before me written in any language." And this is no idle boast. Between the conclusion in this treatise and the index Topsell promises: "Pergamus igitur, (summo fauente numine) si vobis placet ad tertiam de viuiparis historiam, quae est de volatilibus caeli: tenues licet sunt fortunae meae, infinitaeque tum paupertatis, tum pastoralis Euangelicique officii curae me quotidie circumstant affliguntque, non tamen quiescam, . . ." These cares prevented fulfillment of his hopes to complete the projected work on birds.

"Five or six yeares" later, he states in the incomplete MS, that is, in 1613–14, Topsell had finished one-fifth of a work on "the third part of livinge Creatures," *The Fowles of Heauen,* the whole, he estimates, to be "greater then both the former by a third parte." The completed portion, "the first fruicts," Topsell presented to Lord Ellesmere, needing perhaps at this point support to enable him to complete his enormous task, or perhaps realizing the impossibility of achieving the whole. But the quest for new patronage proved unsuccessful, for no part of the manuscript is known to have reached the press.

After Edward Topsell's death in 1625, however, the Stationers' Register contains evidence of an attempt to publish what seems to be either the present MS or a translation of Gesner's *De avium natura,* volume III of his *Historiae Animalium.* On November 16, 1630, an entry in the Stationers' Register records "a Booke called Gesner his thirde booke of birds in English" (Arber, *Transcript,* IV, 242). Though the entry lacks the author's name, Greg (*Licensers for the Press, . . .* p. 90) rightly assigns it to Topsell. As indicated, Topsell's two published works follow Gesner's volumes issued 1551, 1554, and 1587. Naturally the projected work on birds would consist also of an abridgement of Gesner's *De avium natura*, 1555. But *The Fowles* is an out and out translation, not from this work, but from the *Ornithologiae* by Ulysse Aldrovandi, the three volumes issued in 1599, 1600, and 1603. If these huge tomes came late to his notice, Topsell's shift to Aldrovandi as his new authority would be understandable.

Whatever the nature of the work, later record suggests that the above entry was unauthorized. On March 30, 1631, "Upon a Complaint by Mr. Topsell Minister and a Reference from my Lords Grace of Canterburye under a Petition Delivered directed to the Master Wardens and assistant, . . . they so ordered That the Copy called Gesner his Third Book in English entred unto them shoold be crossed out of the Book and made no Entrance" (*Records of the Court of the Stationers' Company,* ed. Jackson, p. 226).* Presumably the "Mr. Topsell Minister" is Edward Topsell's son, Abel, who had inherited his father's books and who now secured a cancellation of the anonymous and probably surreptitious entry of "Gesner his Third Book in English." Then the following year, it seems that Abel Topsell had sold rights to the manuscript to Thomas and Richard Cotes and one Leggat, for on July 16, 1632, under their names a new entry appears, "by vertue of a noate under the hand of master Topsell and by order of a Court a booke called *Ornithologia* or the History of Birdes and foules" (Arber, *Transcript,* IV, 281).† But as no issue of this work is known, the question of its relation to *The Fowles of Heauen* remains. Hence only the uncompleted *Fowles* survives as testimony to the author's ambition to treat "the third part of livinge Creatures."

The Fowles of Heauen

The index for the completed part of *The Fowles* comprises forty-three kinds presented alphabetically from Alcatraz to Cuckoo. The subjects are depicted in colored drawings practically all of which were copied from the crude figures of Aldrovandi. Topsell's descriptions follow this authority closely, even when the Italian depends upon Gesner, Belon, various travellers, even English authors. His only additions are, as will appear, from Luis de Uretta, a Spaniard, and, for a handful of American birds, from his English friend Dr. Thomas Bonham.

Some of the forty-three kinds are species, like Brambling and Cuckoo, but most are genera as recognized by Aldrovandi. Buzzard includes three species, Bittern four, Blackbird fourteen, Bee-eaters two, Birds

* My colleague, Professor William B. Todd, kindly called attention to this entry.

† For this suggestion I am grateful to Dr. James G. McManaway, of the Folger Shakespeare Library.

of Paradise five, Canaries three, Buntings five, Choughs five, Curlew two, Cormorant sixteen, Cock twenty-four (ten domestic species, Heath-cock, Moor-hen, "Woolly" and "Hairy" Cocks, and eleven monsters), "Cocke of the Wood" four (male Capercaillie, Blackcock, Greyhen, and female Capercaillie), Crane four, Coot three, Crow four. Add the American birds and ten "strange birds without figures" (mostly from Uretta) and the total comes to well over a hundred. To appeal to his more gentle readers, the author concludes the accounts of many of his birds by appending the names of English families who carry in their coats of arms the subject just described.

In his Dedication the author had stated that his birds were "neither soe exactly written, figured, and compiled, as I coulde wishe, but as I coulde; and yet fitted with all that I had read or observed, after manie miles trauailes and two yeares labours about these, and an hundred more, which I have readie beside me to be pressed or suppressed at your Lordships pleasure." The end of the MS includes a list of this "hundred more," D through Y, which "together with the former may have their Natures emblazoned to the worlde . . . to expresse in them the wonderfull workes of God . . ." In his desire to include every bird name he knows, in this Projected List Topsell has compiled a new total of one hundred seventy-six English names with their Latin equivalents.

Renaissance Ornithology

The work of Aldrovandi and Topsell can be seen in proper perspective only against the background of the past. Ornithology was just beginning to be recognized as a separate science, although authorities on the subject, almost invariably physicians, were usually much more involved in the study of plants, whose lore they sifted and explored for practical purposes. The need to identify European plants in terms of Greek texts greatly increased the importance of compiling new herbals and commentaries upon Theophrastus and Dioscorides. As for animals, quadrupeds, fish, and insects provided even newer fields for every natural scientist; specialization was for the distant future. Among comprehensive studies of natural history, the following have proved useful for present purposes: Lynn Thorndike's *A History of Magic and Experimental Science,* especially volume VI, "The Sixteenth Century Naturalists," chapter 38, pp. 254–297; Canon Raven's *English Naturalists from Neckam to Ray*, especially "Edward Topsell," chapter 13, pp. 217–226; George Sarton's *Appreciation of Ancient and Medieval*

Science During the Renaissance, Lecture II, "Natural History"; and Wightman's *Science and the Renaissance.* The best history of ornithology is still the Introduction to Alfred Newton's *A Dictionary of Birds,* pp. 1–120. For Aldrovandi, especially for bibliography, Cermenati's "Ulisse Aldrovandi e l'America" and Lind's *Aldrovandi on Chickens* are pertinent. Further information is contained in the Bibliography.

Aldrovandi and, before him, Gesner sum up the vast lore on birds which had accumulated since Aristotle. Accordingly, Aldrovandi's Catalogue of Authors required three folio-size leaves, each containing three full columns of names. Gesner's name is omitted, perhaps through jealousy. Though occasionally named in the text, which draws copiously from his *De avium natura,* usually Gesner is termed merely "Ornithologus." The Preface to the initial volume designates Aldrovandi's prime authority: "Plinius maxima laude dignus est, qui melioribus authoribus optima quemque decerpens integram naturalem historiam triginta septem libris contexuit, . . ." The compiler Pliny thus takes precedence over Aristotle, whose interest by contrast lay in assembling provable fact gained through experiment and travel; and accordingly, those chapters of Pliny which relied closely upon Aristotle are scientifically valid for this reason. Given the lapse of a few centuries, "Aristotle seems merely the name of a remote and legendary sage; . . . in science as in philosophy and religion, the achievements of Greek and Classical Roman civilisation had been transmuted into a traditional lore in which a recognisable nucleus of original authority could scarcely be disinterred from the mass of glosses, accretions, syncretisms, and moralising which pious imagination and fear had imposed upon it" (Raven, *English Naturalists . . .*, p. 6).

Two centuries after Pliny Aelian set the pattern for the future in dwelling upon the admirable behavior of animals in contrast with man: The Diomedean birds, originally Greeks, pay no attention to foreigners, "but at the approach of a Graecian strainger, *diuino quodam munere ab hiis auibus aditur,* . . . with a friendlie spreadinge their winges abroade, doe embrace them, . . ." (29v). Not only in kindness but in intelligence animals point the way, for example, in the cure of diseases by seeking the right herb, a prominent theme in Aldrovandi's Prolegomena as in Topsell's. New editions of Aelian at the hands of Peter Gyllius (Lyons, 1533) as well as of Gesner (Zürich, 1556) prove the continued influence of the *De Natura Animalium.* In spirit the attitude of Aelian to the animal world did not significantly differ from that of the Church Fathers whose hexaemeral writings were not neglected by Aldrovandi; parallels between Aelian and the Hexaemeron of Basil the Great have been noted (Thorndike, I, 322). Analysis of words is the chief theme of Festus, the Roman grammarian, as of the later Isidore of Seville in *Etymologiarum libri XX*, the major authority in the greatest of the encyclopedias, *de Proprietatibus Rerum,* by Bartholomew the Englishman of the thirteenth century (Thorndike, II, 54, 401–435). And aside from the Christian tradition represented in these authors, Aldrovandi drew heavily upon the Roman poets and historians: Ovid and the less known Antoninus Liberalis for delightful accounts of metamorphoses, Virgil and Horace for picturesque descriptions involving birds. But this gives only a sketchy sampling of authorities whose range may be perceived only by a glance at the Notes or at the text itself.

Advance in the study of birds can be measured in terms of the sloughing off of "hieroglyphics, emblems, morals, fables, presages," as John Ray put it, to be replaced by the results of observation alone. Prior to the sixteenth century the figure of Albert the Great in the thirteenth century stands out as one who, recognizing the importance of experiment, repudiated those accepted "truths" which observation did not support (see Thorndike II, ch. 59, esp. pp. 528–548). Contemporary with the work of Albert but without apparent influence is the huge treatise on falconry by the Emperor Frederick II, *De arte venandi cum avibus,* which includes also much direct information on migration and habits of various passerines. Aristotle is almost the sole authority recognized by Frederick, who even so did not hesitate to contradict the Greek. The translation of Aristotle by Michael Scot was made by order of the Emperor. Such an approach to nature is not found again for three centuries.

A just estimate of the work of Aldrovandi requires a more immediate awareness of the writings of a small group of Renaissance scientists, to whom observation had taken on a new meaning.

In 1544, in Cologne, appeared two works on birds—*Dialogus de Avibus*, an unfinished treatise by Gybertus Longolius, a young Dutch doctor who had died the preceding year, the second, *Avium Praecipuarum, quarum apud Plinium et Aristotelem mentio est, brevis et succincta historia* . . . by the English William Turner, who having edited his friend's work based his own commentaries on the two great classical authorities. The importance of these pioneers in the science of ornithology is evident in the readiness with which they are quoted by Gesner and, consequently, by Aldrovandi. Their method and attitude are more significant than their conclusions, and should be summarily noted.

Longolius deplores the dearth of bird studies and the weakness of the ancients in this phase of natural history. Instead, he writes, bookish people have taken over. He attacks the ignorance of natural philosophers, "grammatici," who in explaining classical authors are oblivious of living birds and rely only on "fiction and the testimony of poets." The real problem, he states, is the definition of species, "avium singulas species," and this can be approached only through field observation. This is a new note the significance of which cannot be overstated. Longolius' uncompleted treatise had proceeded only through the "pulveratrices," the dust-scatterers, mainly gallinaceous birds, which involved him in much of the practical lore from Columella and Varro on domestic fowls, including incidentally the best description to date of the turkey, later quoted by Gesner. But many wild birds find place: grouse, capercaillie, bustard; larks, thrushes, sparrows. The most remarkable aspect of Longolius' work is his study of birds in different parts of their range and habitat. Aristotle had commented on the fact that the notes of the partridge vary in different locations. In the Renaissance Longolius was perhaps the first to note the effect of climate and habitat on the appearance, behavior, and above all the song of birds of the same species. In this he anticipated the outlook of modern taxonomists who recognize certain populations as distinctive sub-species.

Longolius' speculative approach is not characteristic of Turner, intent mainly upon identifying species named in the vernacular, English, Dutch, or German, with the birds named by classical authors, a purpose which enabled him to incorporate his own observations. He used the Latin text of Aristotle in the edition of Theodore Gaza, included in separate printings, Venice 1476, 1492, 1495, etc., as well as in numerous *Opera omnia* (see further Sarton, pp. 53–54). Much of the work involved discriminating two or more species covered by the older generic names and supplying English local names. Thus study of classical texts led Turner to observation as the necessary means of identifying birds. In this field "nondum satis explorata" he proceeds cautiously, often by conjecture, stating as his method "inquirere quam pronunciare." Like Longolius, he is willing to take issue with Aristotle, for example, on the transmutation of one species into another: robins do not change into redstarts. As in Longolius, even when there is mistaken identification of a bird mentioned by Aristotle, Turner provides clear descriptions of living birds, their appearance and some details of habitat and food.

In presenting birds Turner follows the alphabetical order, yet at the end he presents a useful classification based broadly on anatomy, food, and habitat. Though, as he writes, this represents only a transcription of notes on the subject, a classification based on such criteria marks the inception of real interest in the living bird.

In his recent *History of Birds* (p. 20) James Fisher refers thus to Turner's work: "If we remove from his 130 recognisable birds those which are domestic or were not seen in Britain, we are left with 105 species . . . of which no less than thirty-seven have appeared as British birds in no previous document, manuscript or printed, that I have seen or heard of." Turner's little book is the work which Longolius noted as most needed. Turner distinguished various species of buntings, finches, tits, which had previously been included in general terms, and recorded his observations of behavior and habitats. Other birds erroneously regarded as different species he recognized as male and female. The Notes appended to our edition bear frequent reference to Turner, whose treatise Topsell knew almost exclusively in the pages of Aldrovandi, who in turn followed Gesner (see n. 4, p. 258; n. 30, p. 260; et seq.).

The work of two other Englishmen of minor importance should not go unnoticed. A brief compilation entitled *De Differentiis Animalium* (Paris, 1552) by Edward Wotton included a section on birds (Bk. 7, chapters 119–153, pp. 103–136) in which the author has assembled much from the past. Termed "the first 'scientific' work on animals by an Englishman" (Wightman, II, 270), this work had been more exactly described by Gesner: Wotton "teaches nothing new but gives a complete digest of previous works on the subject" (Enumeration of authors, in Gesner's *De Piscibus*). As Raven remarks (p. 41), "He read widely, copied his extracts diligently, and fitted them together ingeniously." Finding his name in Aldrovandi and referring to him as "our Dr. Wotton," Topsell appropriates several passages with slight evidence of direct familiarity.

John Caius, known largely for his treatise on English dogs, is also the author of *De Rariorum Animalium atque Stirpium Historia*, issued in London in 1570 (for extracts see Appendix, *Turner,* ed. Evans; for full account of Caius see Raven, *English Naturalists,* pp. 138–153). His influence derives chiefly from the fact that he was another of the many friends of Gesner, to whom he had sent most of his materials on natural history together with drawings, both of which appear in the appropriate volumes of the *Historiae Animalium.* An example of his direct approach to bird study is his rejection of the time-honored notion that the Osprey, which Caius carefully describes, possesses one taloned foot and one webbed. Had Edward Topsell read this description he would perhaps have been less ready to include the "Amphibion" with its mythical feet (see p. 118).

Both Caius and Turner illustrate the increasing contacts between scholars, which included correspondence and the transmission of specimens and drawings. The third volume of Gesner's *Historiae Animalium*, namely, *De avium natura* (Zürich, 1555), bears frequent evidence of Gesner's reliance upon other naturalists (see, for example, quotations from Turner's letters in *Turner*, ed. Evans, pp. x–xiv). Yet here too, as elsewhere, Gesner is philologist more than field naturalist. Textual study outweighs his own observations. He often relies on the reports of others, frequently quoted without comment. For Gesner the definition of a species and the identification of its vernacular name were to be arrived at in the study rather than in the field.

The name of Pierre Belon is famous for his skeletal drawings of man and bird, placed opposite one another as a demonstration in comparative anatomy. In his *Histoire de la Nature des Oyseaux*, published in 1555, Belon devotes chapter 23 to the subject of anatomy and its importance for bird study; "Il fault prendre peine pour acquerir science," he exclaims. Belon's emphasis upon the internal structure of birds doubtless drew Aldrovandi's attention to this feature, for in a letter written in 1558 the Italian lists twenty-eight birds which he had dissected (Cermenati, p. 321). The importance of this phase of study will be discussed later.

Belon grouped birds according to habitat: birds of prey—diurnal and nocturnal, water birds of marsh and shore, birds of wood and field—large and small, the latter divided into worm- and seed-eaters. In this, too, Aldrovandi followed suit, though he objected to Belon's emphasis upon French bird names. Everywhere Belon's approach is direct, unpedantic, and happily neglectful of the lore of the past. His work was freely appropriated by his Italian successor, though not always with acknowledgement.

Aldrovandi and Topsell

In 1565 Conrad Gesner died of the plague in his forty-ninth year. Ulisse Aldrovandi (1522–1605) was seventy-seven when in 1599 appeared the first twelve books of his great work on birds. The two further volumes followed in 1600 and 1603. He lived to assemble a huge library, to found a botanical garden, and to complete a huge herbarium and museum of objects of natural history, bequeathed to the University of Bologna, where he taught botany and medicine. As Sarton remarks (p. 115): "At the end of the Renaissance, the main need was a vast survey such as was provided by Gesner and Aldrovandi." To Edward Topsell belongs the honor of anglicizing the work of Gesner on quadrupeds and serpents and, in part, that of Aldrovandi on birds. As he saw it, his task was to be faithful to his authority and, in abridging, to retain the spirit and major aspects of the Latin text. This resolve was doubtless enhanced by a sense of his own ignorance of birds. Topsell lost no opportunity to impress upon the reader that birds were a wonderful work of Almighty God. Generally speaking, those passages expressing this sentiment constitute the translator's major addition to his original.

In his Preface to the Reader Aldrovandi declares that his treatise is both useful and pleasing. For the first he has provided for each bird "Aequiuora, Synonyma, Genus, Differentiae, Locus, Cognominata, Denomenata"; for the second, "Moralia, Vsus, Mysteria, Hieroglyphica, Historica, Symbola, Numismata, Icones, Emblemata, Fabulae, & Apologi"; and the reader will find precepts "Ethica, Oeconomica, Politica . . . militaria . . . medica." Nothing ancient, medieval, or modern wherein the bird is named does he consider extraneous to his purpose. As the English parson confronted the task of abridging this huge tome, it is little wonder that he concluded only three letters of the alphabet. The title of Topsell's work reflects the extent to which he attempted to embrace the encyclopedic purposes of his original.

With his religious background Topsell sets down his own theological justification for the study of natural history:

> Adams soule had a double knowledge, one *naturall* as yt was considered onelie inseparably reasonable: the other *caelestiall* as yt was assisted, associated, and endued with the extraordinarie, and seperable grace of God. Both these waies was he obliged to the knowledge of the workes of god in livinge Creatures; and both these wayes are we allso tyed of necessitie to looke into their natures, as the obiects of our reason, and to make vses of them, as the gifte of our *Creatour*. . . . with the eyes of grace and illumination to admire the wisedome, bountie, and greatnes of our Saviour. Howe needfull this point is may better appeare by the universall *Theorie* of the Scriptures, and their secret natures wherby in the one they are in a sort incorporated into our faith, and in the other into our lifes action both naturall, politicke, and artificiall. . . . In a word, the scriptures cannot

be rightlie vnderstood without the knowledge, and historie of fowles (6v–7r).

Thus Nature and Grace are inseparably connected, and thus on this firm basis scriptural authority encouraged and laid the foundations for later truly scientific study.

In a minor particular Topsell differed from his authority in choosing the alphabetical order of presenting his birds. Following the example of Belon, Aldrovandi had grouped birds according to habitat—land and water, a recognition at least of one criterion in classification. The alphabetical order had been universal. Even Gesner, for his work on fishes, followed this method on the ground that his work was "grammatical rather than philosophical." Similarly for his birds, Acanthis, finch, with which his volume begins, is followed incongruously by Accipiter, hawk. Both Gesner and Turner were chiefly concerned with names, their aims grammatical. Topsell declares: "I will proceede in Alphabeticall method leaving the knowledge of euery byrd to the description rather then raunge them vnder their proper kindes wherein men many tymes are deceaved, and the readers troubled." Accordingly, "their proper kindes" appear in his treatise grouped together accidentally, as when he presents consecutively all the supposed members of the genera of blackbirds, buzzards, and cormorants.

Topsell sees no reason to doubt that Aldrovandi has followed the best authorities, "multorum grauissimorum virorum testimonia," a phrase that occurs with variations constantly. One can remember that from the example of Aristotle himself natural·philosophers considered, first, the repute of the man, and, second, the basis for believing that which he has stated. To a considerable extent the advance of science can be measured in terms of a reversal of the order of these two criteria.

The effort to include all the authorities usually precluded the possibility of discriminating between them. Ambrose finds place beside Aristotle, an Irishman named Octavian is quoted along with Albertus. At times one is held up over another, yet usually it appears sufficient to the author to have included all.

For example, the vexed question of the generation of the Barnacle Goose—from wood or from sea water, from eggs or spontaneously from shells—requires that the author quote each authority, then observing the weighted scales deliver his own opinion (33v–34v). Hector Boece, William Turner, Alexander Galloway, "a man of greate learninge and judgement," others whose names "I might adde herunto" confirm Topsell's own experience, delivered at length, that Barnacles are bred of sea water. Against such overwhelming authority is the testimony of Albert, Aeneas Sylvius, Belon, and "The Hollanders," denying that Barnacles are bred otherwise than from eggs, like other fowls. To such "it may be aunsweared, that myce ingendred out of putrefaction doe afterwarde couple together and begett other: so may Barnicles engendred out of wood begotten by the humour of the Sea, by a naturall instinct fall to breede by copulation, . . . euen as the first created fowles which God made out of the waters" (34v). It is reasonable, accordingly, to believe that bats, too, "are also engendred out of putrefaction by a certain excretion of the troubled and infectious aer" (37v). Such is the weight of the testimony "multorum grauissimorum virorum." But when, for instance, Antonio Pigafetta, a mere crew member on Magellan's voyage from the East, declared that Birds of Paradise possessed feet, Aldrovandi is prompt in labeling him a liar.

Characteristically Topsell devotes thirteen folios to the Alcatraz, about which so many marvelous stories had accumulated; the commonplace Brambling is given short shrift: "As the bird is litle so there is litle to be said of it . . . ," he remarks. Among the chapters on domestic fowl he finds place for eleven "monsters"—cocks or hens with four feet and the like. Even the new and promising interest in the birds of Africa and of the New World arose less from a desire to extend knowledge of new species than from a habitual emphasis upon the fantastic.

With real interest in birds brought from remote lands to Italy by seafarers (the Curassow, for example) as also those described in the pages of Ramusio's *Navigationi et Viaggi*, Aldrovandi contributed significantly to the knowledge of new species: Peter Martyr on the fishing habits of the New World (Brown) Pelican, Gerrit de Veer on the nesting of the Barnacle Goose. Topsell includes much of this, but goes out of his way to add some fantastic birds gleaned from the pages of Luis de Uretta, a Spanish Dominican, who, though he had never traveled to Ethiopia, professed to describe that land.* These birds of his, declares Topsell, are "the wonderfull worke of Almighty God":

> by admiration whereof wee that are his reasonable creatures for whose sake all these thinges were created, might be stirred vp so much more to magnifie his Greatenes . . . for the newe reuelations of olde Creatures,

* For information about Uretta the editors are grateful to Dr. Nettie Lee Benson, Librarian of the Latin American Collection, the University of Texas at Austin.

whose demonstrations were lost in the losse of paradise and are nowe recouered againe in the tyme of our Redemption: wherein I desire the Readers to stay themselues from scornefull detestacon of their narrations, because their rarities may seeme incredible to them that haue not well scanned the power of God, . . . believinge that all the worlde is in Englande, and that there can be nothinge vnder the cope of heauen which is not visible at home in our oune nation (69v–70r)

As camels, elephants, parrots, and peacocks are now believed in, so "some of these shall growe more credible, familiar, and better knowen to vs and our posteritie." So, beginning with the "Suhayo" (70r), proceeding to the Ruc and others, adding a vulture, the "Nesir," from Leo Africanus via Ramusio, Topsell concludes with the West Indian "Cocuie," a firefly become a bird, and "Amphibion," the two last from Peter Martyr or Gonzales de Oviedo, both in Ramusio.

No Englishman more clearly than Richard Hakluyt recognized the importance of the Spanish explorations and reports of the New World; in 1587 at Paris appeared his Latin edition of Peter Martyr, *De Orbe Novo Petri Martyris . . .*, and both this work and that of Oviedo, *Summary of General and Natural History of the Indies* (1526), were available in English before the close of the century. Topsell says that he received a drawing of a Virginia bird from Hakluyt, a towhee, and from him presumably he obtained also drawings of nine further North American birds. These colored drawings, it has been found, were copies traceable to the first artist of Virginia, John White. Together with descriptions of these birds provided by Thomas Bonham, this windfall represents Topsell's only significant addition to the birds he found in Aldrovandi. Dwarfed beside the bulk of White's historic and artistic accomplishments, it stands as a slight and accidental addition which together with the fantastic accounts from Uretta constitutes Topsell's only original contribution.

Except when one remembers their purpose as pleasant diversions, Aldrovandi's stories of metamorphoses, his emblems from Alciati, and the like appear incongruous beside careful details of anatomy accompanied by drawings representing the results of dissection. Yet as Thorndike observes in another context (VI, 292): "It should be realized that there is no necessary correlation or variation in inverse ratio between an individual's positive scientific achievement on the one hand and his acceptance or rejection of superstition, occult notions and trust in magical procedure on the other hand." The influence of Belon upon Aldrovandi in regard to dissection has been mentioned, and though, unlike the Italian, Topsell reproduced no anatomical cuts, he faithfully and frequently translates relevant passages describing them (36v, 37v, 46r–v, 47r, 49r, 51r, 52r, 87v, 95v, 96r, and 208v). The classification of birds had, since Aristotle, rested upon the slender basis of habitat, with occasional reference to bill, to feet, and to food. For the future a recognition of the greater importance of structure marks the true beginnings of classification. As a corollary the study of the relation of form to function prepared the way for an understanding of evolution.

Accordingly, although neither Belon nor Aldrovandi—nor, least of all, Edward Topsell—recognized the significance of anatomy in classification, their work on birds alone clearly anticipated that of John Ray, the greatest of seventeenth century naturalists. The *Ornithologia,* assembled with Francis Willughby, who died in 1672, was revised and published by Ray in 1676, in English translation two years later. Ray has little patience with the old ornithologists who wrangle over bird names: "Especially seeing if by immense labour it might at last be found out, by what Names every Species was known to the Ancients, the advantage that would thence accrue would not countervail the pains" (Preface). Still, Ray was obliged to make full use of Aldrovandi in identification and description; and, by no means irrelevant, in the same spirit Ray's *The Wisdom of God Manifested in the Works of Creation* (1691) dwelt upon the theme of adaptation. Separated by three quarters of a century, the kinship of Aldrovandi (and Topsell) to John Ray may be glimpsed through their researches in bird anatomy. The European pelican, Topsell's "Alcatraz," offers a hint (24r): "The skull full of braynes but the bones light, white glisteringe and without marrowe, whereby almighty God so provided, that hereby this fowle mighte flie and swymme much lighter." To afford the Bittern a great voice the trachea "contynued without divarication" (54v–55r); in the Crane, too, it is "fastened to the fleshe, as deepe as the ribbes without dependence on the intralls, . . . And this is the true cause why their voices be hearde, before their bodies be seene" (208v). Aldrovandi devoted special attention to examination of differences in the trachea or windpipe of various birds, later to become a key feature in classification; he terms the trachea the "aspera arteria." Dissection of one of the ducks appears thus in Topsell (92v):

the *aspera arteria* or throat-bole, neere the top is very narrowe, but toward the bottome it waxeth broader & thicker, where it is as thicke as the litle finger, being tyed with bones on both sydes & a greate muscle & from thence passe two other muscles to the fore ribbs. Before their diuarication or partinge to the lungs, there is a vessell shaped like a colts hoofe swell-inge in substaunce on the lefte side toward the heart in which there are two passages like windowes broade & marked with this letter A. couered with a thinne & transparent skinne. And from the inferiour or lower partes of this boanye vessell beginne the separation of the arterye, which from the poynt of the tounge to the lungs was aboute ten ynches long.

In his dissection of a scoter, in 1684, Ray thus noted the absence of this "vessell shaped like a colts hoofe," the labyrinth or ampulla of the trachea (quoted from Raven, *John Ray . . .*, pp. 317–18):

In this bird, and in some other of the sea-ducks, which are much under water, that they want that vessell, or ampulla, situate in the very angle of the divarication of the wind-pipe, which, for want of a better and fitter name, we are wont to call the labyrinth of the trachea . . . I am somewhat to seek about the use of this vessel, and I think it were worth the while to examine what sort of birds have it, whether the males have it or in some the females also. I observed it in Mergus cirratus longiroster noster or the Dun-diver and that very large and extended by very strong bones; and yet I thought myself to have sufficient reason to judge that bird to be the female of the Merganser; but I dare not be confident that it is the female because of the labyrinth.

John Ray's *The Wisdom of God* concerns the relation of form and function, a demonstration of "the adapting all the parts of Animals to their several uses." Few parts escape the author's attention: the legs, wings, and tail of swallows, the oil glands from which birds squeeze out "an oily Pap or Liniment." The toes of Woodpeckers "stand two forwards, two backwards, which disposition (as *Aldrovandus* well notes) Nature, or rather the Wisdom of the Creator, hath granted to *Woodpeckers,* because it is very convenient for the climbing of trees" (p. 105). Such observations, he has remarked at the outset, "stir up and increase in us the Affections and Habits of Admiration, Humility and Gratitude," or in the words of Edward Topsell, "with the eyes of grace and illumination to admire the wisedome, bountie, and greatnes of our Saviour." More than any other single book *The Wisdom of God* "initiated the true adventure of modern science, and is the ancestor of the *Origin of Species* or of *L'Evolution Créatrice*" (Raven, *John Ray,* p. 452). A study of Aldrovandi in the abridgement of Topsell strongly suggests that the continuity of which Raven speaks extends backwards as well as forwards, that at least a select group of distinguished naturalists of the Renaissance may not be neglected in a study of the adventure of modern science. Topsell adds little of value to Aldrovandi's volumes on birds which Ray knew intimately in their original Latin. Had *The Fowles of Heauen* been published, it would have popularized the subject through the pious eyes of the translator but affected the serious study of birds very little.

The Fowles of Heauen

or

History of Birdes conteyning their

true and liuely figures with the whole
description of theire natures in readings Gram̄aticall Logicall Philosophicall, Theologicall Hyero-
glyphicall Medicinall and ciuill.

Together with the Coate armes
of noble Persons who beare
in theire Eschutcheons
Fowles or any part
of a Bird.

The first Parte.

[ɪv—blank]

[2r]

To the Right Hon: the Lord Elsmere Lord chauncellor, of England one of his highnes most Hon: priuy Councell the most noble patron of all good Artes and Father of the Church and Common Weale.

All happines bee Continued in Earth and glory be prouided in Heauen.

Right Honorable Lord, and that which is more, Right Blessed of the Lord, for you may say with comfort the words of *Deborah.* Iud: 5. In the daies of Iael, the high waies were vnoccupied, & the Trauellers went thorough by-wayes. The Townes were not inhabited but decayed; there was not a speare, or sheild amonge forty thousand of Israel.[a] The learned Pastours could not gett into Churches by the high-waies of free Donation, but by the by-wayes of Simony & Corruption. Amonge 40000. English there was not the Sheild of Faith or speare of Hope and Charitie vntill you came vp a Iudge in England. Since which time (praised be Iehouah) vnder the broad seale of this Nation so manie learned men haue had free ingresse into Temples, that 40000 at the least haue bin gayned by their preachinge to marche after your Lordshipp and them against our Churches foes to the Kingdome of Heauen. Amonge whome my vnworthy self, commended by that most reuerend Father, [2v] ArchB. Whitgifte vnto your L[ps] fauour at the time of your Honors first and happy entrance to that high Office and Charge you haue soe worthily sustayned, was one and therfore eternally obliged to pray for your longe lastinge life in earthly honor & euerlastinge glorie & heauenly mansion. And pardon me (my good Lord) if I speake a word or two in this my rude gratulation vnto your greatnes concerninge my life, livinge, writinge, and boldnes, while I presume to offer my studies in priuate to your honorable Iudgment before I diuulge them abroad to the view and censure of all men.

Concerninge my life, I was and euer haue bene whipped with the smart of tongues, and haue not wanted accusations because I stood not vpon the fauors of Lordes or Ladies; yea vnto your owne most noble selfe haue I bin so traduced, y[t] if your great Integritie had not giuen leaue to so poore a Subiect as my selfe, to answer, & wash away my Aduersaries accusations, I must needs haue perished in good opinion, and lost the fauour that I most honour aboue all the Lordes of Great Brittaine, for with your Lordship, *Æquum est cognoscere, et ignoscere.* And my comfort was y[e] wordes of *St. Augustine* against *Petilian;*[b] *malam Conscientiam non sanat laudantis præconium, nec bonam convulnerat convitiantis opprobrium.* The best stay of livinge, which by Gods mercie I enioy, I must next after him giue most humble thankes to [3r] your Lordshipp, whose onelie hand hath bin my Saviours Instrument wherby I haue had *oleum pro opera Nephalium sacrum: Ex phelleo venire,* and fearfull modestie, not vnthankfull forgettfullnes hath hitherto hindred my publique acknowledgment for the same. ffor as I am in your Lordshipps bookes *per lapsum,* so would I (if I had durst, or if I might anie waies haue encreased your greatnes Honor, or content thereby) more often consecrated my Bookes vnto your Honor *pleno iure pertinentes.* But not for any satisfaction *diis, parentibus, patronis non sufficiens reddi potest compensatio*; and therfore as a Philosopher not able to make retaliation vnto his freind Diotimus Carystius prayed so will I. *Deus tibi largiatur tantum, quantum animo cogitas, et cupis.*[c]

Ælia. Lib. 4

My writings, especiallie of the livinge Creatures haue nowe passed in the world to a *non plus.* I considered that almost all Nations had bred some learned men, that with industry, labour and charges, & especially for the glorie of the Grand Creatour, and the benefitt of their Countrymen, had pressed and written somethinge both of the figures & natures of Gods liuinge Creatures. Although I were the least able of 5000 in England (beinge oppressed in suits of Lawe, & therby empouerished, charged with preachinge an hundred times [3v] a yeare for twentie yeares together, and sometimes enfeebled to write thorough a paraliticke righte arme, euen from my birth, yet for the benefitt of my Nation, and the glorie of him, to whome the glorie of all workes, witts, and natures are due, did vndertake the taske, and five or six yeares agoe finished the Histories of Beasts & Serpents in some fashion, to my great trauaile, & charges diuulginge them to the world to the Stationers great proffitt, and my owne empouerishinge. ffor (I beseech your Lordship, giue me leaue to say it) they are the men which are rich by makinge schollers poore: and schollers are poore by makinge them riche. And if I had respected either reward from Patron or Printers, I had vtterly failed, and neuer gone further. But my first resolution beinge whetted on, by the daylie verball encouragements of some Lords, Gentlemen, and men of worth, hath preuailed with me, to vndertake the third part of liuinge Creatures, The fowles of Heauen, and this greater then both the former by a third parte. The first fruicts wherof I most humblie here offer to your Hon: viewe not printed, but written, neither soe exactly written, figured, and compiled, as I could wishe; [4r] but as I could; and yet fitted with all that I had read or obserued, after manie miles trauailes and two yeares labours about these, and an hundred more, which I haue readie beside me to be pressed or suppressed at your Lo[ps] pleasure. I am bold to presume of your Honors leasure to reade these thinges, for I read this historie of Saint Iohn the Evangelist in *Fulgosus,*[d] He delighted manie times to play with a tame quaile, and one day a yonge man espyinge him at this recreation, founde Fault with the holie man for an action of such leuitie. The Apostle perceuinge the yonge man had a bowe at his backe (for a readie answer) bad him shoote twice or thrice at a marke he appointed him, which the yonge man did accordinglie, first bendinge his bowe, & then after he had discharged it twice, or thrice he did vnbend it againe. The holie man asked him the reason of lettinge downe the bande. He answered, *Vt cum eo vti necesse fuerit agitationi, non ineptum inveniat.* Euen so, replied the Euangelist, *Nos honesto studio interdum relaxamur, vt maioribus viribus orationi, et ieiunio sufficere possimus, Quod fieri non posset si semper eodem tenore viueremus.* Pardon me I beseech you my good Lord allso, for that with Pharaohs Butler I do so late remember Ioseph. [4v] My former labours, nor these are worthy of your Patronage. Yet, *Insuaues esse solent foetus primi, amoeni magis, & iucundi subsequaces.* The Swan singeth sweetest when he is old, and whitest, and peraduenture my last labours wilbe sweeter then the former, howsoeuer I am sure the subiect is more excellent. And therfore both labour and Author do cast themselues at your Honors feete.

Semper in oblita repetam tua munera mente,
Et me Posteritas audiat esse Tuum.

In all deuotion, seruice, and gratitude.
Edward Topsell.

[5r–v—blank]

[6r]

The dignitie, necessitie, & delightfull vses of this Historie of Fowles

Of all livinge Creatures Man is the youngest. Before him were made the same day *Beastes,* and *creepinge thinges* and before them *fowles and fishes.* This order the Allmightie obserued, to make the waters before the earth: and the waters to bringe forth livinge Creatures before the Earth. *Simplex præcedit composito generatione, Compositum simplici corruptione.* ffor in Philosophie that which is simple goeth first to generation, and that which is compounded goeth formost to Corruption. Therfore the waters more simple then the earthe do first bringe forth *fowles* & fishes, for yt is trulie saide *Aqua & pennatorum, & pinnatorum mater, vtrisque participant nam sunt & pisces volantes, et volucres natantes,* and these corrupt sooner then the waters. Afterwards the earth brought forth beastes, and creepinge thinges immediatlie before Man was created because perfection rested in the last. ffor even as when *Alexander* had builded and finished his Cittie *Alexandria,* and fullie peopled the same, he put therinto last of all his owne picture to remember them of their ffounder and foundation. So Allmightie God havinge finished this whole world and stored yt with all kinde of Creatures like people to inhabite the same, last of all he made Man, and put into him his Image, and so placed him in this world givinge him authoritie over all other precedent Creatures of Earth and water. Accordinge to the methode of the *Philosopher** which [6v] teacheth to beginne a *nobis notioribus* I haue allreadie in some sorte described both the figures, and natures of *Beastes* and *serpents,*† and nowe by the

* *the Philosopher* Aristotle (so throughout)

† Reference to *The Historie of Fovr-footed Beastes,* 1607, and *The Historie of Serpents,* 1608

mercie of God assistinge, haue attempted the like labour vpon the *fowles of Heaven,* because in order of Creation they were next made and therfore in the methode of my pen are next to be handled. And because the Prologue of a Booke is like a faire porche or shop windowe that sheweth what is within, my preface shalbe prefixed in the front to teache the reader that wanteth skill both the vses, and necessitie of this *History.*

And first of all to beginne with the Necessitie, without which neither the vses are profitable nor dignities honorable. Allmightie God havinge made them, subiected them to man, as a knowen subiect to a knowne *Lord.* Neither is he a worthie owner that knoweth not his possession, as he is accompted a seelie Shepherd that knoweth not the brand sett vpon his owne sheepe. In the Creation Gods image appeared in man by two eminent faculties, *Knowledge* and *righteousness*: whereunto we are restored by *Christ*: soe as the Lordes sheepe must weare these marks, first as they are men, because difference of knowledge maketh difference of Men. Secondly as they are iustified because difference of Righteousnes maketh difference of Saints, and as one starre differeth from another, so doth the glory of one Saint exceede anothers by the surpassinge measure of *righteousnes.* But Adam's soule had a double knowledge, one *naturall* as yt was considered onelie inseperably reasonable: the [7r] other *cælestiall* as yt was assisted, associated, and endued with the extraordinarie, and seperable grace of God. Both these waies was he obliged to the knowledge of the workes of god in livinge Creatures; and both these wayes are we allso tyed of necessitie to looke into their natures, as the obiects of our reason, and to make vses of them, as the gifte of our *Creatour.* Neither may we behold them with Curiositie onelie of naturall contemplation, as did the *Philosophers,* but with the eyes of grace and illumination to admire the wisedome, bountie, and greatnes of our Saviour. Howe needfull this point is may better appeare by the vniversall *Theorie* of the Scriptures, and their secret natures wherby in the one they are in a sort incorporated into our faith, and in the other into our lifes action both naturall, politicke, and artificiall. ffor the scriptures doe make frequent mention of fowles both in the good and evill parte touchinge both their substances in the letter, and their actions in the figure: makinge some of them cleane, and some vncleane, and yet by and from the natures of the vncleane enforceth cleane actions: and by the natures of the cleane dehorteth*

* *dehorteth* dissuades

from vnlawfull things. In a word, the scriptures cannot be rightlie vnderstood without the knowledge, and historie of fowles. As for example, when yt mentioneth the lawe of cleane, and vncleane fowles *Leuit: 11.* Noe man livinge can rightlie interpret those places without some philosophicall knowledge of those which are forbidden or tolerated for foode. Wherupon yt shall not be inconvenient nor of evill sounde in this our preface to expresse the speculations of Divines about these fowles, remittinge [7v] the literall prohibition of their flesh to the actions which their natures followe, not befittinge the people of God. You shall not eate (saith the *Text*) the *Eagle*, and why saith the *Glose,*[e] the *Eagle* soaringe aboue the cloudes signifieth God. You shall not eate him therfore least you be *Theophagi,* Eaters of God. Againe the *Eagle* is a proude bird, and it becommeth the people of God not to feed vpon proude meates, least their soules should be infected with the distemper of their bodies. *You shall not eat the Goshawke* and *Osprey*, and why saith the *Glose*, they are cruell, and devourers of other small birdes; therfore you shall not eate them, least by their example you learne to be vnmercifull and cruell allsoe. *You shall not eate the Kite or Glead*, and whie saith the *Glose*, It is a treacherous Creature, and watcheth aduantage against the weake and younge Chickens, and *God* abhorreth treacherie, for more noble is the nature of the Bald-Buzzard which will never take a small bird in ye nest or sittinge still on the earthe or on a bough, but flyinge in the aire. *You shall not eate the vultur,* because yt killeth nothinge, but liveth vpon dead carrions which yt findeth. There is nothinge worse beseeminge a man then to live in idlenes vpon the labours of others, and they allso are to be abhorred which wish the deathe of their freindes, that they might possesse their goodes. *You shall not eat the Raven*, because beinge sent out of the *Arke* he never came againe but rested himself amonge the Carions that remayned after the flood, nor the *Ostriche* because yt hath winges and flieth not, soe must hypocrites be [8r] avoided and idle persons as vncleane, and vnfitt for ye kingdome of God. They lay their *Eggs* in the sand, and hatche them not. Men must not onely beginne a good worke but contynue yt vnto perfection. *Nor shall you eat the Nightcrowe* which ys sharpe sighted in darknes, but blinde in the light. *God* approueth not such people as are wise in the affaires of the world which are but darknes, but very fooles in matters of *Heauen,* which are the onely daylight of happines. Nor the *Seamewes* because they liue amphibiouslie on lande and water. Such signifie their vncleanesse which hold with the hare and runne with the hound, being like the Company they frequent, and makinge but one Element of *Good* and *Euill*. Nor the *Hawke* which havinge nothinge to eate taketh away the life of small birdes to sustaine hir owne. Nor the *Owle* because yt is a fowle lovinge darkenesse. Nor y^e^ *Cormorant* because yt doth never labour but for the Belly. Nor the *Swanne* because yt seldome vseth the winge, nor the *Alcatraz* or water *Pellican,* because like the Covetous yt hordeth vp more meate then yt can devoure. Nor the *Redshanke* because nothinge ys good in yt, besides the beautyfull outsyde. Nor the *Lapwinge* because yt breedeth in myre, and counterfayteth mourninge while yt singeth. Nor the *Storke* because they eate *serpents*. Nor the *Batt* for their doubtfull shape betwixt a bird and a mouse. Nor the *Partridge* because to avoide the *Hawke* yt stoopeth too neare the Earth. *God* cannot abide them which denie him thorough feare of Tyrants, And so of the residue, wherby yt is apparant, that they were not onely forbidden *propter vitiosum succum*: for their evill nourishment (for what is better then a *Partridge?*) but *propter mystica mala*; [8v] for some misticall evills adhærent to their nature, which Allmightie God forbad his people, because he will not allowe them soe much as the apparance of Evill.

Againe, on the other side, we reade in particular the prayses of manie birdes which we cannot vnderstande vnlesse we first vnderstand their actions by their naturall knowledge. Why did the Lord allowe the sacrificinge of a payre of *Sparrowes* and a payre of *Turtles,* but to signifie his Sonnes *Charitie* in the *Sparrowe*, and his *Chastitie* in the *Turtle?* Whie are the *Quailes* allowed for suche desired, and delicate meate, yet they eate the seedes of poysonfull herbes. Soe doe *Divines* and all good people heare, and see the evills of this wicked world, and are never the worse: when they fall into the *Sea,* thorough wearines, they holde vp one winge instead of a sayle, and the other they vse like an oare to stirre forward, and supporte their Bodies from sinkinge. Such (say the *Diuines*) is the Case of penitent soules, for they could not chuse but perishe betwixt shame, and sorrowe for their sinnes in the bitter and dangerous sea of this world, yf yt were not for the one winge of faithe which they hold vp towardes *Heauen* and the other of repentance which keepeth them vp, and stirreth them forward to saluation. The *Storke* is *auis piissima*; a bird of *God*, and therefore although forbidden to be eaten yet commended by the *Prophet Ieremy** vnto the people of God to imitate because they obserue their seasons. Nowe who can tell their

* *Prophet Ieremy* Jeremiah 8.7: "Yea, the stork in the heauen knoweth her appointed times; and the turtle and the crane and the swallow observe the time of their coming; but . . ." (A.V.)

seasons [9r] without knowledge of their naturall story? But herein allso they resemble the people of God because the *Crowes* are their friendes, and fight for them against all their naturall Enemies. Euen soe All-mightie God makethe evill persons, Tirants, and *Pagans,* yea sometymes the evill Angells to worke the benefitt, and defence of his chosen. The *Swallowe* is spoken of in the scriptures because of manie vertues; they are temperate, and never sitt but flie, and eate: they are industrious in buildinge their nestes, and instructinge their younge ones not to defile yt. They are fearfull to the *Eagles,* for though their bodies be small yet is their mouth or bitinge venemous. When they growe blinde they let themselues blood in the winge & therewithall annoynt their eyes to their recovery, wheruppon *Saint Austen* maketh this note, *pœna aperit oculos, quos culpa clausit*, Punishment maketh men remember that which Prosperity made them forgett. It were too longe to speake of the *Pellican*, the *Doue*, the *Cocke*, the *Hen*, the singing *Birdes*, the *Rauens* that fed *Elias* and such other vpon whose mention dependeth some notable point in scripture. I will end them all with that sayinge of the princely *Prophet Dauid. Psal: 111. The workes of the Lord are great, & ought to be sought out of all them that feare him.*

And to conclude the necessitie of their knowledge with one discourse and so proceede to their dignitie, and vses. The *sacred scripture* doth manie tymes make mention of *sooth-sayinge,* as *Deut: 18. Gentes istæ quarum possidebis terram augures & Diuinos audiunt. Tu aliter a Domino Deo institutus es.* Saith *God* [9v] to *Israel: The Gentils whose land thou shalt possesse doe heare their soothsayers, and Diviners: but thou art otherwise instructed of the Lord thy God. Balaam* could say that *God would blesse the People bycause, non est augurium in Iacobo*: there was noe soothsayinge in *Israell*: and manie tymes in the *Prophets* we read of *Sooth-sayers* and *Diuiners,* whome we cannot vnderstand vnlesse we vnderstand the *Historie of Birds.* Yt shall not be tedious to me, nor vnprofitable to the Reader to discourse a little vpon ye knowl-edge hereof, that soe he may vnderstande the originall progresse, and vanitie of this damned thinge in holie writt, which are not to be founde in every *Comment glose,* or *exposition. Non enim scire, sed facere malum, malum est.* Yt is evill to doe ill but not to knowe yt onely.[f]

Birdes (as shalbe said afterward) by a naturall instinct, because they liue by their senses without reason, or because of their imbecillitie doe perceiue externall affectiones and changes of the aer before other Creatures: which beinge obserued by superstitious antiquity, they grewe from the opinion of a naturall, to a divine and heavenly prognostication of events and accidents foreshewed by the flight of Birdes, euen in suche workes as proceede from the secret prouidence of *God* or the operation of Men. This is a wonderfull folly because the knowledge of such events dependeth not vpon naturall causes as do *cold, heate, drought, moisture, winter,* and *sommer,* but vpon divine revelatione. As for example by the flyinge of [10r] birdes they would coniecture of warres, of wares, of iourneys, of Merchandise, of particular battells, and combates, and allmost of every worldlie matter, as yf God had made birdes of his privy Counsell to declare his secret will vnto vs, or our actions and their successe did stande vpon noe other termes, then the movinge of a bird in the aer. Although it were granted that our externall actions were in our power, yet we see by daylie experience what occurrences and impediments are interposed betwixt them, and their most expected issues, wherof neither the witt of man, nor ye winge of Birdes could ever forethinke or foreshewe the contrarie. Yt seemeth that this sooth-sayinge learninge (I should say folly) began in *Italie*, and was called *Hetruscorum disciplina* the learninge of the *Hetrurians** which had spread yt selfe into all Nations as farre as the *Græcian Hellenisme* or *Idolatry* even vnto *Canaan* and *Egipt,* which occasioned the Lord by his *Prophetts* so wonderfully to forbid yt to his owne people ye Children of *Israell.*

The Professors of this Art were called *Augures* and *Auspices,* of *Auis garritus,* and *aues specere,* or *inspicere*: and yt contayneth two kindes: *Oblatiua,* thinges accidentally offered, and *Imperatiua* or rather *Impetratiua,* thinges desired and commaunded. The first kinde contayned both *fausta* and *nefausta, good* and *euill,*[g] and the vnlucky evill diuinations were called *piacularia, Cliuia,* & *caduca.* These Augurismes were made by ye flight, by the voice, and by the feedinge of birdes. When ye birdes gave divination by flyinge alofte in the aer they called [10v] them *præpetes,* and by flyinge alowe or neare the ground *Inferæ.* By the voice they were called *Oscines,* of *canendo ore,* and the yssue thereof they called *osmen,* or *omen.* The Augurisme by their feedinge they called *Tripudium solistimum*; and *Tripudium,* saieth *Tully,* was first called *Terripauium,* feedinge vpon the earthe, and *solistimum a solo,* the soile. This last was not a voluntary but *coactum augurium,* an enforced and constrayned divination, because they coniectured by Chicken killed by famine within their Coopes or by lettinge fall their meate out of their mouthes as they did hastily devoure it.

* *Hetrurians* Etruscans

This Curious and paganish folly was not soe vniforme as learned Men might haue made yt, neither did their *Sooth-sayers* agree in the obseruation of good and evill, lucky or vnluckie augurismes. ffor the *Græcians* interpreted those to be luckie which came vpon the right hande, the *Romanes* those on the left hande. *Tacete habete animum bonum, liquido exeo foras auspicio, Aue sinistra* (saieth *Plautus* in *Epidico*).[h] Be still, and of good courage, I goe out with good fortune, for the bird flieth vpon the left hande, and thus I may say of these wise men our english *Iambick.*

As the foole thinketh
so the Goose winketh.

Yet that learned *Dionysius Halicarnass* describeth both the Custome and reason of the *Roman* augurismes,[i] sayinge that by imitation of the *Hetrurians,* their Teachers, they sett their faces toward the East when [11r] they obserue the flyinge of birdes because on that Coast arise both *Sunne, Moone,* and starres. And so lookinge vpon the *East* they haue the *North* on their left hande and the *South* on their right. Nowe the *North-pole* ys ever more conspicuous then the *South. Arcticus e' quinque coeli circulis magis conspicuus circa quem mundus voluitur quum Antarcticus delitescit.* The whole vniuerse ys moved about the *North* in a more visible and apparant manner then in the *South* or anie other of the Circles of heaven, and therfore the best motions in the world are on the *North-part* and so by Consequent the most happy and lucky augurismes vpon the left hande. So *Seruius, sinistra a sinendo* because they suffer our actions and desires when yt was said by *Plautus* in *Asinaria, picus et cornix a læua Coruus et parra a dextra consuadent.*[j] The Crowe and the Pye persuade on the left hand but the *Rauen* and the *Colmouse* on the right. *Tully* asked this question, *Quid habet augur cur a dextra coruus, a sinistra cornix faciat ratum?* I pray what reason hath the *sooth-sayer* to perswade *men* that the *Crowe* prophecieth on the left, and the *Rauen* on ye right hand? The *Eagle* on the right hand, saide the old *Græcians,* yet *Homer* in the person of *Hector* εἴτ ἐπὶ δεξί' ἴωσι πρὸς ἠῶ τ' ἠελιόν τε, εἴτ' ἐπ' ἀριστερὰ τοί γε ποτὶ.[k] He cared not for the *Eagles* flight, neither on the right nor the left hande.

When the Pullen did eate they gaue them branne or loose meale which they could not take vp so waryly [11v] but that some of yt would fall out of their mouthes, and this fallinge out of their mouthes they interpreted for a good diuination, but yf the Pullen let fall none or vtterly refused to eate, then they tooke that Recusancie for an evill and ominous augurisme. Yet you shall reade in ye *Historie* of the *Cocke* and the *Hen*[l] of a *Roman Sea-Captaine* beinge to ioyne a battell on the sea with his Enemies, called (before he fought) for theis divininge Pullen, whome when the Soothsayer had brought forth they refused to eate, which evill signe he told to the *Captaine* thinkinge that it would haue abated his Courage from fightinge that day. When the *Captaine* heard his relation, and sawe indeed y[e] truth he tooke the Pullen and cast them all into the Sea sayinge, *Comedere cum nolint, videamus an bibere velint.* Seinge they will not eate let vs see yf they will drinke, and so after the Pullens castinge away obtayned a very happie victory.

Yt might be overtedious to define their *Arculae, Enebræ, Inebræ, Remores, ffecilytræ, voisgræ*, and suche like as were ominous, and of evil signification. The *owle* seene in the *Citty* in the day tyme was of such an evill interpretation that yt droue the people to their prayers and holy water. On the other side the *Eagle, magnarum rerum auspicia faciebat.* So did the *Lame hawke Circus*, the *Buzzard* and the *vultur*, as shalbe seene in their seu[r]all descriptions: but the Crowes, Ravens, and Colmouse were most commonly interpreted evill. And such like vanityes were the lamentable Religion of the *forlorne hope* [12r] of *Adams* posterity. When their *Sooth-sayers* went about this busynes, they were apparrelled like their Preists, and had a Chappell called *Auguraculum* in the vpper part or quier wherof they sate with their rods in their hand diligently observinge the birdes flyinge both on the right and left hande with their other gestures, notes, and voyces. Sometymes allso they lay downe and made prayers to the gods to guie them prosperous answers and significations, the summe of which prayer is thus described by *Virgill 3 Æneidos.*

> *Quem sequimur? quove ire iubes? vbi ponere sedes?*
> *Da, Pater, augurium, atque animis illabere nostris.*[m]

Whome do we follow? whether shall we go? or where make resting place?
Giue's happy signes, o father great, our mindes adorne with grace.

None might be a *Sooth-sayer* which had a blemish or a sore, or were *Lunatique* although he had *Lucida interulla, neque morbidæ aues augurium faciebant.* Sicke, lame, & maymed Birds made no Augurismes. And for their greater honor they instituted a *Colledge* of *Augurs*, and adopted into yt very noble *Senators, Orators,* and great Magistrates. *Cicero* reioyceth that *Hortensius* had adopted him into that Colledge.

Of this societie was *Q. Mutius*, and of their authority *Paulus Æmilius* witnesseth that without their prescript the *Senate* did not meete togither, observinge both tyme and place by them decreed. And Cicero, *Rem bellicam nostri maiores administrari nisi auspicato noluerint*, Our Ancestors did not go to warre but by their direction. Therefore Liuie taxeth the *Commaunders* in *prælio Alliensi, quod nec auspicato, nec litato instruunt aciem,*[n] for settinge their battel without sooth-sayinge and sacrifice. By the Counsell and direction of this Colledge they made lawes and abrogated them againe, they called assemblies, and dissolued them, they chose *Consuls* [12v] and deposed them againe, they gaue the people their popular gouerment, and tooke yt away againe, prouided yt were not done after *August* till the Springe came in againe. Their *Sooth-sayers* were exempt from all criminall Courts, and had the precedence of Preists beinge never removed out of their office duringe life vpon anie occasion, and they stiled them the *Messingers* or *Interpreters of the Gods, Troiugena, interpres Diuum qui volucrum linguas & præpetis omina pennæ* [*sentis*].[o] ffrom henceforth yt came that they obtained such power to depose *Scipio,* and iudge of his Election, and to punishe *P. Claudius,* and *L. Junius* for takinge ship contrary to their direction. The *soothsayinge* Magistrate went out of the Citty, and performed his diuination, *sub dio* vnder the Cope of heaven, where he sate till a Ceremonie was performed and then retorned into the Citty substitutinge another to finishe the action; and these *Sooth-sayers* Magistrats might sometimes vndertake without their fellowes Counsell yet with respect to the dignity of the Colledge. ffor they must attribute all to this *Augurisme,* the buildinge of their Citty, the waginge of *warre,* the orderinge of *peace,* and the gouerment of *Houshold.* ffor, saith *Liuy,* most superstitious in this kinde, *Quid si pulli non pascantur? si ex cauis tardius exierint? si occinerit auis? parua sunt hæc; sed ista parua non contemnenda; maiores nostri maximam rem hanc fecerunt.*[p] What yf Pullen doe not feede? What yf it be longe before they come out of their Coopes? What yf the bird chirpe or peepe? these are but small thinges, yet such small thinges are not to be despised, for our Ancestors made great Accompt of these small thinges. *So far Liuy.*

But (alas) for the seduction of this old world, howe [13r] simple were they that thought Allmightie God would reveale his will to *Crowes* and *Pies,* and yet conceale yt from *Angells*? *Varro* calleth such Goddes *otiosos et feriatos, idle & lazy gods. Cicero* beinge himself of the *sooth-sayers Colledge* laughed at *Nonius* when he said *se spem optimam habere, quod septem aquilæ in castris Pompeii essent captæ,* I am of good hope because there were seauen Eagles taken in the Tents of *Pompey. Recte moneres* (saith *Cicero*) *si contra picas nobis pugnandum foret.* You say well, those Eagles would stand vs in some stead, yf we were to fight against an hoast of *Pies.* At another tyme one complayninge vnto him for feare of some evill presignifyed by the extraordinary Crowinge of Cockes: he bad him be of good comfort, for yt was naturall with Cockes to crowe, but (said he) yf ffishes had crowen so loud you might haue iustly feared. This old Serpent the Divell which like an Ape imitateth the inventions of God, would make men beleeve that instead of *Angells,* the *Birds* haue a diuination, and so call mens thoughts and hartes from heauen vnto the aire wherein himself ruleth. But the Magicians alleaged the examples of *Clodius* and *Flaminius* who refusing these Augurismes lost the feild, and of *Regulus* that observed them and won the victorie. And is it to be thought that Cockes did fight on his side or that the birdes gaue him aide? Why then did *Mancinus* and *Paulus Æmilius* loose their lifes? and whie did *Cæsar* speede soe well in *Afrique* goinge thither against the minde of *Sooth-sayers,* and workinge wonders? Surely they are but vanityes. Saith *Homer,* εἷς οἰωνὸς ἄριστος ἀμύνεσθαι περὶ πάτρης. / ἡμεῖς δὲ μεγάλοιο Διὸς.[q]

> *Let vs obay the will of Ioue above,*
> *Tis best our strength for Contries good to proue.*

[13v] I will conclude the idlenes and impiety of this *sooth-sayinge* learninge with this one historie.[r] When *Alexander* was come to the red sea, he and all his Companie were comaunded by his *sooth-sayer* to make a stande vntill he had made a divination by the Birde which sate singinge in a bush beside them. Nowe there was in the troope a certaine *Iewe* called *Mosolam* that knewe well enough the vanitie of this knowledge to be condemned by the *Lord* of *Heauen.* Whiles the *Augur* was in his obseruation, the *Iewe* shott his arrowe and killed the *Bird,* wherat allmost the whole Armie mutyned because nowe they knewe not which way to take, for they expected direction from the Bird. The *Iew* was called in question wherfore he slewe that bird, who made this answer: They were not forbidden by *Alexander* to kill birdes; & therfore he thought to try whether this bird could foresee hir owne deathe by his arrowe. For yf she had forseseene her owne perill, and avoyded yt, then was she the better to be beleeued, but yf she could not knowe when an arrowe might kill her, *quomodo de itinere nostro prædicere potuerit?* how should she knowe howe to direct our iourney? *nescia mens hominum fati sortisque futuræ.* There is no truth nor credit in

sooth-sayinge, and therfore let them looke to perish that seeke vnto yt. And soe much for the necessitie of our history bringinge light, to and for the better interpretation of *Scriptures.*

By this which hath bin said may well be collected as well the dignitie of our present historie as the necessity, for yt must needes be very noble that encreaseth light in the hart of man to vnderstand the reuealed will, and word of God. And this kinde of diuination you shall finde in our historie which teacheth the meaninge of textes of [14r] Scripture but not of events and matters to come. But besides this the Dignity may appeare by many arguments, but especially because *God* hath termed them *Volucres celi,* thė fowles of heauen. There are but three thinges or workes of God that are soe phrazed in the booke of God, *angelos cæli, signa cæli, & volucres cæli,* all of them emplyinge an excellencie aboue other Creatures not soe muche dignified in title. Therfore as it is an honorable and most worthie pointe of learninge to knowe ye history of *Angells,* or of the *starrs* and signes of heauen, so is it of birdes, and the ffowles of heaven, and so much the rather because the precept of the *Lord Iesus* leadeth vs vnto this labour. *Intuemini volantilia cæli.* Behold ye ffowles of heauen, for the *Angells* are winged aboue soe are the fowles beneathe in so muche as the fowles are and may be called *Angells* on earth, and soe the *Angells* the fowles in heauen, but their dignitie appeareth by the great loue that great and excellent men haue borne vnto some one of them; and therfore *maior est gloria vniuersitatis quam vnius.* All of them decyphered together are more noble and worthie our knowledge then anie one never soe well instructed. That men delighted in them may appeare by these Testimonies. There was one *Marthes,* a kinge of *Egipt,* which nourished a *Crowe* and made yt so seruiceable that it could vnderstand places and messages and would carry a letter manie miles to any Citty, and there lett yt fall to be deliuered to ye party to whome the kinge sent yt. *Agrippina,* that famous *Roman Lady*, kept a *Thrushe*[8] and by great care & tokens of *Loue* made yt to vnderstande and speake many words [14v] after men. There was a *Rauen* in *Rome* which would come in publique assemblies, and by name salute *Tiberius Germanicus*, and *Drusus* first, and then afterward all the whole assembly in Generall. *Cecina,* a noble and riche knight, carried swallowes with him in the warres and would by them send letters home to his freinds of victories and occurrences of *Warre.* At the seige of *Mutina* when *Brutus* was *Consul* they taughte Pidgeons to carry letters out of the Castle into the tentes, and againe out of the tents into the Castle. The like thinge hath bin practized within our memorie in the Lowe Countries at the seige of *Harlem* and other places; and for such purposes allreadie spoken of, no Creatures in the world are so fitt for speede and messages as are fowles. *Seuerus,* an Abbott, and *Maxentius,* a *Monasticall Eremite,* taught Sparrowes to take meate at their handes, especially the later leadinge a solitary life. The birdes of the woods were his Companions and his housholde table freindes. Manie such other things you shall read of in this following historie arguinge the excellent nature of fowles which serue for the vse of man, not only by constraint but in a voluntarie, familiar, and free kind of subiection.

I will not tarrie vpon their dignity when as we see for singinge, *Thrushes, nightingales, canaries, Lynnetts, finches* are highlie prized, and I haue knowne an hundred pound a yeare land offered for one *Hawke.* I will not prevent my history in my preface, but like a Merchant hange out for shewe the baser [15r] wares, promisinge much better within the lists of my succeedinge discourses. The vses which are made of fowles are many, and so greate, as neither mans Nature can want, nor my pen discourse sufficiently, for it is easyer to finde a beginninge then an end of their narrations. ffrom an *Eagle* haue manie famous men, manie places, and many worthie things receaued denomination or ells cognomination, for where the birde hath bin before the man, there the man called by that name is thought to be named by and of the bird. *Aquila* called allsoe Ponticus, St. Paules Companion. There was another of that name deare vnto *Hadrian* the Emperour who afterwarde made a translation out of *Hebrew* into *Greeke* and *Chaldee* of the old Testament. There are herbes, starres, wood, chymicall salt, precious stones, rivers, Townes, and Cittyes called by the name of *Aquila,* and especially the birth place of *Salust* the Oratour called at this day (yf I be not deceaued) *Aquileia* within the *Venetian Territorie.*

Fortia belligerans Aquilæ sub mœnibus altis, saith *Mantuan.*[t] And in *fferrara* they haue a kinde of money called *Aquila* because of the *Eagle* stamped therupon. Soe the *vultur* signifieth a starre, a *Gulon* or eatinge beast which killeth not, but eateth what he findeth dead: a River in *Apalia* and a mountayne. *Dice* are all soe called *vulturs* because beinge dead things they consume Mens estates as livinge *vulturs* doe dead Carrions. *Hawkes* called *Accipitres* gaue names to Men, as there was one *Accipiter,* a builder of *Ceres temple.* The *Chirurgions* haue a bone they call Accipiter, and the litle gunne called a *Muskett* is named from that litle hawke so called.* The *Owles* [15v] haue not wanted

* *Muskett* the Sparrow Hawk *Accipiter nisus*

their honor in this parte. *Bubo* hath called a Citty in *Licia* by hir owne name, hath giuen title to the inflammatons *in pudendis* amonge the Phisitians, and there was (saithe *Atheneus*) a kind of daunce called *Bubo* the *Owle*. *Bubonia* was the old name of *Bollen* in *ffrance* and *Bubonium* the name of an herbe. The *Batts* haue founde some honor amonge the names of Men, as *Nycteris,* the surname of *Chærephon,* a great Philosopher and freinde of *Socrates,* and *Nyctiporus,* a River. I shall not neede to searche into *Latine, greeke,* and forraine examples for proofe hereof. Our owne language will speake what names of men, instruments of labor, places and other memorable thinges are amonge vs. We have *Bird, Doue, Pidgeon, Crane, Crowe, Swan, Ducke, Buzard, Teale, Drake, Nightingale, Wren, Hawkes, Howlet,* and manie such other for names, for tooles, for places, as all wise Englishmen haue obserued. ffrom hence come their seuerall Coates and Crests of honor which are hereafter expressed. Without ffowles we should lodge hard not hauing feathers in our bedds, fare harde without manie rare delicates, live sicke without manie singuler remedies and parts of physick, and manie places would be eaten vp or soe annoyed with flies (especiallie our fennes) that yt were impossible for men to dwell in them as I will manifest (God assistinge me in convenient place[ )].

But the delightfull vses of this *Historie* are manie and infinite euen of our knowne fowles in England, and other forraine worthie our speculation. [16r] ffor a tast wherof to shewe the varietyes of ye faculties natures, inclinations, and propertyes giuen them by the great Creatour and obserued by men it shall not be greuious to my pen to expresse some of them in this my prologue, and entrance of my Booke.

ffirst yt is obserued that artes haue receaued their encrease and supplement from fowles. The *Greekes* haue added fower letters to their Alphabet by markinge the order of *Cranes* in their flight . γ . λ . φ . ξ . wherupon (said *St Ierome*) *Grues vnam sequuntur ordine literato.* Cranes fly like an *Alphabet,* and this obseruation ys ascribed to *Palamedes,* wherfore they are called *Palamedis aues.*

Turbabis versus, & litera tota volabit,
vnam perdideris si Palamedis auem.[u]

Yf that you loose but *Palamedes* Birde
the letter flieth, and verses want a word.

The Learninge of *Rhetoritians,* and *Poets* is illustrated by examples, similitudes, and notes taken from fowles as may be seene in all writers sacred and prophane. The affections of our mindes, and *ideas* of vice and vertue are enforced and prohibited by the inspection of fowles. *Cranes* teache vs wisdome to waigh our owne selfes, and what we want in nature to supply by industry. Wherfore when they flie they carrie a stone to giue poize to their bodies, and by the fall of that stone as they fly alofte in the aire they can tell whether they be over the earth or water, when to rest, and when to goe forward. They describe the best forme of a *Common-weale*, for [16v]in their Iourneys they haue guides by course like an *Aristocracye,* they haue drivers behinde like *Iudges* that execute the lawe, they haue supporters at the sides y[t] they erre not on the right hande nor the left, and they haue succours for the weake to beare them forwarde when they haue done their vttermost. They teache the tyme of plantinge and sowinge and the whole arte of warre, for in the night they keepe a watche which is changed twice at the least that the whole burden lye not vpon a fewe, the *Captaine* or Guide walkinge the round. They obserue buriall of their kinde, and other suche laudable, and instructive *Ceremonies.*

The *Nightingale* when she bringeth her yonge ones abroad out of their nest instructeth them to singe with as greate sedulitie as anie parentes teach trades and sciences to their growen Children. The arte of graftinge and inoculatinge was learned from fowles, for (saieth *Pliny*) *Semine raptim, fame auium deuorato solidoque, ac alui tepore madido, cum foecundo fimi medicamine abiecto in mollibus arborum lecticis etc*: Seedes taken by fowles in their hunger and so hastily deuoured that they come out of their bellies whole, sound, and warme with their fruictfull excrements into the putryfied and soft hollowe places of trees cause one roote to beare diuers fructs, as *plantane* in *laurell, bay* in a *Cherrytree, vines* of diuers colors, *plumms* in *apples.* Soe doe Dawes by hidinge seedes and sprigges, so doe Crowes with wallnutts. Manie other arts haue had their perfection from fowles, as Painters by beholdinge the varyetie of Colors mixed and elegantly compounded in one birde. [17r] The feather makers haue their livinges from these fowles who were first taught that trade in *Europa* by y[e] *Indians* of *Florida.* Their quilles make pens for schollers, and writers, the *Rauens* quilles and *Crowes* for *geometrike* lines and musique in *Virginalls.* The Pictures of sondry birdes were a great parte of *Hieroglyfican* learninge, and the *Pyes* and *Cuckoes* teache Housholders to lay vp store of foode in sommer against the cold of winter. The Swallowes haue bin our Masters to teache vs to make walls of earthe which they performe in suche excellencie, as no playsterer can attayne vnto, wherfore they are by the *Greekes* called *Ornithas Tectonas, aues fabras,* birdes that be builders. By the *Kites* who guide their iourneys in the aire by windinge their Tayles, haue Nauigatours learned to guide and turne their shippes by a sterne, or Rudder; for what a feather can doe in the aer that can a peece of wood effecte in the water beinge wisely managed. In the Isle of *Taprobana* they saile not by Compasse or obseruation of the starres because they cannot see the *North-pole,* wherfore when they goe to sea they carry with them diuers birdes, which they let goe one after one, and direct their courses after the birdes flight.

Without the knowledge of fowles naturall *philosophy* was very maymed, and especiallie *Physicke,* for out of fowles haue Phisitians founde a wholsome diet for their patients and a direction for suche as be sounde without perill of their healthe. Allso they haue learned manie materiall, and naturall remedies against greuious diseases and maladies. The *Storke* is good in a *Palsie* and *Apoplexy.* The *Larke* against the *Chollicke,* the *Pye* against the tremblinge of [17v] the *hart.* The *Sparrowe* against the *Stone* and difficulty of vrine. The *Woodwall* against the yellow Iaundise. All theis birdes cure and bringe ease by their only sighte, especially this last, for the sicke man shall liue, and the *bird* dye when once yt is beheld by a party so infected.[v] The skinnes of *swannes, vulturs,* and *Eagles* applied to ye brest strengthen yt to the helpe of concoction. ffrom these Masters haue the *Phisitians* learned (by their own confession) the vses of manie herbes, and plants, as *Hawkeweede* from the *Hawke, Selendine* from the Swallow. *Origan* from the *Storke,* the stone *Ætites* from the *Eagle, Cichory* from the *Goshawke,* white bramble from y^e *Kite, Venus* haire from the *Hoope,** mirtle branches from the *Thrushe,* and liue roote from the *Peacocks.* The *Heron* cureth herself with a sea-crabb, the *Ringdoues, Choughes, black-birds,* and *Partridges* with a laurell bough; *pigeons, turtles,* and *Cocks* with *pellitory,* the water fowles with wall-sage. *Cranes* and *Storkes* with bull-rushes and the Crowe beinge poysoned with *Laurell* cureth himself of that poyson by a dead Chamelaeon. Yt were infinite to speake, all that may be spoken, and yt were to put all my historie into a preface.

Astronomers haue bin benefited by birdes for the better diuision of the tymes of the yeare, for the swallowe by hir first comminge proclaymeth the first aequinoctiall, and by her departure the second. The

* *Hoope* the Hoopoe *Upupa epops*

Nightingale chaungeth colour, and note in ye sommer solstice. The *Storke* and the *Quaile* proclaime the springe. All the Musitians confesse that birdes are ye cheifest [18r] Daughters of *Europa*, the mother of musick. *Hymen* could not singe sweeter layes then one *Indian* birde doth in *Ælianus Lib*: 17 *cap*: 22.[w] Their affection and loue towardes men are exceedinge greate and allmost miraculous, as shalbe manifested in every parte of the particular *Historie*. *Semiramis* (saieth *Diodorus*) cast out by her cruell Mother was nursed by the Birdes *Semiramides*, who brought the Infant milke gathered vp from the grounde where the Shepherdes milked their sheepe, and afterwarde cheese which they tore out of the Shepherdes bagges vntill they were espyed & followed to the Rocke where the young Infante was founde. So the old *Rômanes* beleiued that a *Woodspiker* did helpe to nurse *Romulus* and *Remus*.

I will conclude their vses with their naturall presages, by obseruation whereof Mankinde receiueth yearly no small aduantage, especiallie Husbandmen, Merchants, & Mariners. Raine and tempests are foreshewed by the flight, voyces, and washings of Waterfowles. So doe the Tree-fowles when they make hast from the Cornelandes to ye greene Trees. Yf Larks, and other Birdes of the Earthe drawe neare to waters, and liue in silence about them, yt foresheweth calme weather, and a greate drought. Yf Stares and such other Birdes flocke together in Ilandes, yt betokeneth inundation; and when strange fowles appeare where they were strangers, to the harme, and damage of the Countrey, then they signify the wrath of God, from whome (like ye Locusts of Egipt) they are sent to spoile, ruyne, and [18v] destroy. Wherfore Allmighty God speaketh by *Jeremy Cap*: 15. 3. *I will appoint ouer them fower kindes* (*saith the Lord*) : *the sword to destroy, the doggs to teare in peices, the fowles of heauen, & beasts of the Earth to deuoure & destroy.*[x] Therfore yt is requisite that we obserue them least we vnderstand not our owne misery nor seeke for remedy in the right place. When Birdes forsake ye feildes and woodes wherein they abide naturally, and make to houses, Townes, or Cytties, it signifyeth famine, and scarsitie. But yt is better to instance in some perticular then thus to discourse in generall of matters of this Consequence. And withall I desire my Reader not to attribute these presages in fowles to anie Metaphisicall or Celestiall prediction, but onely to their severall natures giuen them of the great Creatour for their owne preseruation, and obserued by Men of deepest skill, and Judgement in nature.

ffirst, therfore, the *Eagle* strivinge to fly Eastward foresheweth winde, when the *Hawke* keepeth a tree and therein picketh her owne feathers, and killeth vermyn bread vnderneath them, yt betokeneth raine, saith *Theophrastus,*[y] and the same thinge is premonstrated by the appearaunce and noyse of *Owles* either before the Sun-sett or more then ordinary, for so she prouideth foode till faire weather come againe, but yf in raine she howle more frequent, yt signifyeth the approche of Calme and faire weather. When Rauens flocke together and croake hoarsely thorough the operation of ye Southwinde (as often we heare in Cocks and hawkes), yt betokeneth stormes, and by beatinge and flappinge [19r] their winges, as they sitt vpon Trees, for the cold which bringeth the rayne worketh vpon their bodies, and they by motion of their wings studie to avoide the same. When Crowes doe cry muche, and wash themselues or sitt in flocks by water-sides yt signifyeth rayne, for at such times their vapours growe over hott, and therfore they gett them to the waters to coole them. When Choughes drawe to houses, and pull themselues or returne late to their nests and lodgings, they foretell raine. The squeakinge voyce of a *Iay* sheweth the same thinge. The like is obserued in the crowinge of Cocks, yf they vnwillingly come off from their roosts in the morninge, and walke not abroad to feede as they are wont, yt allso signifyeth fowle weather and soe doe the Pidgeons for the same cause. *Peacocks* cryinge in the night and *Sparrowes* in the morninge presage Tempests and stormes at hand. When Cranes forsake the waters they forshewe great raynes, and when they fly mute faire weather. The *Swallow* doth manie wayes shew rayne, so doth the little *Wren,* the *Redbrest, Swannes, Ducks, Cormorants, Cootes, Herons* and manie other fowles as shall appeare in their particular Histories, all of them proclayminge the infinite wisedome of our grand-maker by whome such rare qualities were engrafted into theis aeriall Creatures wherby they foresee aeriall mutations, and call vppon men like livinge and flyinge Bookes to meditate of their chaunges allsoe from sinne to *Grace,* from life to dust, and from dust to resurrection.

I will add for delight sake some shadowes of the obseruations within this historie, that by them the [19v] Reader may take a scantlinge of the residue, and so with brevity conclude the porche and preface of my discourses. There ys every yeare in *Licia* about ye Riuer *Xanthus* a battaile betwixt Crowes, vulturs, and other Carnivorous or flesh-eatinge fowles on the one partye, and *Alcatrazes, Storkes,* and such like fowles on the other party. Yt is a wonderfull and furious skirmishe, and the Inhabitants watch the yssue of the victory, for yf the land or Carnivorous fowles overcome they haue the next yeare plenty of Corne, yf the water fowles overcome then haue they the yeare following plenty

Reader may take a scantlinge of the residue, and so with brevity
conclude the porche and preface of my discourses. There is
every yeare in *Licia* about the River *Xanthus* a battaile
betweene Crowes, vultures, and other Carnivorous or flesh=
eatinge fowles on the one partye, and *Alcatrazes*, *Storkes*,
and such like fowles on the other party. It is a wonderfull
and furious skirmishe, and the Inhabitants watch the
issue of the victory, for if the land or Carnivorous fowles
overcome they have the next yeare plenty of Corne, if
the water fowles overcome then have they the yeare followinge
plenty of Cattell. And the victorie is adiudged by the
Inhabitants accordinge to the number of the slaine, for they
deeme the Conquerours side to have lost fewest of their companie.
The *Alcatrazes* are water fowles, and yet never drinke; and
when they sleepe or take their rest their head lyeth upon
their backe with their Eyes open toward heaven. There is
a fowle called *Artennah* or *avis Diomedea* from whose
neste in banke and sides of ditches men are thought first to
have learned their excellent worke of vaultinge and archinge.
They have two holes passages in their neste one to the
East another to the west, everie morninge they go forth
at the East, because there light first appeareth, and
returne at night in at the west because there the light last
of all departeth and closeth. *Barnacles* are not onely
engendred but unto this day created and growinge out of
trees, maste, and shippe sides in the Northwest seas of
Ireland and *Scotland*. *Backs* or *Batts* beinge younge
never lett goe the breste of their damme although she be

dead

of Cattell. And the victorie is adiudged by the Inhabitaunts accordinge to ye number of the slaine, for they deeme the Conquerours side to haue lost fewest of their companie. The *Alcatrazes* are water fowles, and yet never drinke, and when they sleepe or take their rest, their head lyeth vpon their backe with their Eyes open toward heauen. There is a fowle called *Artennah* or *auis Diomedea* from whose nests in banks and sides of ditches men are thought first to haue learned their excellent worke of vaultinge and archinge. They haue two holes, passages in their nests, one to the East another to the west; everie morninge they go forthe at the East, because there light first appeareth, and returne at night in at the west because there the light last of all departeth and closeth. *Barnacles* are not onely engendred but vnto this day created and growinge out of trees, masts, and shippe sides in the Northwest seas of *Ireland* and *Scotland*. *Backs* or *Batts* beinge younge never lett goe the brests of their damme although She be [20r] dead, for all that a Man can doe, but the damme being aliue setteth them off and on at her pleasure. They are not Runnagates, but whersoeuer they sommer there also they winter, and carryed from the places of their birthe and breedinge never prosper. The *Buntinge*, an english fowle, in winter are fatt when their foode is least, and in sommer leane when their meate is most, *flante austro macrescunt & aquilone pinguescunt*, the warme southerly winde maketh them leane, and the cold northerne winde fatt againe. The *Bustards* haue taught marriners to attend the winde, for they beinge heavy yet with the helpe of the winde fly over seas, so do shippes laden. Their fleshe is sweete, but the marrowe of their bones stinketh like the actions of *Iacobs* sonnes when they sold *Ioseph*; out of a filthie intention they bred a wholesome action to them all. Birdes seeinge a Buzard over their heades doe soe much hate to be spoyled by their owne kinde that they sitt still immoveable and rather chuse to fall into the handes of men or mouthes of dogges then to be killed aboue in the aer. The *Bitter* beinge tamed endureth not opprobrious wordes, but discerneth disprayses and scornes. The birdes of paradise, livinge alway aloft in the aer till they die, are Emblemes of men whose soule goeth vpward when his body falleth into ye earthe. Amongst the Canary or singinge birdes the least are the best singers, and they all singe best after they haue eaten sugar. The Quayles cannot change Countreyes except the Cenchram be their guide and Tutour, and he it is (although but a little bird) that directeth, [20v] awaketh and prouoketh them to

OPPOSITE, *the author's hand*

their iourneys end. Yt is a wonderfull note in the *Chaffynche* that buildinge her nest in the highest tree placeth yt in the lowest boughes, and in the lowe trees she maketh yt in the highest branches so that aduersitie doth not depresse her nor prosperyty extoll her aboue her proportion. They neuer singe but in colde weather, and then they liue a parte, the male from the female and come not together, hauinge this rare inclination that in the sommer they couet the hottest Countries and in winter the coldest, one tyme beinge a pennance to the other and accustominge themselues to bodily extremities. Howe greate is the loue of one Chough to another? *Graculus Graculo assidet* saith the prouerbe to signify and expresse vnto vs the straightest and firmest band of freindshipp that may be, for they never change mates, mourne perpetually after one of the Couple are dead, reioyce at the picture of another though paynted on the wall. And yf they see one of their kinde hanged vp in a Corne feild by the legge they will never dare to come into that place to behold such a sorrowfull sight. The *Colmouse infausta, et nefausta auis,* yet is the kindest to his parents of all birdes, for they tarry not till age with their remuneration (as do the *Storkes*) but as soone as they [are] able to forrage feede their parents and suffer them not to raunge abroad for meate, but onely for delight and recreation. They fly with their tayle forward because by that meanes they take the more flies. The *Cormorantes* being [21r] hunted, dive vnder water, by which they doe not onely avoyd the perill of their hunters but alsoe take fishes for their meate and sustentation, turninge necessitie into a benefitt, and drowninge into a Commoditie. Yea when the waters are roughest they are safest, for then are other fowles gone away for feare and soe the waters are theirs alone. And to conclude the dunghill household Cocke is a Creature of such worth that he is an excellent patterne of a husband lovinge his wifes the hennes, and for them he fighteth to death, of a householder for he scrapeth all the day longe (and is not wearyed) to feed the troope he leadeth; of a good and watchfull ffather, for yf the hen dye he hatcheth the egges, and feedeth the Chicken, and while he hath one eye to ye earthe to looke after foode he casteth another eye vpward to heauen to preuent ye incursions and violence of *Hawkes* and *Kites* aboue head; of a bountifull and liberall man, for when he hathe found meate he calleth the hennes and pullen vnto yt, takinge the least part to himself and givinge most to other; of an armed Soldier hauinge his Combe for a helmett, his spurres for a sword, his beake for a speare, his taile for a standard, and after combate his owne voice to proclaime his victorie and singe his triumph. Manie and manie more shall the history contayne which the preface cannot admitt. Yf these suffice not for this booke, make the whole booke but a preface to other which I am ready to diuulge: and yf the worke shall not content the Readers because the Author is not exquisite enoughe, yet I desyre you not to neglecte the Creatures of the *Trinitie,* for they are the miraculous [21v] workes of God although they are not opened in oracles as they deserued.

The Birdes in Alphabeticall Order Conteyned in this worke

A.

Alcatraz. Onocrotalus. Osina. Truo.
Alchata. Vn Angel. Oenas. Vinago.
Aiussaco. Virginia.
Artennah. Auis Diomedea.
Artamokes, Aupseo. Aushouetta

B.

Barnacle. Brenthus
Batt. Vespertilio.
Byrgander. Vulpanser
Byttor. Botaurus
Blackbyrd. Merula
Bramblyn. Montifringilla
Bulfynche. Rubicilla
Buntinge. Terraneola
Bustard. Tarda auis. Otis.
Bald Buzzard, Subbuteo
Buzzard. Triorchis
Byrdes of Paradise. Manucodiata. with other strainge birds without figures.

C.

Canary bird. Chloris
Capon. Capo.
Cenchram. Cynchramus.
Certyon. Cercyon
Chaffynche Fringilla.
Chalander. Chalandra
Chawankus. Virginia
Choughe. Graculus
Chungent, Chuguareo, Chuwheeo } Virginia
Colmouse. Merops
Corlieu. Numenius
Cormorant. Mergus
Cocke. Gallus
Cocke of the wood. Vrogallus
Coote. Fulica
Corrier. Trochilos
Crane Grus
Crex. Auosetta
Crowe. Cornix.
Cuckoe. Cuculus.

[22r]

[I]

The Alcatraz

Even as it is with men, so is it with the Creatures. Princes and eminent persons haue all their actions on the stage; so the Worlde taketh knowledge both of their vices and vertues, for both their good and evill is written in their forehead, as Henry the fourth of Fraunce saied to the Earle of Salisbury beinge Ambassador with him for Queene Elizabeth.[1] ffrom hence it cometh that Historyes and Chronicles are filled with the lyves and doinges of greate persons whose actions beinge made publique came to the knowledge of euery writer and either for loue or hatred were so proclaymed that euery man may reade a Lecture vpon their naked Anatomye because there was nothinge that euer they did, but all men tooke notice therof. The fowles of heauen which haue different qualities are so respected like the Nobles of the earth, for by reason of their vses, amitie, or enmitie with men their natures, originalls, properties, and dispositions are better knowen and more fullie described: but if they live in obscuritie (or as the [22v] Greekes saied of the Barbarians) where their deedes cannot be knowen or written, though neuer so notable they must be contented to haue litle saied where little was knowen of them. I shalbe forced through want of Authors to saie but little of many strainge fowles which in their oune

Regions haue not ben described by the naturall inhabitants but casually noted by Christian Nauigators. ffor when a man is not knowen by any better marke, it is not vnreasonable to describe him by his garments and outside. And when wee can say nothinge of a strainge fowle it shalbe sufficient to name him and expresse him by his colours.

I must beginne with this strange fowle for orders sake because I will proceede in Alphabeticall methode leavinge the knowledge of euery byrd to the description rather then to raunge them vnder their proper kindes wherein men many tymes are deceaued, and the Readers troubled.[2] This Alcatraz is described by Baptista Ramusio, a greate Trauayler of Venice. Vol. 3 fol. 49. & 136.[3]

The Alcatraz

[illustration]

[23r] This fowle is very neere as bigge as a Swanne and it is the same which the Latynes call *Onocrotalus* which St Iherome saieth is meant in Holy Scripture by these Hebrewe wordes *Kik* or *Kisk* or *Hakik chasida,* and a greate Rabbyne amonge the Iewes calleth it *Kaath a vomendo* for vomitinge his meate out of the bagge vnder his throate. The Arabians call him *Balazub,* the Grecians *Onocrotalios, Pelekan, Pelekinos,* and *Ramphios* because of his longe bill. Albertus called it *Osina,* but the most comon name is *Onocrotalus quod collum mergens spiransque velut ruditum asini edat,* because when he diveth with his necke into the water he brayeth like an Asse. It is called also *Truo* because the throate thereof resembleth a vessell called *Trua,* which floteth vpon the waters and sinketh not like one of these Alcatrazes. ffrom the corruption of the Latine worde the Italians and Spanyards call it *Grotto* or *Groto,* the Venetians *Croto,* the Frenchmen *Liuane* and *Goetteuse,* that is, greate throate, the Germaynes *Vogelheyne* and *Onuogel,* that is, foolish bird and *Eselschryer,* that is, Asse crier, and *Kropffuogel,* the Flemings *Vogel-vanetna,* the fowle of Ætna, in *Finland,* it is called *Surpesi,* amonge the Turkes *Sackagusch,* but the Indians where it is most naturall call it *Alcatraz,* and therefore without libertie of invention of any other name I will binde my pen to it in this History, although some out of no similitude but that it wanteth a gall doe tearme it a *water pellicane.*

This Alcatraz is a water fowle bigger then a goose and verie little inferiour to a Swanne, but exceedinge a Vultur, and one of the greatest water-fowles. Bellonius sawe one at Rhodes tamed and conversinge gentlie with men and Tame-fowles. And our Countreyman Dr. Turner[4] sawe one at Machlin in the Netherlands, and describeth the same, which afterwarde Iohn Cukman, a learned man of that Countrey, did more exactlie figure and sende vnto Dr. Gesner, both of them agreeinge in the quantitie that it was in bodie bigger then a Swanne but the necke much shorter. Aldrovandus bought one that was brought from Ferrara, which he also describeth more particularly. And therefore I will in this description followe his auctoritie. It was higher then a man when his necke was stretched vp at leingth, for in measure it exceeded [23v] tenne spannes* yet it was a yonge one and not come to his iust and naturall proportion. It weighed not aboue eighteene or nyneteene pound: whereas in their full grouth Gesner affirmeth that they weigh fyve and twenty. His breadth exceeded his height or leingth, for the wings stretched out he was twelve spannes, that is, very neere fiue dutche elnes.† ffor the most part a man stretched out at leingth is no broader then his height, but this fowle was exorbitant. His beake was of a browne colour, and a most stronge bone whereof the vpper part was three fingers broade and two spannes longe, crooked at the ende like a hooke, and of a saffron colour wherewithall he holdeth the fishes in his mouth when he casteth them vp from his throate vntill he haue eaten them: withinside this vpper part resembleth a plantane leafe wherein are five sharpe swellinge lynes, wherewithall he presseth the fishes to death before he swallowe them into his throate bagge. The neather part of his beake, measured from the throate where it is ioyned vnto the necke, exceedethe the vpper part a hands breadth in leingth and both of them opened at the widest were two feete distant one from the other. Vnder this hangeth that greate bagge, which is like a thicke yellowe sachell or bottell of such a nature as it stretcheth more or lesse accordinge to the will of the birde or the violence offered thereunto.

Perottus[5] affirmeth that he sawe a man of a greate stature thrust in his legge with a boote thereon into the same with little or no offence and so pulled it furth againe. Franciscus Sanctius, a learned man, writeth that one of these beinge heauily laden with meate was taken because she coulde not rise quicklie from the earth, and a whole Blackamore infant was found within this bagge. Peter Martyr and Ramusius affirme that they haue seene taken out of one of their throates a Souldiers coate, a hatt, and three paire of shoes, which is no incredible thinge, as wee

* *tenne spannes* a span is about nine inches

† *dutche elnes* the Flemish ell was twenty-seven inches

shall manifest when wee come to their feedinge. The eyes very round with a blacke pupill, and the iris of a loame colour. The head feathers white and softe but black quills at the rootes and some longe feathers hanginge downe from the Crowne or hinder part of the head. The wings [24r] partlie black or browne and partlie white but the endes of the feathers all white and so are the other feathers. The leggs like a goose legge and shorter then such a proportionable greate body required. The feete or clawes all ioyned together with the thicke membrane, all of them beinge of a leingth to spread in the water when they swymme whereas in the Swannes feete one of them was vnprofitable and of no vse. It was a female wherein were eggs of the quantitie of a pease. The milt round, as bigge as an hasell nutt and very hard. The ventricle or crappe was very hard, not aboue two fingers broad but tenne in leingth, the gall was ioyned to the hollowe of the lyver, the gutts much shorter then in Duckes and geese, the throate bole or windpipe was flesh and greate in the middle, but small at both ends both aboue at the head and beneath at the crappe. In the broader part the meate is halfe disgested before it descend downe into the mawe. The heart was greate, and therefore it is coniectured to be fearefull.* The skull full of braynes but the bones light, white glisteringe and without marrowe, whereby Almighty God so prouided, that hereby this fowle might flie and swymme much lighter. The naked wings are couered with a stronge membrane, out of which growe foure and twentie quills or longe feathers which noe force is able to drawe furth, and this is the cause of her stronge flight: ffor Culmanus reported that Alcatraz of Machlin did flie vp so high aboue the head of his keeper, that it seemed no bigger then a swallowe.

Concerninge the Regions and places of their abode it is confessed at all hands that it is a West-Indian fowle, so Ramusius, Odoricus,[6] and Martyr, which in the vpper India in the prouince of Manzi they call *Cela,* because they abound about the Citie Ceuscala, and Eucherius graunteth also that they lyve in Nilus. *Onocrotalus, Aqua vt anser vtitur cum salsa, pascitur tum dulci, magis tamen frequentat marinas.*[7] The Alcatraz (saieth Albertus) vseth the water like a goose, and is found both in freshe and salt water, yet it delighteth most in the salt water. The reason is, because noe freshe waters can fill her throate [24v] with sufficient foode. But the freshe waters of the Southe as Nilus freese not in the winter, and therefore they withdrawe themselues

* *fearefull* inspiring dread

thither in wynter tyme, even as Cranes and quailes forsake Europe and flie into Asia; when cold weather or the sommer aequinoctiall approacheth they haue ben found in Italy about Rauenna which caused Martial to write thus.

Turpe Rauennatis guttur Onocrotali.[8] So in the lake of Mantua and in Padus about Ferrara in the Coasts of Florence about Port Hercule and Orbitellus, and in Sauoy in Lake Lemayne. Once in Heluetia within a litle of Zuricke neere a place called Tugium, there appeared one of them in the latter end of February which was brought to Gesner because no man had euer seene the like in those parts. When they flie, they shrinke vp their neckes so short as a man wolde thinke they had none at all, or a very short one, but when they sitt still, swymme, or walke they stretch it out to a greate leingth. They liue principally vpon fishes yet will they eate also wormes, swallowe vp stones, gravell, chippes, and almost any other thinge. Which caused Pliny to call it *inexplebile animal obuium quemcunque piscem etiam quinque libralem vel maiorem in os imponet ita inuertit vt rostro præmisso deglutit.*[9] An vnsatiable Creature devouringe euery fishe it meeteth although it weigh fyve pound or more, turninge it with such arte within his crooked beake, that it shall neuer escape his throate. Oysters, Crabbes, and other shellfishe escape him not but he loadeth his bagge with them till the heate thereof cause them to open of themselues, then he vomiteth them furth out of his bagge into his mouth and with the Crooke of his beake picketh furth the fishe and casteth away the shells. Gesner saith he fisheth like a swanne, thrustinge his head into the water and keepinge his other parts aboue water, his tayle standinge highest. Peter Martyr saieth otherwise: *More Miluorum & petulantum in sublimem eleuatæ aërem circumrotant &c.*[10] As Kytes and other birds of prey flye highe with a croakinge voice, aboue the waters lookinge earnestly downeward when the fishes appeare on the brinks or vpper face of the waters, then sodenly they fall downe like a greate many hounds after one [25r] hare or boyes to scramble for one musse, whereby the astonished fishe becommeth a prey without stirringe: for their nomber and weight parteth the waters and openeth them the leingth of halfe an arme. Therefore, saieth Ramusius, they followe the skulls* of herrings and take of them aboundantlie because they swymme alofte and in greate troopes. ffirst they prepare them in their prolobe or throate bagge, then after a while they vomitt them furth into their

* *skulls* schools

mouth and take them into their throate where they lye till they be halfe disgested, then they lett them sinke downe into their mawe where the first concoction is perfected, which is very speedy because it is narrowe and longe, & *venter nullum habet diuerticulum quo cibum retineat*: their bellyes want roome to retayne their meate longe. And it is a wonderfull worke of Almighty God, that hath so made the bagge of this fowle to retayne at one tyme water, sand, stones, chipps, fishes, and whatsouer els they devoure, and yet none of these annoy the throate itselfe, and passage to the mawe, beinge so neerelie conioyned as is the entry of a house vnto the open hall: without muscle, v[e?]yne, or synewe to keepe the passage for the naturall foodes either to open or shutt the same: but like a bladder wideneth and contracteth of it selfe accordinge to the fulnesse and emptines wherewithall it is charged: beinge made of a double thicke skynne full of fibres transparent and yet very stronge whereby it is dilated and contracted and so when they haue filled it, they feede vpon the best as hath ben declared and the residue of any burden they cast vp from beinge a trouble vnto them. The Alcatraz of Machlin beinge tamed did eate bread steeped in broath and other liquid things. A pore olde woman had of the Emperour foure stiuers* a day for the keepinge of the same. Dr. Turner writeth that notwithstandinge they lyve in the waters, yet they drinke but twice a yere, the certeintie or reason thereof he expresseth not, and it may seeme incredible that lyvinge perpetually in the waters it shoulde be endued with so greate a temperance *posse & nolle nobile*. It was a brave part of a Noble Iewishe woman, the wife of Philo, to refuse riche clothes yet had ability and opportunitie to weare them. This therefore beinge true in this [25v] fowle, must reproue the intemperate humours of them that can obserue no meane in superfluitie, but esteeminge all lost which they spend not vpon themselues, repyninge onelie at the narrownes of their throates and bellyes because they are not capacious of more then ynough. Temperance is the playne songe vnto euery vertue without which no mans life is harmonious or melodious to God or his Countrey. Another memorable vertue or naturall part of the disposition and inclination of this fowle is their alacritie and aptnes to be tamed: for they quicklie lay aside their wildnes as may appeare in the forenamed fowle of Machlin who wolde take meate at the hands of the Queene amonge all her trayne, and flie from the house of his abode vnto the Courte and back againe, and so remayne with his keeper very tame. An excellent

* *stiuers* approximately five Dutch cents or one penny

propertie for yonge men to imitate that they may lay aside their obstinate wilfulnes, as this birde doth her wildnes, and neuerthelesse her wings were not impaired, but that they coulde support hir mounted vp aboue, or almost out of the sight of mortall men. No more wolde their honors be lessened if they were made more gentle, but vertue wolde giue them wings to soare aboue the strayne of comon persons whereby their glorie shoulde be extolled amonge men, and yet their soules flie nearer vnto heauen. Wonderfull is their loue to their younge ones, they breede in ditches and make themselues neasts like swannes with stickes layed together: they lay eggs in quantitie and nomber as swannes and obserue the same tyme of hatchinge. When they haue brought furth their younge ones they fetche them foode vntill they may adventure on the waters and fill them out of the storehouse of their oune throate. The Spanyards of the West Indians sent to Panama and Spagniola where they breede and take both the olde and the yonge by this stratageme:[11] when they finde them on the land they make fire about them, the olde ones presentlie runne to the fire, and labour with their wings to quenche the same that it burne not vp their younge ones: but *flatus vnde ignis extingui videtur inde roboratur*: the colde winde of their wings encreaseth and not extinguisheth the same. This harme shee reapeth by her labour, for the flame siengeth her owne wings and so maketh her vnable to flie away whereby the olde and yonge are both taken prisoners by the fowler. In this extremitie [26r] of their naturall loue they resemble an Asse, because shee will for the loue of her yonge ones runne through fire. Arsinoe, the noble Egiptian Dame whome Kinge Ptolomye desired in marriage bycause she was next heire to the kingdome, receaued many wounds in defence of her two younge sonnes whome her treacherous brother caused to be slaine in the armes of their mother. Bycause this fowle beareth such an extraordinary loue to her yonge shee hath ben stiled *Onnoget*, a foolishe birde, but who can dispraise Arsinoe for her naturall pietie to her children? none but such as are voide of humanitie. And why shoulde it not be more admired in a beast then a reasonable Creature? In one it is taught by reason, in the other it is ingrafted by Almighty God.

The voice of this birde is like the brayinge of an Asse, for when shee will make a noise shee pitcheth her beake in the water or in the earth and roareth like a horn winded by a weake breath or one that hath noe skill. They flie by troupes or Companies and all the defects of their bodies are supplied by their wings: for in them they paralell the Eagle or the best flyinge creature: beinge the largest and strongest parts of there body. The Alcatraz of Machlin so often remembred did remoue with Maximilians Army and went before it some yeres: it liued foure-score yeres, for one woman and her father had the custodie thereof fyftie and foure yeres.

The enemies vnto this fowle are all manner of flesh eaters as Rauens and Crowes, vultures and also Iayes: and the friendes hereof are onelie the storkes. They keepe yerelie a constant warre in Licia, about the riuer Xanthus which is thus described by Kiranides: *Mox primo vere pelagi* [*id est Ciconiæ*] *simul procedunt vt & aliæ aues anseres feri anates aliæque* [*quæ*] *ab Ægipto* [*Lybia*] *& Syria aduolant &c.*[12] In the beginninge of the Springe first the Storke with wilde geese, Duckes, and other fowles that come out of Ægipt, Libia, and Syria sett forward vnto Xanthus in Lycia, where they combate with Rauens, Crowes, Vultures, Iayes, and all flesh eatinge fowles: for those are alsoe foretellers of seasons and come thither about the same tyme. On the one side of the Riuer sitt the storkes and Alcatrazes: on the other side their enemyes before named where they sitt and feede within their seuerall Circuites and shores, that sixth month which is Aprill. They attend the onsett [26v] which is to be enterprised by two onelie, one for each side: which they beginne by a signall or greate crye, and that soundinge, both armyes meete with rare and remarkeable fury, tearinge from one another feathers, skynne, bloud, and fleshe. The feathers are yeerlie gathered vp by the Lycians wherewithall they fill their beds. When the Combate is ended they finde the water bloudy and many slayne on both parties: and the greater nomber they obserue curiouslie. ffor if the victory be with the water fowles (which they gather by the nomber of the dead) then they assure themselues of plenty of all manner of grayne: but if the Land fowles ouercome, then likewise they are perswaded of plenty and store of yonge Cattell. And so both parties depart away, bycause they are beasts and knowe not howe to vse victorye. Quayles and Alcatrazes are also greate enemies, although the imparitie be greate as witnesse Philes and Ælianus: and so much for their battells and hostilitie.

There are also certeine Allegoryes made out of these fowles and are appliable to the life and state of man for whome all things are made. ffirst this fowle sleepeth on the earth layinge her necke on her backe and her beake standing vpwards lookinge into heauen: which she doth to be the more ready and better prepared against her enemyes the land fowles. ffor althoughe it be one of the greatest yet doth it not want adversaries who being often tymes overcome yet watch opportunitie to reuenge more by policy then by streingth: whereof the nature of this fowle is not ignorant and therefore waiteth with sworde in hand and pistoll charged, to the intent that when it shalbe assailed it may not be surprised. Other thinke that it is a type of pietie, that when it resteth and by necessitie is constrayned to remayne beneath, yet the disposition is to be aboue: whither the beake tendeth and looketh. It is no matter whether way it be applyed: ffor in policy it becommeth men to be alwaye prouided for enemyes which watch[ing] advauntage to destroye doe neuer giue warninge: therefore they are the wisest that take warninge by their oune prouidence and preparacon. Let your loynes be girded and your lightes be burninge, saied the wisest and best that euer was: and againe, Beholde the fowles of heauen. *In signem sunt factæ, vt in hiis nostrorum morum vitia videremus & caueremus ea,* saieth St. Ambrose.[13] They are made for signes and tokens, that in them we might beholde our oune vices: [27r] and avoide them. Happie is the man, that takinge his sleepe on earth yet hath his minde lookinge towarde heauen where is appoincted our eternall rest and quietnes.

Our Sauiour Christ maie also be compared to this fowle who perisheth by fire to sauegarde her younge: *saluti filiorum intenta potius quam suæ vitæ: sic mortis atrocissimo genere conficitur: tanta in eo charitas, tantus Amor.* Intendinge more the Welfare of her Chickens or Cygnats then her oune life; and therefore dyeth a most cruell death. O greate charitie, O greate Loue: So did hee to quenche hell-fire burninge of vs vndergoe the most vnspeakeable paynes that euer man suffered and by death in them overcame paynes, hell, and death. O superaboundant Loue, O vnspeakeable Charitie, O incomprehensible mercie: *Vbi tuta nobis securaque requies nisi in vulneribus Saluatoris.* We are neuer in safetie but in the wounds of Iesus Christ our Sauiour.

They are also the Allegories of euill, ffor, saieth Orus: *Ægiptii: in Pelicano picto Amentem & imprudentem significant: non enim in alto nidum struit, sed in scrobe in terra parit: & ignem ab aucupibus circa nidum excitatum dum alis extinguere conatur seipsum comburit:*[14] The Ægiptians make a water pelican to signifie an vnwise and a madde man, bycause it hauinge wings to flie alofte yet maketh her nest belowe in a ditche vpon the earth, and seinge fire kindled by the fowlers about her nest, burneth vp her selfe to quench that fire. So doe the vnwise worldly men chuse to builde here where all thinges, yea, themselues shalbe destroyed with fire, whereas wiser men regarde perpetuitie aswell as present commoditie and therefore builde not in earth but in heauen made without hands. Neither doe they rake for their best foode out of the puddles, lakes, and brynishe waters of this worlde, but out of the pure runninge fountaine of the water of life which is aboue and descendeth from heauen.

A Glutton was signified by an Alcatraz such as was Dionisius, the sonne of Clearchus, Kinge of Heraclea, who was inclosed in fatt as a man in a Chest, hauinge to be seene but* his head, and fallinge into a lethargy thereby the Phisitians were constrayned to make longe sharpe needles to pricke him through his fatt vnto the quicke before he wolde be awaked: and Appicius also, another Nobleman of Rome, who spent a very greate patrimony vpon belly cheere, and at last [27v] fearinge least he shoulde want meate before he died, poysoned himselfe when yet he had ynough left to maynetaine an honest man. Of both these Alciatus made this Embleme inscribed *Gula.*

Curculione gruis tumida vir pingitur aluo
Qui Laron aut manibus gestat onocrotalum
Talis forma fuit Dionisi & talis Apici,
Et gula quos celebres delitiosa facit.[15]

A man that's shapte with swellinge panch and necke of Crane
With Alcatraz in hand or a sea gull
Apicius may or Dennis blase in fame
or any whome the trencher hath blowen full.

In like manner a loude and vnpleasant talker or prater together with a liquorous mouthed man are ioyned together vnder the signe of this bird.

Voce boat torua, prælargo est gutture, rostrum
Instar habet Nasi multiforisque tubæ:
Deformen rabulam addictum ventrique gulæque
Signabit volucer cum Truo pictus erit.

Paint Alcatraz and hee will shewe the man
That eates and rayles, for wide throates onelie praise:
A voice vnpleasinge and vnseemelie face him frame,
whome eatinge much and speakinge ill doth raise.

The vses of these fowles are briefelie these: Their fleshe is hard and worse then a Swannes whereof there is little vse: Cotys, Kinge of Thrace, caused them to be serued at table: and besides him I reade not of any that euer eate of their fleshe with approbation. *Grauis & ferini odoris neque grati est saporis,* saieth Gesner. The smell is stronge and the tast vnpleasant. Who wolde eate such greate fowles (saieth Iulius

* *to be seene but* i.e. nothing to be seen but

Alex) for there is not one good morsell in an Eagle or an Elephant or such like: and therefore our englishe prouerbe holdeth good: a Winge of a larke is worthe the whole body of a kyte.[16] So I conclude it is not good for the table.

The medicinall vses are not many. Onelie the Phisitians praise [28r] the gall; yt taketh away the morphewe* and cleanseth all externall blacknes vpon soares and other parts of the bodye: and rustie golde or siluer it cleanseth and restoreth to the prime and purified colour.

The skynne and bagge vnder their throate together with the skull is vsed by Fishermen insteede of a souppett† to cast water out of their boates bycause it is so compounded by the Workeman of nature that it will not corrupt by moisture, and so it lasteth for that vse many yeres together. It is also vsed for windowes insteede of glasse because it is transparant and suffereth the light to goe through like parchment or paper oyled. The skynne with the feathers is also vsed for Childrens beds because it is not harmed with their vryne and yet is softe to lye vpon. They growe exceedinge fatt in India after herringe tyme wherefore the Spanyards kill them with their pieces in greate aboundance and fleay them so they take out their fatt which they trie and melt, and therewithall make verie excellent Lampe oyle which smelleth sweete and burneth cleare. And thus much for this Alcatraz.

[II]

The Alchata, called in France *Vn Angell,* and in Greeke *Oenas.*

[illustration on p. 40]

[28v] This birde is of the kinde of Stockedoues called in Italy *Sassarolo,* in Arabia *Filacotona.* And Auicen calleth it *Alfuachat.* The Frenchmen in Monspessulum perswade themselues that it is the same which they call *Vn Angell,* whome I will not crosse, but consent vnto them. Aldrouand maketh this all one with the *Oenas* or *Inas* which Rondoletius sent figured and described vnto Gesner in these wordes: *Alchata est genus Columbarum siluestrium quarum alæ oblongæ sunt, pennæ & plumæ coloris coturnicum & Cutis extrema prædura: Quamobrem Medici in Orientalis regionibus præcipiunt huiusmodi Colum-*

* *morphewe* a leprous or scurvy eruption
† *souppett* properly "soppet" or "sopper," a dipper

bas excoriari, vt cutis remoueatur. Vulgo visae sunt in Syria pedibus nigris & valde breuibus. That is, The Alchata is of the race of wilde Doues whose wings are longe, but their feathers and quills of the colour of a Quaile, the outmost skynne very harde, for which cause the Phisitians doe advise to fleay it of before the fleashe be eaten. They are comonly seene in Syria, their feete being very blacke and shorte. All these thinges agree with the Oenas, and therefore the Reader shall not expect any more descriptions thereof. They are in quantitie like a partridge, the beake and clawes of the feete blacke, the feete redd, and the other feathers either a darke browne or an earthie colour tendinge to redd loame or sometyme gray or Ashecolour, the longe feathers of the wings blacke, which are very stronge and make the birde to flie apace. Some saie that the Greekes called it *Inas* or *Oinas* bycause the colour was like a wyne grape ouer ripe, other suppose it to be so called, because

it commeth in the tyme of vintage, and thereof it is called in Latine *Vinago. Oenas autumno potissimum conspicitur & capitur.* The Alchata is found in the Autumne and then taken when they bend themselues forward to drinke.[17] They liue in Mountaynes and amonge the Rockes beinge thereof called in Italy *Sassarolo,* that is, *Saxatilis* and thought to be the birde called *Semiramis* which also breedeth in Rockes. The necke is greene wherein are interlaced some blacke feathers. They are very good meate; especially for such as haue the dropsie, or an ill languishinge disposition. They breede twice in the yere and two at a tyme even as Doues. Athenæus relateth a miracle of this kinde sayinge: *Arbores non producturæ Ixiam nisi super quas auis ventrem deponens, deuoratum cuius semen excreuerit.*[18] The trees yelde no gumme except this birde leaue her egestion vpon the trees after shee haue devoured the foode thereof. And so much for this Alchata, which Dr. Turner professeth hee neuer sawe in Englande.[19]
[29r]

[III]

The Artenah or Diomedean Bird.

This Bird was not knowen to Plyny or the Auncients by any other name then *Auis Diomedea,* the Bird of Diomedes. Whereupon there are many auncient and not vnpleasinge fictions which I will relate to the Reader in the beginninge of this Birdes History, reservinge the moralls thereof vnto the Conclusion. Strabo[20] saieth that there are two Ilands of Diomedes whereof one is desert wherein Diomedes vanished away, the other inhabited by much people standinge in the Sea Adriatique; wherein was once a statelie and sumptuous Temple of Diomedes. This Temple was besett and as it were environned with certeine water fowles on euery side, of a very greate bignes hauinge harde and crooked beakes. If any Græcians came vnto the saide Temple they sate still, and stirred not either for their handlinge or presence of their persons: but if any straingers of other nations, they wolde arise, crye out, and smite one another with their beakes as if they wolde giue and take mortall wounds. And the poets fable that theis fowles were once men, and the Companions who holpe him in his warres against Mars and Venus, and therefore were turned into these birdes by the saide [29v] Heathen gods who watch perpetuallie about this Temple of Diomedes.

Ælianus doth somewhat vary from this narration, for, confessinge their transformation and that they were Greekes and the olde Companions of Diomedes, yet he differeth sayinge that they stirre not at the comminge of Barbarians or straingers but remayne in their places quiet and still: but at the approach of a Græcian strainger, *diuino quodam munere ab hiis auibus aditur,*[21] by a divine inspiration they goe vnto them, and with a friendlie spreadinge their wings abroade, doe imbrace them, as one friende taketh another in his armes when he giueth him most kinde salutations, and suffer them to handle their bodies without all terrour and dread, flyinge about their tables and into their bosomes: as if they did still professe themselues Græcians and studious to advaunce both their Countrey and Countreymen. So Ælianus.

Olde Silenus[22] telleth the fable another way. And saieth that when Diomedes returned home after the Troian warre, wherein he had wounded both Mars and Venus, in revenge of this bloud, his wife Ægialia fell in extremitie of passion to loue Comutas of Cyllabarus, the sonne of Stenelus, in so much as he was in danger to be slayne by her, hardly escapinge to the Altar of Iuno Argiua, where hauinge a while remayned in the Sanctuary of his person without hope of returne or recouery of his wife, fell into a desperation of that benefitt, and so forsakinge his oune Countrey came vnto to [*sic*] Kinge Daunus, raigninge at that tyme over a people called *Dauni* after his oune name. At which tyme it also happened that the saide Kinge, beinge much distressed with hostilitie and Warre, made greate accompt of Diomedes, whose fame and valour in the Troian warres was sounded throughout all Italy. Daunus promised him a part of his Kingdome if he wolde assist him against his enemies; which he performed happilie, and afterwarde built therein the Citie Agrippina. But Daunus proposed moreover vnto Diomedes, that for his rewarde he shoulde choose either all the spoile or all the Countrey of the Enemye which hee had conquered. But Diomedes wolde not choose for himselfe least he shoulde seeme overcouetous yet was very desirous of the enemyes Countrey, referred the matter by consent of Daunus to the election of his [30r] bastard brother Althæus. Nowe this his brother beinge fallen in loue with Euippa, the daughter of Daunus, and to gratifie the Kinge hopinge thereby to enioye the Damsell, gaue away the land from his brother to the Kinge: which bredd a greate indignation in the minde of Diomedes: and in greate passion he implored the aide of the gods for revenge. At whose petition they graunted that neuer seede or tree planted or sowen in that land shoulde prosper nor any livinge thinge engender to perfection without abortment except the Companions and people of Diomedes planted, sowed, or begott the same. So in short space all the Countrey became a desert, and as the dead sea, wherein nothinge liueth, to the greate astonishment of Kinge Daunus aboue all other. At last he consulted with an Oracle about this matter: from which he receaued this aunsweare: that the prayers of Diomedes and anger of Venus that had made Althæus in loue with Euippa was the true cause of all this desolation: and vntill that Diomedes was taken away or satisfied it coulde neuer be better. This aunsweare wrought murther in the minde of Daunus, for insteede of satisfaction, a fewe dayes after he caused Diomedes to be slaine as an enemy to the gods and him, which brought so greate a lamentation vnto his fellowes and other his followers that the gods in their compassion turned them all into this fowle: which nowe wee will describe accordinge to our first proposed methode.

It hath ben fondlie imagined to be a kinde of Sea gull or els the Alcatraz before handled bycause Ouid thus describeth it with notes common to one and other.

Si volucrum quæ sit dubiarum forma requiris
Vt non Cygnorum sic albis proxima Cygnis:
Magna pedum digitos pars occupat oraque cornu
Indurata rigent finemque in acumine ponunt.[23]

If forme of doubtfull birds thou doe demaunde

Which are not Swannes: as Swans yet lyly white
A broade clawe foote, and beake horne straite doth stand
Yet sharpe at ende his dyett fishe to byte.

[30v] These foure thinges agree with the Alcatraz: yet bycause he writeth of Diomedes bird, which is no where founde in all the worlde, but in the Island Tremiti, once called *Diomedea,* which is nowe possessed by a Cloister of Augustine Monkes, and their tenants: I will applie it onelie to this fowle in hand: seinge that the Alcatrazes are founde in many places of the worlde and neuer in the Island Tremiti. They are all water birds broade footed, crooked beaked, and very stronge, neither hath it any likenes with Herons or Fenduckes, sauinge in the starre* or baldnes in the forehead. But I finde it thus described by other whose footesteppes I will followe as neere as my englishe skill or labour can attayne. It is in quantitie as bigge as a fatt and fleshye henne, the necke and leggs being much longer, the colour was browne or darke ashecolour, the belly white like a white pigeons, the beake hard and crooked like an Eagles whereof the crooked end was blacke and the residue redd. And Pliny addeth that the sides of the beake both aboue and beneath had litle sharpe points like small teeth.[24] The eyes small, very fiery redd and beautifull, and the colour of the feete and legs was redd like the beake. They are onelie bredd in the foresaide Island Tremiti and are there called by the inhabitants *Artenna,* saieth Aldrouandus. Wherefore without studie or alteration of the name they haue in their oune Countrey, I haue here expressed them by that title. They flie by troopes and flockes like Cranes, whereof one is Guide flyinge foremost to leade the way, another is the dryver, behinde to constrayne them that loyter and be idle forwarde. When they haue occasion to emptie their bellies they slippe the ranke and sinke downe, turninge their head into the winde that so they may avoid their excrements without annoyance to themselues or their fellowes, by a kinde of naturall instinct obseruinge cleannes in euery feather.

When they make their neasts they digge with their beakes a hole in the earth in the side of some ditche which they frame and vnderproppe like a vault in a Rocke and so they make it hollowe with two passages, one toward the East, another toward the West. In the morninge they goe furth of the East passage because the light doth there first appeare: to awake and stirre them vp: at night they returne home by the West

* *starre* unfeathered area

because there the light lasteth [31r] longest. They cannot well abide the Sunne light, but avoide it: they are very fruitefull layinge many egges and hatchinge many younge ones.[25] Albertus writeth that they hatch in the winter and not in the sommer: because of the thunders in sommer which are very hurtfull to thir eggs. They liue vpon fishes which they take and hunt onlie in the [r?]ight season: they bite verie fiercelie and their voice is not much vnlike to the whyninge or ballinge of a Childe: which caused the Duke of Vrbinum arryvinge late in that Island by night and hearinge their voices to affirme confidentlie that it was the cryinge of Children, vntill the aforesaide Augustines shewed him one of theis fowles makinge such a noice where by he found he was deceaued.

The fleshe of this fowle is not for the table: bycause it eateth poysonfull or venemous fishes whereby they growe fatt aboue all other fowles so as their leggs cannot sustaine their bodies. Therefore Albertus thought to giue them a newe name more proper, callinge them *Gurguliones* which had ben good if *Gurgulio* had not before hand ben taken vp for weauills destroyinge malt. This their fatt is nothinge els, but bloud concreted; for it is of a saffron colour, and is most wholesome for an oyntment against all colde diseases, aches, and gowtes: but hurtfull to the whott.* They kill the fowle, and pull of his feathers, so they hange them vp in the whott sunne, settinge a vessell vnderneath it to receaue the droppinge fatt distillinge from the dead fowle. And thus much for the naturall history of this Artenah.

Touchinge the Morall of the first related fictions, it is concluded by the opinion of the learned, that Diomedes thus punished after that hee had warred against the gods: doth signifie that men in their felicitie spare not God himselfe but wound and wronge him which iniury shall neuer escape vnpunished. But Diomedes and all vngodly men shall tast of bitter death, and then their friends and followers shalbe turned into fowles, that is, take their wings and flie away from his adversitie, whom they so much admired in prosperitie. Orells they shall remayne without comfort, sorrowinge as beasts which haue lyved like beasts. Who [31v] had noe gouernement in their ioyes, shall haue noe end or measure of their lamentations.

* *whott* hot (diseases)

[IV]

Virginea birds without descriptions

Aushouetta

[illustration]

Aupseo

[illustration]

Aiussaco

[illustration]

[32r]

Artamokes

[illustration]

This is a Virginia bird the description whereof I had from Dr. Bonham. It is the thirde kinde of woode-spikers, hauinge a loftie Combe or Creste arisinge highest at the two Corners behinde and before: The colour of the feathers for the most part blewe from the toppe of the Creste vnto the rumpe, there are some browne blacke feathers and it hath also diuers white spotts, the belly is white, the beake and feete blacke. It is not good for meate bycause it liueth like other Woodspikers vpon flys, spiders, and oakwormes. ffor this thinge onelie the people of the Countrey admire it, and I doubt whether there be any Creature in all the worlde to paralell it: for it imitateth readilie all the seuerall voices of other birdes, so as Cleopatra Epiphanius or Kinge Mithridates which had three and twentie languages are not to be compared to this siely birde, that can singe with the thrushe, croake with the Rauen, crowe with the Cocke, mourne with the turtle, hisse with the peacocke and soe imitate the residue: for which cause our Countreymen in Virginia doe call it a Linguist, as if it had skill in many languages, and the people of the Countrey call it Artamokes.

[32v]

[V]

The Barnacle

This fowle vnknowen to the Auncients hath no certeine name amongest the Greekes, although some thinke it to be the *Chenerotes.* Amonge the Latynes also it is taken for the *Vulpanser,* which is not likelie to be true bycause then it had ben no strainger in Greece as all men knowe very well that vnderstand *Chenalopeke.* ffor this cause the learned haue invented Latine names either from the Originall, as *anser arboreus,* or from the branded colour thereof callinge it *Branta* and *Bernicla.* Issidore calleth it *Barliatam* and Albertus *Barbates.* In France they call it *Crabrans* or *Crauant* or *Oye Nonnette,* the Germanes *Baumganss*, *Wiewolanch*, and the Scotts *Clakis.* Yet Gesner casteth a doubt hereof and saieth that the Baumganss is not of the colour of the Barnicle, and liveth in fresh waters sometymes aboue and sometymes vnder. Notwithstandinge this difference I can finde no diuersitie but a

Barnicle and a *Baumganss* may be both one. And so I will proceede to the description.

They are lesser then a wilde-goose, and bigger then a Ducke, their colour inconstant, sometymes about the head and necke brownishe or a sandy colour: the breast white, the backe a blacke ashecolour, the belly a pale white or ashecolour, the wings a pale browne, the taile very small but of the same colour. [33r] It hath a halfe ringe about the necke white, the beake like a gooses but shorter and the head like a peacocke but without a Crest of feathers: the eyes very yellowe: the legs a bright browne with blacke spotts some round and some like halfe Moones, the feete broade and distinguished into clawes like a gooses foote. They resemble wild geese in their flight, voice, feedinge, and abode in moist, wett, fenny places. And Bellonius saith that the Males resemble the attire of a Monke and the Females of Nunnes, and therevpon in France they call them, as wee haue alreadie declared, *Oye Nonnette.*

They abound in Scotland and in Wales toward the Seaside and almost in all Ilands which are frequented with shippinge. But concerninge their originall there is a greate difference amonge Authors, where in some affirme that they are ingendred vpon the sides of shippes as they saile, or vpon trees, and nourished out of a putrified humour vpon the masts of shippes in the Sea, or plancks of shipwracke, other out of apples putrified without couplinge like other fowles; or out of shellfishe as Oysters and such like. The contrary is affirmed by Albertus, Bellonius, Æneas Siluius, and the Hollanders in the thirde part of the Dutche Voyages[26] wherein they relate that in a voyage which they made to the Northe pole they landed in Greenland and they founde many Barnicles sittinge vpon their eggs and hatchinge them: and when they came to their neasts they flewe away cryinge *Rot, Rot, Rot.* These *Rotganssen* or Barnicles come yeerelie into Holland and are there taken in greate multitudes: no man knowinge either their neasts or eggs and therefore they are wrongfully supposed to haue their origin all in Scotland or the Orcades vpon a tree, hanginge by a thicke skinne which groweth within the barke: or from the braunches hanginge over the water and droppinge their fruite thereinto: So they. Albertus calleth it an absurde opinion to belieue that they are engendred without couplinge, sittinge, hatchinge, out of wood or masts of shippes putrified: *Ego enim & alii complures mecum vidimus eas coire & oua fouere & pullos alere.*[27] ffor I myselfe and many with mee haue seene them tread, lay eggs, and hatch yonge ones. So Albertus. Æneas Siluius beinge in

Scotland a Nuntio for the Pope with James the 4th. enquired diligentlie of the tree whereupon it is reported they growe vnto perfection of feathers and lymmes till they fall off into the water and flie away. But hee sayed, [33v] *miracula remotius fugere*:[28] that these miracles fledd farre from him, and that the tree when he was in Scotland was remoued into the Orcades. So Æneas.

On the other side many haue most constantlie affirmed that they are engendred vpon trees or shippes or Masts in the Seas and that very often both in Englande, Scotland, and Wales: such haue ben seene and found cast vp out of the Sea, whose generation is thus described by Hector Boetius. Many haue curiouslie enquired after the beginnings of these Clakes or Barnacles, some attributinge their origin all to a tree, and some to the Sea water. But I (saieth Boetius) haue most dili[gen]tlie attended and applied my minde to the perfect knowledge of this so rare and miraculous worke in nature, and must needs attribute their generation rather to the nature of the Sea of the Hebrides then to any tree. If you tost a piece of wood into the Sea, after a certaine tyme it groweth full of wormes whose heads cominge furth of the wood, first doe grow to the head, wings, feete, and feathers of Barnicles, and at last fall of and flie away like other fowles of heauen: ffor the proufe hereof he alleageth two famous experiments, one in the yere 1490. at Buthquhan, and the Castle of Pethslege where arriued a logge or piece of wood with an infinitie Company of Barnicles vpon the same, whereat the Lord of the Castle beinge amazed, caused the same to be sawed asunder in the middle, which beinge performed he found the wood made hollowe within with wormes aliue in the same aboue number, and the Barnacles without, hanginge by a skynne, some formed, some vnformed, some with feathers, and some without feathers. So he caused the same to be conveyed to St. Andrewes of Tire where it was preserued a longe tyme. Two yeres after this there came a Shippe called the Christopher from the Hebrides (which was made of the wood of that Iland) vnto the Castle of Bruthe and afterward was brought to Leith neer Edinburghe, after it had rode at Anchor three whole yeres about the foresaide Ilands. When it was brought a land, they found it eaten of these wormes whereof it was verie full, and some of them were formed and other infourmed Barnicles. The like did I see at Brithelinston in Sussex about the yere 1596 vpon the mast of a shippe, which was drawen by the Inhabitants ashore, out of the Sea, and lay thereon the land, and was seene of many hundreds.[29] I say I sawe the fashion and shapes of an infinite nomber of fowles growinge betwixt two skynnes transparant, and hanginge by a litle thicke round skynne, like white leather hauinge their head, wings, and head visible within the saide skynnes. and some of them well neere feathered: but all dead, and no life appeared in them bycause (as wee that sawe them (beinge Scholers) coniectured) it had ben taken out of the water, about a weeke [34r] or eight dayes before. Nowe that this shippe mast came from the Hebrides into that part of Sussex I cannot easilie belieue, consideringe the wonderfull distance and contrary flouds betwixt the Scottishe Seas and the Ocean against Sussex. Therefore seinge there is not any doubt of the thinge, let vs enquire, whether there be any other Seas or Coast of England or Ireland wherein such fowles are so bredd beside the Hebrides. An Irishe man called Octauian did sweare vpon the Gospell vnto Dr. Turner[30] (as I thinke) that hee had seene them and handled them with his hands aliue in Irelande hanginge vpon shippes boughes fallen into the water and such like. And our Countreymen nowe in Ireland doe advertise me of the truth and daily experience hereof: so as I coniecture the aforesaide shippe mast loaded with Barnicles which I sawe in Sussex, was driven from Ireland vnto vs, and therefore they are bredd in moe places then one. And yet the Seas of that Climate wherein Ireland and Scotland are placed are most fitt for their generation, of what kinde or Countrey soeuer the wood be wherein they are bredd.

And that I may consent with Boetius, that the Sea and not the wood is their Mother or burden: I will proceede to some more experiments which hee vpon his credit hath recorded to all posteritie. If the wood were the cause of their generation howe came they to breede within shells? as is well knowen by this History followinge and the testimony of many thowsand that liue and are able to witnesse the same: Alexander Galloway, Minister of Kilde in Scotland, a man of greate learninge and judgement, ioyned in zeale with his Religion, drewe out from certeine Clifts of the Sea the weede Alga, seagrasse or reite,* whereunto he sawe growinge and cleauinge shells as if they had ben full of fishe, whereat he wondered to finde such things so vnited and conioyned together. But after he had opened it, and in steede of a fishe found a birde or fowle therein ingendred, he wondered much more then euer before, runninge speedilie to Boethus to acquaint him with his noueltie or miracle: bycause he knewe very well howe much that learned man was addicted to such raryties. And hereby it is manifest that the Sea is the cause of their generation (as once all the fowles were created out

* *reite* a sea-weed

of the waters) and not the seede of birdes, or any putrified trees or fruites [34v] thereof. And therefore Homer and Virgill did not without greate reason call the Sea *Patrem entium,* the parent and breeder of many things. Vnto these testimonies may be added some other that be more auncient. Isidore saieth, *Barliatæ e ligno putri crescunt*[31] *&c.* Barnacles, a kinde of fowle, doe growe out of putrified wood in the Sea or Sea Water, which hauinge floated in the same a certeine tyme sendeth forth a thicke humour. which groweth harde, is by litle and litle fourmed into a birde of the quantitie of a larke naked and vnfeathered, which soone growe to haue feathers, hanginge vpon the wood by the bill, and so moueth in the waters till it be ripe and perfect, and at last beinge full fligge,* vnlooseth his holde by the beake and flieth away. So Isidorus citinge the testimony of Iacob, a Bishop of Athens, to confirme his relation. I might adde hereunto the witnesse of Dentatus, an olde writer before Alexander ab Alex. and of learned Iulius Scaliger, Aristotle, Lobelius, and other, beinge moe in nomber and greater in auctoritie then those who deny the same. And for the obseruation of the Hollanders in their Northerne voyage, and Albertus that sawe them tread and sitt vpon eggs, hatch and bringe vp their younge, it may be aunsweared, that myce ingendred out of putrefaction doe afterwarde couple together and begett other: so may Barnicles engendred out of wood begotten by the humour of the Sea, by a naturall instinct fall to breede by copulation who were begotten by putrefaction and operation of the Sea, euen as the first created fowles which God made out of the waters.[32]

They liue vpon fishe in the waters and their oune fleshe is not precious for foode, neither are they very plentifull, bycause of their perill in generation. Yet England, Wales, Scotland, and Ireland knowe them. And Aristotle speaketh of a fowle called *Ephemeros* which is engendred in Hypanis out of certeine leafes which growe in the same Riuer. And againe, *Genus testatur ex nauigiis putrescente fæce spumosa adnasci,*[33] a kinde of fowle is bredd out of the putrified lees or froath of the Sea, cleauing vnto shippes. And so with admiration of this wonderfull worke of God, who yet worketh in the daylie creation of his olde Creatures, and not newe kindes I will conclude this discourse with some verses of Scaliger.

Idem canoris cantibus canunt lætæ,
[35r] *Qui pisciculentis nidulantur in stagnis,*

* *fligge* fledged

Herbilis anser, atque anas quiritratrix.
Qui corpus vrinantium Colymbarum
Suo æmulantur corpore et putris ligni
Ortum Crabranes Santones recognoscunt.[34]

Sweete songs they singe with ioyfull mery note
Who builde them neasts midst pooles of scaly race
Planten breedinge goose and whyninge ducke I wote
Whose body dyves Colymbus shape to face
Crabrans him call the Xantours for his birth
Bred in the sea of rotten wood, and not on earth.

[VI]

The Batte or Backe or Flittermouse

[illustration on p. 54]

I may beginne this History with the wordes of Varro, *Quid multa? Factus sum Vespertilio neque in muribus plane neque in volucribus sum.*[35] A Backe is neither a fourfoote nor a fowle. [35v] Bycause it seemeth to haue leggs vnder the wings some haue raunged it amonge myce and denyed it any place at all amonge birdes: but I will not followe their example bycause I finde in it more parts or qualities of fowles then of myce. And therefore, *Oportet pauciora sequi plura,* the fewer shall giue place and followe the greater and more noble Company. The wings I graunte are not feathered. *Volare est proprium auium,* yet it is the propertie of birdes to flie, and therefore I will rather ranke it amonge birds for the flight then for the feathers. It hath noe vse of the two leggs vnder the wings to walke or runne as a mouse; when it cleaueth or resteth to a tree or a wall, it standeth vpright vpon the hinde leggs like a birde. And therefore except wee take from it the wings and chainge the leggs wee must make it a bird rather then a beast. The sacred Scripture calleth it *Ataleph,* Leuit. 11. The Chaldees *Atalæpha,* the Arabians *Baphas,* the Persians *Anseb perak,* the Grecians *Nycteris* and *Nycterida phalke, Nyctalops,* and *phylesperos* bycause it cometh after sunne settinge. The Latynes call it *Vespertilio* and *Vespertillus* which Nonnius defineth, *animal biforme, dictum, quod vespere se ad volatum proferat noctis,*[36] a Creature of two formes so called bycause it flieth in the eueninge. Therefore Ouid.

Nocte volat, seroque tenet a vespere nomen.

It flies not in the day but night:
Therefore tis named of eueninge flight.

Albertus anatomizeth this worde *Vespertilio* of *Vespere vtens alis,* vsinge his wings in the eueninge. Valla tearmeth it *Semimus,* a halfe-mouse. The Italians *Ratto pennago,* a winged mouse, *Nottola, Sporte-gliono, Barbastrello, Pipistrello, Vipistrello,* & *Vilpistrello,* all of them corruptions of the Latyne worde. In Portugall it is called *Morcego,* or *Murziegalo,* a Blind mouse, *Ratte pennade* or *Ratte volage,* a flyinge mouse. In Germany *Fleedermauss.* The Belgians *Vledermuys* or *Vler-muys.* The Polonians *Metoperss* and the Illirians *Netopyrz.*

By all the names, the reason of the doubtfull nature appeareth, by-cause it partaketh both with beasts and birds. Aristotle therefore saieth: *Vituli marini & Vespertiliones quoniam ambigunt & vtrorum participes & neutrorum.*[37] The Seale and Batt walke on the land and water, flye in the aer, and walke on the earth; therefore they are saied to be partakers with all, and with none. The Backe [36r] wanteth both the taile of a beast and of a birde. Plato and after him Athenaeus call it *Auem non auem,* a bird no bird. Whereupon Plato made this riddle: *Vir non Vir, videns non videns, percussit non percussit, lapide non lapide, auem non auem, super arbore non arbore.* A man and no man, blinde and not blinde, strooke and did not strike, with a stone and noe stone, a bird and noe birde, vpon a tree and noe tree; which he expoundeth: *Eu-nuchus luscus excussit talictro pumicem in vespertilionem super sam-buco.*[38] A purblinde Eunuche fillippinge a pummyse stone did hitt a Batte sittinge vpon an Elderne tree. And hereunto I may adde another riddle of this birde made by Sempronius.

Nox mihi dat nomen primo de tempore noctis,
Pluma mihi non est, cum sit mihi penna volantis
In tenebris sedeo, nec me committo diebus.[39]

What call you mee whome nights first part doth name?
I winged am like other flyinge fowle:
Yet bald and bare, noe feathers hide my blame,
I sleepe in light, in night I flie like Owle. Vespertilio.

Macrobius is the greatest and stiffest defender or opponent to the birdlike nature of this Creature and most desirous to make it a beast, but his reasons are alreadie refuted in part and shalbe more fullie in the description. It was wittilie fayned of Ouid, that Aristippe, Leucippe, and Alcithoe, the three daughters of Minyas, were by the anger of Bacchus turned into Batts because they despised the Orgian sacrifices of that drunken god:

Adhuc Minyeia proles
Vrget opus spernitque Deum festumque prophanat[40]

The daughters of Minyas did despise
The god, the feast, and prophane sacrifice.

By the transformation of which three sisters I note the treble and threefolde difference of these Creatures. ffirst they differ in sexe, and therefore are they both male and female, as is most visible by inspection of their bodies. Secondlie they differ in parts, for they are not all æquallie proportioned, with one and the same specificall members. For some haue a head like a mouse and some like a dogge, [36v] some haue a taile and some none except a thicke skynne; and such are ours in Europe: but in Affrike they haue tailes like myce. Some haue but two

eares and some haue foure. Lastly they differ in colour: for they are founde some blacke, some yellowe, some pale, and some of an ashe-colour. Aldrouand doth thus describe the seuerall parts of a Batte that had foure eares, and was found nere vnto Bononia, of which race Bellonius saieth, that there are many in France.

The head was like a mouses head, and the eares grewe two at a side whereof the one was aboue the other and the vppermost was the greatest and conteyned the inferiour eare: for they exceeded the other foure folde. The beake was diuers from all other fowles: and gapinge it opened wide. The nosethrills like a calfes. Within the mouth it had foure and twenty teeth, twelve vpon a Chappe: and the foure foremost both aboue and beneath different from the teeth of myce, for they were not longer, but shaped like a doggs teeth yet all of them vpon both chapps were like a sawe, smooth and longe. And Bellonius obserued sixe and thirtie on a chappe, eighteene on a side. The Cheeke without side was couered with blacke longe haire. The tongue longe like a dogs, and other such beasts as eate fleshe, the apple of the eye blacke. They haue breasts like a woman or an Elephant, and therefore Macrobius cannot endure they shoulde be fowles but rather beasts, aswell for their teeth as for their breasts. But such examples wee haue of Apes that haue hands and besides walke vpright like men and yet are not to be accounted amonge men. So there are hennes which are couered with haire or woll like Catts or sheepe, and not with feathers and yet they are hennes. Even so the diuersitie of teeth and breasts in these birds maketh them not beasts. But to proceede with their breasts, they nurse their younge ones gyvinge them sucke and their milke is called by the Arabians *Sizarach*. Their wings are nothinge els but a skynne foulded vp in foure plights: beginninge at the shoulders, and are so fastened downeward to their leggs: they haue certeine articles wherewithall they foulde and contract them: or ells open and dilate them. Vpon the middle of their articles they haue crooked clawes or fingers whereby they sustaine themselues when they rest vpon a wall. Their wings are three fingers broade apiece, but from one winge to the other stretched out is more then halfe a foote: Their feete are foure ioyned to the lower parts of the wings, and are so stretched out from their belly not much vnlike the palme of an hand. Broade, diuided into fyve clawes and [37r] armed with sharpe nailes, their feete are ioyned to the sides of their tayle, although some Auncients haue denied that they had any at all, but resolueth better. *Qui negant volucrem vllam sine pedibus esse, confirmant & Apodas & Nycterin habere.* They which deny that there be any fowles which want feete doe with the same breath confirme that swallowes and Battes haue alsoe feete. The colour a more darke yellowe then a Mouses, they have a short tayle much like their wings. And Bellonius writeth that he sawe in Ægipt vpon the greate Piramides them that had longe tailes like mice hanginge downe beyond their wings three inches. And thus much for this kinde.

There are other kindes of Batts with two eares or at least with hollowes on the sides of their head like eares. Their breadth when the wings are stretched furth are two spannes, their members genitall are more visible behinde in the females, and of the males vnder the belly like a dogs. The Males haue blacker haires, and the female more yellowe, yet their colour varyeth as they growe in age. The eares blacke, the inwards are like a mouse. Pliny saieth that it hath but one hippe bone or rumpe like a birde. And so much for their description.

The generation and education of this birde sheweth the wonderfull worke and prouidence of Almighty God, for they lay not egges as other fowles but breede their younge ones in their belly like myce and Conyes. Therefore saieth Pliny, *Volucrum vespertilio parit tantum.*[41] Of all flyinge Creatures the Batte breedeth her younge without eggs. They are fourmed perfect in all their members before they come forth of their dammes belly: therefore their generation is vniuocall* proceedinge immediatelie from the seede of their parents, and not growing by addition of any parts after their litteringe. They make noe neasts, but leaue their younge in the chinke of a wall or in a hole ready fourmed to their hand. They neuer breede more then two at once accordinge to the nomber of their duggs, for if they bringe furth any moe, they cannot giue them sucke. As soone as they come out of their dammes belly, they take holde on the breasts and neuer giue ouer, or lett goe their holde, although their damme be killed or dye. Neuerthelesse when she flieth abroade shee maketh them lett goe, and leaueth them stickinge to a wall. She flieth not from them, till two dayes after their litteringe or hatchinge; then she forageth for foode, and first teacheth them to eate the secondines† wherein they were bredd: ffor Bellonius saieth that in Crete he dissected aboue twentie females which were all full of younge, and found them wrapped in membranes, [37v] beinge like to field mice in all things inward. They liue at the first vpon the milke of their damme, afterward they delight in all meates like mice, and ouer besides they are

* *vniuocall* according to normal generation between members of the same species

† *secondines* afterbirth

best pleased with the gnatts and small flies, which they take and hunt after in the Sommer euenings by their greediness. They will fall into trappes while they search after meate hanginge at baites. They are also engendred out of putrefaction (as Aldrouand writeth) by a certeyne excretion of the troubled and infectious aer; and hereof it commeth that there are such plenty of them in moist weather and moist places.

They loue darkenes and not light, therefore they covet holes and caues, dungeons and vaults, wherein they flie in the day as in the night. There is in Crete a pseaudo laborynth in a rocke within the earth betwixt Gnosus and Cortyna, which is soe darke that in the day tyme one cannot enter without a torche, and when you are therein the Batts flye so thicke about that they endanger to putt out the lights. And by the heapes of their excrements which lye in the Center or bottome of the place it is coniectured that their nomber in that rocke is very greate. The like are in the Caues and dennes of the Apennines whereunto they resort from all places about Puteoli. And at an Abbey in Misina* they found whole cartloades of their dunge, *Tectaque non syluas celebrant* (saieth Ouid),[42] they frequent houses rather then woods and deserts. They avoide colde, and flye not in the winter like Cuckowes and such other fowles; they sleepe and lodge in the place vnmoued, wherein they haue delighted in the Sommer.

The reason why they loue darkenes better then light is bycause they see better in the darke then in the light or day tyme; and the cause why they see better is thus discoursed by Aphrodysæus: *Feles, Hyænæ, & vespertiliones interdiu nihil fere videant, acute omnia per noctem conspiciunt, spiritum quidem illum visorium & tenuissimum & dilucidissimum habent, ita vt per noctem incrassescens modice, idoneus ad rerum conspectum reddatur &c.*[43] There is a certeine spiritt of seinge in the eyes of all that haue sight which beinge of it selfe thicke maketh them to see better in the day then in the night, bycause it groweth more congealed in the absence of the Sunne, and therefore cannot reache vnto the visible obiect. But Catts, Hyænæs, and Batts doe see better in the night then in the light, because the spirit of their sight is thinner, and so thickeninge in darkenes is more capable of a visible obiect then in the day, wherein the Sunne did extenuate the humour aboue measure. They flie therefore both eveninge and morninge, whose flight is thus described by Petrarch.

[38r] *Son animal al mondo di si altera*
Vista che contra il sol pur si difende

* *Misina* Messina

Altre però che'l gran lume[li] offende
Non escon furor se non verso la sera.[44]

The sight of some is of such state & pride
That gainst the sunne they both flye & gaze
And other are so weake & tender eyed
That night[s?] their ioy & light is their amaze.

The parasyte in Athenæus which watcheth all tymes and all occasions of artificiall content, seemeth to confesse that they flie al the night longe, and not onelie morninge and eveninge. *Si frigus sub dio merula sum sine minimum dormiendum, vespertilio aut Lepus.*[45] In the day tyme I am a blacke birde, and if I must watch, and not goe to bedd, then can I play the hare or the Batte. And this was the cause of that pleasant fiction of Lucian,[46] that there is a certeine Riuer which is called *Nyctiporus,* of the Battes that liue about it, which neuer ceaseth runninge about the Island of sleepe wherein are bredd these birds in aboundance, and vpon the same Island there are greate woods of Poppey and Mandragoras wherein they sitt and solace themselues. They were consecrated to Proserpina, the fayned Goddesse of darkenes, bycause they flie in the night when darkenes causeth men to sleepe. Their voice is not the voice of myce nor of birds but a softe barkinge or schriechinge. Therefore Ouid.

Minimam pro corpore vocem,
Emittunt peraguntque leui stridore quærelas.[47]

Small is their body, but smaller is their sound:
ffor in a softely schriech, their whyninge they propound.

The onelie and principall thinge which maketh it as a birde is the flighte, and winge-crafte thereof, although it want feathers, wherein appeareth the power and wisedome of the blessed Trinity who without feathers and quills causeth this Creature to mount aloft in the aer.

paruos membrana per artus
porrigitur, tenuesque includunt brachia pennæ:

By synewes small, they stretch their flyinge skynne,
and weake bare quilles their armes contayned in.

St Basill saieth they flie not direct but wyndinge and in a compasse bycause of their continuall feare: neuer very high from the earth or much aboue houses; when they rest they vse not their leggs, [38v] or sitt as birds, but the crooked clawes vpon and vnderneath their wings which Homer saieth Vlisses did imitate when he came to the braunches of a tree, *οὔτε στμρίζαι ποσὶν ἔμπεδον οὔτ᾽ ἐπιβῆναι·*[48] Whereupon he coulde not clymbe nor walke. At their rest they are many together so ranked as if they were in a chaine, which caused also the same Homer to compare the soules which Mercury carried to hell, *ὅτε νυκτερίδες μυχῷ ἄντρου* like Batts one cleauinge to another as they flie out of their dennes, yea, sometymes they flie carryinge their younge ones about them hanginge at their breast, who will not be lost or fall of but lyve and die with their holde; and without any other helpe of their dammes. When they flie not abroade but keepe home it is a signe of rayne and tempestuous weather, but if they flie many and frequentlie, it betokeneth heate and a very calme season, saieth Gratarolus. Hiero the Tyrant of Sicily beinge but a yonge man, and desirous to proue his fortune in the warres, by the prouidence and Counsaile of the Soothsayers, did tell them one day that he found sittinge vpon his shielde an Eagle and vpon his speare a Batte: whereupon they promised him that he shoulde be stronge and wise. But the inconstancie of the heathenishe learninge may appeare in this: That whereas the Augurs of Sicily did attribute wisedome and circumspection to the Batte, on the other side the Ægiptian Hieroglyphikers did paynt a Batte to signifie a bold, rashe man that will needs be flyinge without feathers. They also deciphered a good mother that bredd vp and nursed her children by a Batte. They are but litle in body but cruell in mynde, for they will bite perniciouslie, and cominge to naked members drawe bloud out of them: especiallie the Indian Battes. ffor Peter Martyr writeth that when the Spanyards came first into the West Indies, they were extreamely annoyed with the bytings of batts, whereby many of them lost so much bloud, that their lyves were endangered, and some consumed and died. And not onely men but Catts, dogs, and hennes.[49] The Inhabitants of Peru were so annoyed with them, as the poets haue fabled of the Harpyes and Stymphalides,* that they were forced to forsake their Countreys and seeke newe habitations, because in the first part of the night before midnight they came like madde dogs and bitt them; for in that Countrey they are as bigge as Pigeons. And the like is reported by Pompilius Azalius, the Portugall, of one Countrey of East India where they sett vpon naked passengers, and

* *Stymphalides* odious birds of prey in Arcadia, their destruction the sixth labor of Hercules

many tymes so beate them with their wings that they overthrowe and kill them. If these thinges be true Pliny may be well controwled* for accusinge antiquitie that it fabled. One Prince Herodotus,[50] goinge to [39r] gather that pretious Cassia about the Marshes of the East Indians, h[ee?] was constrayned to fight with Battes and winged Serpents, that with incredible fury sett vpon him and his Company; and this, saieth Pliny, was but an invention, *augere rerum prætia,* to enhaunse the price thereof, and make men pay the dearer. Euen so the Spanyards and Portugalls to encrease the credit of their adventures, and for the commendation of their oune valour and piety, haue written what Giants and Monsters they haue conquered in those nations, whereas they haue not ben opposed but with naked men, not with weavers beames in their hands,[51] but with reedes and arrowes headed with flints, or such stones, and yet their valiant deedes haue exceeded the Romans and the miracles by which they prospered those of Ioshuah and the Israelites. Those fewe honest men amonge them which haue blazed their cruelties doe sufficientlie convince their valour, for crueltie cannot admitt courage as Mauritius saied of Phocas, *Si timidus crudelis est,* If a Coward then cruell.

The enemies of Battes are many, for I knowe not what friends they haue. The storke and they are at greatest feude, as Pliny, Elianus, and Zoroaster haue written; for if a Batte touch the egges of a storke, they corrupt and neuer come to good. Wherefore the storkes doe guard their neasts with Plantane, for that (say the former writers) causeth an astonishment and terror to fall vpon the Battes, when they touch it; *Platanus aduersatur Vespertilionibus.* Plantane is an enemy vnto Battes, and therefore if it be hanged vp in houses, they dare not enter. So are they compelled to flie away from perfume of Iuye. There are, saieth Tully and Delachampius, a kinde of venemous Emmetts, which are driven away from those places where the heart of a Batte is preserued. The Locust is afraid of Battes, for (saieth Democritus) they will flie ouer a tree where a Batte hangeth dead. They are saied to loue Pigeons, for if the head of a Batte be hanged vp in the toppe of a doue coate, the Pigeons thriue the better. They loue not light, as some say, they loue any bright things as a torche, candle, or bright sworde, for if you sett vp one of these in a house they will instantlie flie vnto them, whereby they are offended, fall doune, and taken. But the secreate reasons of their amitie or enmitie are vnknowen to vs, and I haue written these thinges more out of the creditt of other men then myne owne

* *controwled* called to account, reproved

experience. And therefore if any man can teache me otherwise, I shalbe as willinge vpon better [39v] reason to change and believe him before them.

Allegories, Emblemes, and vses of Battes

St. Basill writinge vpon the 2. Chap. of Isaiah ver. 20. where the Prophet threateneth the people, sayinge: In that day shall a man cast away his siluer idoles, and his golden idoles (which they made to themselues to worship) to the mowles and to the Backes &c. hath these discourses followinge. *Est vespertilio animal nocturnæ caliginis appetens,*[52] &c. The Backe or Batte is a lyvinge Creature desiringe darkenes, and not abidinge the light of the Sunne, flieth into secreate and solitary corners. And are not the divells also such Creatures? doe not they loue darkenes more then light? doe not they flie from the true light? who saieth, I am the true light, that lighten euery man which commeth into the worlde. The Batte hath Winges without feathers by which she flieth, beinge nothinge ells but skynne. So the devills are incorporeall: flyinge without the feathers of humane desires, but sett vpon naturall lusts, doe harden themselues and others till they be consumed. The Batte is fourefooted and yet flieth, beinge neither good of foote nor yet of flight. Such are the Diuells, neither good flyers like Angells, nor good walkers like men, that is, neither good Angells nor good Creatures, bycause they want the dignitie of the one and the nature of the other. Noe other birds haue teeth besides the Battes, and the divells are more greedie of revenge then any other Creatures. The Battes lay noe egges but breede their younge perfect without the delay of broodinge and hatchinge. Euen so the devills doe more speedilie giue perfection to their evill workes then any other, insomuch as they are no sooner seene and borne, but they worke a malicious end. So farre St Basill.

Others compare Batts and their qualities to the diuersities of sinners. ffirst they say leacherous persons are like Batts bycause the eyes of the Adulterer wayte for the twylight; so doe Batts. Againe they liue by eatinge dust of walls and in narrowe chinkes: so doe the Couetous, for they care for nothinge but this worlde: like the enemyes of our Lord, they licke vp the dust makinge more reckoninge of one droppe of

Aurum potabile [40r] then a whole viall of *Aqua Coelestis*. More-over this bird will eate the oyle out of the Churche Lampes: so the envious rob good people of the grace and praise which belongeth vnto them; they are glad of another mans harme but sory for another mans good.

Inuidus alterius rebus macrescit opimis.[53]

The envious heart lookes leane and wan:
To see the weale of another man.

They sticke to the walls and liue in secreate holes betwixt the tiles of houses or ruynes of Chimneyes. Euen so doe proud persons advaunce themselues aboue their neighbours by the goods, lands, and fauours of other men. And thus farre of the evill that is obserued in this fowle.

The good nowe followeth. As they flie into the holes and ruynes of Rockes wherein they finde diuers mansions, so they are types vnto vs of pietie, for our Sauiour Christ is a Rocke and his blessed woundes are the holes whereunto we must flie to hide ourselues vnlesse wee will want protection. And St Basill againe: *Commoueat te quæso mutuus amor vespertilionum qui longa veluti catena constricti inter se cohærent ne vnquam seperationem ac vitam solitariam societate atque communi-one præstantiorem esse existimes.*[54] That is to saie, I pray be moued by the mutuall loue of Battes, for they agree together and flie together and rest together, as if they were tied in one chaine: so doe you avoide seperation and neuer thinke that a solitary life is better then a societie and friendshippe: And thus much may suffice for their Allegoryes. Whereunto I will adde this one Embleme of Alciatus.

Vespere quæ tantum volitat, quæ lumine lusca est,
Quæ cum alas gestet, cætera muris habet.
Ad res diuersas trahitur, mala nomina primum
Signat, quæ latitant iudiciumque timent.
Inde & philosophos, qui dum cælestia quærunt,
Caligant oculis, falsaque sola vident.
Tandem & versutos, cum clam sectentur vtrumque,
Acquirunt neutra qui sibi parte fidem.
Assumpsisse suum volucri ex Meneide nomen,
Socraticum Authores Cherephoonta ferunt.
Fusca viro facies, & stridens vocula, tali
Hunc hominem portuit commaculare nota.[55]

[40v] In Englishe thus.

What meanes that purblinde Batte which day light flies?
  Wingde like a bird and membred like the myce:
To diuers things applied and first to men of evill fame
  they are. They lurke and feare the Iudge revenginge vice:
Then heathen Sophyes searchinge thinges of heauenly name,
  but without truth with false and darkesome eyes.
Then Ambidexters praysinge good and ill they touche,
  yet neither side may trust their subtile faith.
So Authours write Cherephoon was such
  a versipellean [*sic*] man[;] notes of a batt he hath:
A swynishe face, a voice with whyninge strayne:
  defilde with craft, which playnesse he did fayne.

Nowe followe the vses of this birde. ffirst it is apparant by the Lawe of God. Leuit. 22. that it was forbidden to be eaten because of the doubtful nature thereof. Yet men ignoraunt of the lawe, haue eaten of them: for Strabo writeth thus: *In Borsippa vrbe Babiloniæ quæ Mesopotamiæ coniuncta est inter Euphratis conuersiones maximam esse vespertilionum multitudinem qui longe maiores sunt quam in cæteris locis capiuntur eosque in cibum condiri.*[56] In Borsippa, a City of Babylon standinge in the windinge of Euphrates, there are greater Battes then those that are taken in other Countreys, and they are salted and eaten. In the East Indyes in the Island of St John they doe the like: but first they scalde them in whott water, and then flay them so their fleshe looketh as white as anie Chickens. And Iulius Scaliger writeth that in Catigan within the Sea called *Mare del Sur* they eate Battes, *Aquilæ magnitude & Gallinæ sapore*, beinge as bigge as an Æagle, and as good meate as a henne. And thus much for the artificiall vses.

Nowe followe the medicinall vses wherein it shall appeare that this birde is not onelie phisicke but also a phisitian, ffor Aldrouand telleth this History followinge vpon his oune credit.[57] A certeine Monke lay sicke of a pleurisie, ioyned with a burninge feaver, whereupon a Chirurgeon was sent for to let him bloud, beinge the onelie remedie in this Case. But he assayed in vayne, for vsinge all the arte he coulde, yet he failed, and coulde drawe no bloud: whereupon he was giuen over as a forlorne hope, and his fellowes forsooke him, takinge their last farewell [41r] of him, thinkinge neuer to see him walk againe in this worlde: or that he shoulde haue seene the next morninge light. But the next day came; and they returned to visite him, because they heard he was alive, and beinge come vnto him, they found him comforted and in good hope of life, wherein hee was not deceaued. And they demaundinge the cause of his ease and soe sodaine alteration hee made this aunsweare: Oh (saied he) your Chirurgeon did not strike me in the right place, for this night I had another which hath drawen bloud sufficient, for as I lay with my legge out of bed bycause of heate, there came a Batte and bitt me, with furye hanginge fast, vntill she had sucked her belly full; and left the veyne open as you may perceiue, and so hee recouered. ffor as we haue alreadie shewed, they will bite in the night pernitiouslie like gnatts and not be afraied. By which History it must needs be confessed, that by accident they may be Phisitians and fedd with a mans sicke and superfluous bloud: doe good vnto themselues and also to the pacient. But we will for conclusion adde their corporall medicines, and so shutt vp this History.

Against the swellings of the melt* Auicen prescribeth this medicine or Composition: ffirst take off the head of a Batte, and then drie all the residue vntill it may be bruised to powder. Afterwarde put that pouder into your drinke, the quantitie as much as you can take vp in three fingers, and drinke them with syrrup and vineger. Againe take seauen fatt Battes, cast away the heads, and cleanse their bodies verie pure. Put them into a vessell full of vinegar and so boile them in a furnace, the mouth of the vessell beinge stopped vp close with clay. So after it is throughlie boyled, take it forth againe and coole it, and then bruise in the boiled vineger those bodies with your fingers, and cast them away. Drinkinge thereof every day two drammes, and it is an approued medicine. Galen teacheth howe to apply them against the gowte. ffirst seeth three Batts in rayne water, and afterwarde adde vnto them bruised lyne seede foure ounces a piece, three rawe egges, one cuppe full of oyle, of oxe dung and waxe foure ounces apiece, mixe and worke all these things and apply them warme to the place and partie diseased. In like manner he prescribeth an oinctment to take away haire out of Battes taken aliue, and putt into lyme wherein they must continue till they putrifie.

[41v] There is an oyle against the gowte and all paynes of the synewes which they make out of this Composition. ffirst they take twelue Battes and the hearbe called St Iohns wort, and sixe ounces of olde oyle, hartwort, oyle of Castors, and herbe Mary, foure drammes of the first and three of this last. Seeth them all to an oyle and then vse

* *melt* spleen

them. Against the cleauinge of the eyeliddes the bloud of Battes is good, as Serenus writeth sayinge.

Ergo locum crinis vulsi continge cruore
Quem dat auis tremulis simulat quæ pellibus alas.[58]

ffirst plucke the haire, then touch it with red dye:
Of bird thats plumeles yet with skynnes doth flie.

Yet the most iudicious writers of our tymes adde the seede of Hemlocke, thereunto alledginge that otherwise it wanteth the force of refrigeration, for the bloud of a batte is not colde ynough without some colder addition. Pliny addeth moreouer a magicall medicine out of the bloud of a Batte torne in pieces, for hee saieth that if a mans belly be annoynted therewithall it keepeth him from the belly ache a whole yere afterwarde. The gall of a Batte mixed with vineger cureth the bitinge of spiders or shrewe mise. The milke cureth the white spotts and thicke skynnes of the eyes. The bearinge about of the heart of a Batte kepeth a man wakinge vntill he lay it aside againe: and the same vertue is ascribed to the head beinge tyed to the right arme of the watchman. Whereas also wee haue shewed that the bitings of Battes especially in West India is venemous and hurtfull, I thinke it also requisite to expresse the remedie for the same: which is effected by warme water, or by sea water, or by whott ashes out of the fire, so as they may be endured vpon the wounde. Whereas also the heart and head beinge eaten are poison, the same remedies cure it which doe also cure the bitinge of a madde dogge, vomitinge beinge first prouoked by butter and vineger and newe milke powred vpon the head of the pacient. And thus much for the History of this Nightbird.
[42r]

[VII]

The Birgander or Bergander

[illustration on p. 66]

This Birde is the same that the Auncients called *Chenerotes, Cerамides*, or *Chenalopex,* bycause the shape is like a goose but the disposition like a craftie Foxe: Chenalopex was the race of Laconian dogs, begotten

betwixt dogs and foxes. The Latynes called it *Vulpanser,* the Frenche *Bieure*: bycause like a beuer, it feedeth both on land and water. Gesner thinketh it may be the same which in Italy they call *Ciccus* and *Oca sterna,* which is found in one of the Islands of Poe, and called by the Germanes *sternganss*; havinge the winges and backe of an Ashecolour, the other parts white except the spotted breast, the feete whitishe and broade footed like a goose. But it seemeth this fowle is nowe no where so frequent as with vs in England, especiallie in the Isle of Tenett, yet sometymes they are seene in the Riuer of Thames. They are bigger then Duckes and lesse then geese lyvinge in the waters but breedinge and layinge their Egges in Conyholes which they finde in the Rockes. And it is coniectured by some learned men that our Forefathers the Englishe Saxons did call it *Bergander*, bycause it loueth Mountaynes or Boroughes which were auncientlie called *Bergh* and by corruption of that worde a *borrough* and by addition of the Male goose a *Bergander.*[59]

[42v] Ælianus praiseth the Latyne name *Vulpanser, quod ex ingenitis naturæ suæ rebus trahit, Cum enim anseris speciem habet, tum probe cum vulpe callida improbitate comparari potest &c.*[60] bycause it taketh name from the inbredd and vndeceiuable disposition of its oune nature, ffor althoughe in shape of body it resemble a goose, yet in the improbitie of minde, it may be compared to a foxe. And although in bulke of bodie, it be inferiour to a goose, yet in the internall subtilitie of minde it farre surpasseth, and in courage to invade or offende his enemye. ffor yf any bird of prey or Catt of the earth sett vpon it, hee defendeth himself by his owne prowesse. Hee vseth the same arte to defende his younge ones which the partridge doth and for their safe-

guarde doth fall into the hand of the fowler, rather then that they shoulde miscarrye, ffor which cause the Olde Ægiptians made a Hieroglyphicke thereof, to signifie a sonne beloued of his parents. ffor if it happen that any of their younge ones be taken, both the Male and female will offer themselues alsoe, either to dye with them or deliuer them.

There was a tyme when our Forefathers did as much esteeme of the fleshe of this fowle, as of any other water fowle, which caused Pliny to write, *Eo suauiores epulas non nouisse Britannos.*[61] The Bryttaynes knewe no meate more delicate then the Bergander. And their egges alsoe were much sought after, for next to the peacockes they were accompted the best, and were preferred before the egges of hennes in the opinion of Epanetus. The Medicines or Ciuill vses of this fowle are fewe or none that I can reade, more then I haue expressed: except this obseruation of Aretæus, *Sarmentorum cineres admistos adipe Leonis pantheræ vrsi vel Chenalopecis contra facie tumores illitos iubet.* Annoynt the swellings of the face with the ashes of vinespriggs mixed with the fatt of Lyons, Beares, Panthers, or Berganders. And so I must cutt of the farther description of this fowle, by reason of the want of necessary matter. ffor I may resemble it to a poore profitable Citizen which cannot haue his deserued praises, least they shoulde eclipse the glory of other men.

[43r]

[VIII]

The Bramlyn

This litle Bird is called by Aristotle *Orospizes,* of a Mountayne, and a *Fynche,* and thereupon the Latynes giue it the like name *Montifringilla,* a Fynche of the Mountaynes. In Italy it is called *Frenguello Montanino,* in France *Pinson Montain,* in Heluetia *Maldfinck* and *Thanfinck* and wee in England a *Bramlyn.* The Germanes *Rouuert, Schneefyncke,* and *Winterfincke,* bycause it commeth in the wynter tyme. As the bird is litle, so there is litle to be saied of it, beside the description which must be attended bycause it is the Worke of God, wherein is lesse error then in the most exquisite invention or doctrines of the wisest men of this worlde. The quantitie or bulke of bodie exceedeth not a sparrowe. The beake sharpe, thicke, and of a Clay colour: but a little blacke at the ende: the tongue sharpe and thicke, the crowne, backe, and necke of an yron and black colour entermingled, a little white on the rumpe. The taile consisteth of twelue feathers, and they are distinguished into blacke and white, that is, one blacke and another white. The wings are parted with two little white bands or laces, which also are seperated by another blacke. The vppermost of the two is the greater, beinge a clay or darke white aboue, and more bright beneath the throate; next the beake blacke, and from thence to the breast, a colour compounded of yellowe and earth colour. The belly white, and the feete like a Chaffinche [43v] but stronger and better coupled. The female is more redd vpon the Crowne, necke, and backe and not so blacke as the Males. And of the laces or lynes in the wings the vppermost scarce appeareth. The Male looked vpon and held vp against the Sunne, seemeth to haue some blewe feathers in his necke: but the females head is more white then the Males. And thus much for their description.

The voice of this litle birde is not very sweete when it singeth, and therefore is not nourished for the Cage, as is the Chaffynche except for traynes* or foode of haukes, for it will squeake out a litle, and then breake of like a man interrupted in a sentence, or as the meawinge of a litle Catt. They haue other voices alsoe, especiallie if they be kept tame in Cages: where they may heare the voices of sparrowes and other like birds: for then they endeauour to imitate them: and take vp the shredds of many tunes, which make as good musicke as dry chippings doe good meate. They are tamed quicklie, and taken with no greate difficultie, beinge nothinge so subtile as other small birds to avoide the snare. They liue and flie by flockes inhabitinge the coldest Countreys in the Sommer, and in winter come into other places of a more moderate temper. Aris-

* *traynes* a train is "a live bird attached to a line, or a lame or disabled bird, given as an enticement to a young hawk during its training" (*OED*)

totle saieth they will eate small wormes, and in all other things resemble the Chaffynche. They are good meate for such as will eate them. In immoderate colde weather they are so enfeebled that a man may take them in his hand; therefore they flie in temperate regions and come to vs in the beginninge of winter, accordinge to this olde verse with which I will conclude.

Aduenisse hyemem fringilla renunciat ales.[62]

The wynters tyme, that men may knowe:
Bramlyns come the same to shewe.

[44r]

[IX]

The Bullfynche or Blutfynche

[illustration on p. 70]

This also is a small and wormeatinge birde called by Aristotle *Pyrrhula*, and by the Latynes *Rubicilla,* by the Italians *Suffuleno* and *Stufflotto,* and sometymes *Franguello montano,* and about the Alpes *franguel Inuerneng,* a winter fynche. By the frenche *piuoine* and *pion,* by the Germanes *Gutfinck, Brommeiss, Bollenbysser, Bollebick,* and *Rotuogel, Hail Goll,* and *Blutfynck,* from whence cometh our Englishe worde *Bullfynche,* ffor the worde *Blutfincke* is giuen bycause of the bloud-redd necke it hath. It is also called in Austria *Gympel,* in Heluetia *Gugger,* in Brabant *pilart,* in Saxony *Laubfincke* and *Thumpfaff* and *Gumpel,* and the female *Quetschfyncke* and about Francford *Pfafflyn,* and the Illyrians *Dlask.* I will nowe leaue the names, and proceede to the description. They are distinguished, I meane the female from the Male, on this manner, for the female is a pale Chesnutt colour on the breast, but the Male, a bright redd like bloud, hauinge a blacke beake very short and broade in forme like a triangle, the tongue broader then any other birdes of that bignes, beinge at the ende bare, tender, and fleshie, where it tasteth the meate, but vpwarde couered with a thicke skynne like a horne. The backe is of a grayishe colour, with some blewnes therein, the Crowne of the head, tayle, and typpes of the Wings blacke: and the wings white next to the belly. Their leggs and

feete very small and brownishe: the rumpe feathers white vpon blacke quills: and two or three of the longe feathers in the wings [44v] are couered with small white feathers. But their onely beautie lyeth in their breast, the vnderpart of their throate and forepart of their belly which is like the purest redd leade or pomegranate liquour. And so much for the description.

Our Dr Turner writeth that in Sommer tyme it keepeth in the Woods, Mountaynes, and fields: but in the Winter it descendeth to the valleys and draweth neere to mansion houses.[63] It breedeth in bushes or hedges where it maketh a round neast of small strawes and dried grasse, and layeth not aboue foure or fiue egges in the same before it sitt, and hatche the younge ones. They eate wormes, small buds, and tender leafes of trees: also plants, as night shade, and whatsoeuer looketh redd in the winter: hempseede, water elderne, and the blossomes of apple and peare trees, and grapes. It is a birde easilie taken, quicklie tamed and taught to imitate the sound of a pipe and some wordes also of men, by reason of the broade tongue. They neuer chainge colour, but remayne constant all the yere longe. Both Male and female singe very sweetelie, especiallie when they are caged in houses, where they heare blackbirds, thrushes, or pipes musicallie tuned by the voices and art of musique. And so I will lett this bird flie away from my penne.

[X]

The Buntinge or Heathlarke.

[illustration on p. 71]

[45r] This litle bird was not knowen to Aristotle, or at the least not described by him, the best Latynes call it *Terraneola, rubetra,* & *Alau-*

dula. The Italians *Lodola campestre, petronella,* & *Regio.* The Germanes *Heidlerch* and *Sanglerch* and *Himmellerch* and *Holtzlerch,* and the frenche *Alouette.* The quantitie is lesse then a Larkes, it wanteth a Creast on the head, it is shorter beaked then a larke, and the clawes are all of equall length. The head somewhat blackishe, hauinge in it some yellowishe feathers, the breast spotted with little small browne markes, the belly a pale white, the backe a mixt colour of a bay ashe and blacke. The wings and taile like the backe, except in either of them two pale white feathers. The Male is somewhat blacker then the female. They make their neasts on the ground especiallie delightinge in heath and such like places, or els in iuniper and amonge thornes. Their voice is preferred before the Larkes, as much sweeter and more acceptable: wherefore the Germanes call it *Sanglerch,* a singinge Larke. They also flie higher then Larkes, for which cause also they call them *Himmel-lerche,* for they also seeme to haue stronger wings bycause they flie oftener, and tarry a longer tyme in the aer then Larkes. In other thinges they are altogether like larkes, and are taken by fowlers with the same snares, netts, and devises. They liue in Sommer by couples a male and a female, but in winter by greate flocks and troupes together: so as they resemble the fashions of reasonable men who in the Sommer of prosperitie part asunder and desire a solitary life, more for desire of wealth then content of nature, but in the winter of adversitie they cleaue together and desire company, partinge stakes* with multitudes when they haue litle, who refused to diuide with a fewe when they had greater plentie. ffor this cause [it] is to be noted as a Wonderfull Worke of Almighty God, who hath so ordered their condition that in the Winter, wherein they finde lesse foode yet they growe much fatter: so is it with poore men, whose bodies are in farre better estate then the richer mens, and many tymes the adversities of this life make mens soules in better

* *partinge stakes* sharing belongings

likinge then their welfare and prosperitie. These birdes are well accepted in all nations for the sweetenes of their fleshe, especially in the winter. *Quia frigus cogit ne effluat pinguedo,* bycause [45v] the colde weather keepeth in their fatnes. And that which is more admirable: *Flante Austro macrescit Aquilone pinguescit,* they growe fatte or waxe leane by the turnings of the winde, for with the north winde they growe fatte, and with the south winde fall to be leane againe. I shall not neede to expresse their manner of dressings, boyled, roasted, and baked: it is sufficient that they are laufull, and delicate foode ordeyned by our greate Creator. And therefore although they seldome come to the mouthes of the poore, yet lett the riche praise their maker for such a greate sweetnes in so litle a fowle.

[XI]

The Bustarde or Bistarde

[illustration on p. 74]

The Iewes at this day call this fowle *Anapha,* althoughe our olde Interpreters translate it a kynde of kytes. Auicen calleth it *Alhabari* in Arabian. The Greekes *Otis* and *Lagodia quasi gradipes,* for it delighteth more in walkinge then in flyinge or sittinge. The Latynes call it *Auis tarda,* a slouthfull bird, *Quod graui & tardo volatu detenta, nequaquam vt ceteræ volucres pennis attollitur.*[64] The heauines of the body doth hinder it from risinge vpon the winge like other birdes and therefore wee call it a *Bistard* or *Bustarde,* beinge tardy in the flight. ffrom our Englishe worde Aldrouandus is of the opinion that the Romanes called it *Tarda.* But I rather thinke that when the Romaynes were in greate Brittayne, and first sawe this bird, they called it *Auis Tarda,* and *starda,* and our Countreymen by corruption called it thereupon [46r] *Bistard,* and so at last it came to the vulgar *Bustard.*[65] The Germanes call it *Trap,* and the Belgians *Trapgans* and the Scotts *Gustardes* bycause they resemble geese; though they be not so agill and nimble; the Frenche *Bistarde, Oustarde, Ostarde,* and *Outarde* and the Illyrians *Drofa.* And so much for their appellation.

This fowle is farre greater then a Goose, and not much lesse then a Swanne. Gesner saieth that he weighed a couple of them, and found them to weigh twentie three pounds and some odd ounces. Aldrouand saieth that he weighed one that was sent him from the Cardinall of Trent which alone æqualled both the other. I will first describe this of Aldrouandus and then consequentlie that of Gesners. It had an vnhandsome and ill fououred head, like a vulturs, being very thicke. The beake also stronge and pointed like a fighting Cockes: the head and necke of an ashecolour downe to the breast or mawe: the inferiour or lower part of their wings white: the other grayishe or ashecolour exceptinge two of the longe feathers which were blacke at the endes. The backe full of spotts of Chesnutt colour vpon white: the leggs like the necke. The holes of the eares so broade that you may put into them a mans finger, yet they are couered vnder the feathers, and cannot be discouered vntill the feathers be remoued: within the holes are two passages, one windinge forward to the beake, the other direct vnto the brayne. The quills of the feathers are redd, the thighes white: the leggs playne without feathers and naked, beinge as thicke as a mans thumbe and as longe as halfe a foote: their feete thicke, and vnder them a hard and greate heele: but their Clawes were onelie three and very short: the taile aboue was of a Chesnutt colour full of blacke spotts, and beneath toward the earth a white; the breast round and thicke, the tongue notched like a sawe: beinge sharpe on both sides and hard at the ende. And so much for the first fowle.

Gesner describeth his Bustards on this manner. The colour of the vpper parts exceptinge the necke is an Ashecolour, resemblinge a Bittour or lesser Partridge but more redd, elegantlie besprinckled with blacke spotts. The beake sharpe like a hennes, the head and necke of a pure ashecolour, but whiter on the vpper part of the necke: the breast, [46v] belly, and legges white vnto the middest of the thighes, the tayle fyfteene inches longe consistinge of beautifull reddishe feathers distinguished into many blacke spotts aboue runninge in rancks like filletts or laces, and vnderneath white spotts: and so at the ends white. The necke about halfe a foote longe, the bodie beinge about fifteene inches longe. The greate feathers of the wings white and blacke at the endes, the leggs browne and about eight inches longe, hauinge onelie three feete* and clawes vpon them stretchinge forwarde, but no spurre or clawe behinde, having a thicke palme or hard fleshie muscle insteede of a heele growinge at the lower ende of the leggs, out of the vpper part whereof the feete and clawes issue. And so much for the description of Gesner. Unto whome I may adde in worde the consent of the

* *feete* toes, for it lacks the fourth, the hind, toe

Auncients. *Otis auis fidipes est tribus insistens digitis, magnitudine gallinacei maioris, capite oblongo, oculis amplis, rostro acuto, lingua ossea, gracili collo.*[66] A Bustard is a clouen footed birde goinge vpon three feete, as bigge as the greatest kinde of Cockes, hauinge a longe head, broade eyes, a sharpe beake, a hard and bony tongue, and a cleane necke. And so much shall serue for the description hereof.

These fowles loue the open and plaine fieldes, neuer cominge to the waters except to quenche their thirst, nor yet restinge themselues vpon any trees, but like ostriches walke vp and downe vpon the earth vntill they be frighted. They are common to many Countreys, to Spayne, Greece, England, Scotland, and in Scotland they exceede all other in quantitie, yf it be true which is reported by Hector Boethius, who writeth in this manner: *In Merchia Scothiæ regione nascuntur aues Gustardes, vernaculo sermone dictæ, colore plumæ ac carne perdicibus non dissimiles, sed quæ olores corporis mole exuperant.*[67] In Marchland, a piece of Scotland, are the fowles bredd which they call *Gustardes,* beinge in the colour of their feathers and tast of their fleshe not much vnlike a partridge, but in the balke* and quantitie of their bodies they exceede a Swanne: whereby it must be collected that the Bustards of Scotland are farre greater then in other Countreys: for ours in England which my selfe haue seene were bigger then geese but lesser then Swannes. In Belgia, especiallie in Holland, they alsoe are very plentifull, and in Heluetia, especiallie in the winter tyme, for in the latter end of Sommer after haruest they flie away from England, Italy, Spayne, [47r] and other warmer Countreyes into those colde Regions. ffor

* *balke* bulk

althoughe some say that they flye away with the quailes, yet the gravitie and ponderous heauines of their bodies, especiallie being fatt, doth hinder them from any longe flight, and as they arise from the earth by iumpes and leapes three, foure, or five tymes before they can gather wynde ynoughe into their wings: so with the like difficultie, they contynue aboue beinge not able to sustaine themselues in any tedious course, like the Cranes or Wildgeese, vnlesse they enioye the benefitt of a prosperous winde which they attend as dulye as the most watchfull Marryner bound for a voyage: for els she falleth downe into the hands of the fowler. They are very fearefull of the sight of men, and if they receaue but a small wound they quicklie faint like Cowardes and die thereof. They breede and lay their egges vpon the ground and by the sagacitie of their nature, they discerne whether in their absence men haue handled or breathed vpon their egges, which if they perceiue, they leaue and forsake those egges and lay other in a newe place, whereon they sitt, and hatch them about the beginninge of haruest after thirtie daies like other greate fowles.

There is some difference about their meate and manner of foode: for Albertus saieth, that they eate dead fleshe as Lambes and such like Carrions, and on the contrary other affirme, that they liue vpon hearbes and grayne left in the fieldes after haruest. Gesner and Longolius say that all is good meate they gett to satisfie their hunger: hearbes, fleshe, stones, grayne, seedes, and any other thinge. Wherefore Gesner did anatomize one that came to his hands taken by a fowler, and found in the mawe all kindes of hearbes and two white stones, and at another tyme the barke of trees and stones in snowye and harde weather. By reason that the beake of this fowle is somewhat indented like the teeth of a sawe, some haue affirmed, that amonge all the flying fowles, this onely after he hath eaten his meate doth chewe the cudde like the fishe Ruminalis. And of this opinion is Eustathius and Athenæus: they are neuer or sieldome tamed, and therefore it is hard to knowe the truth hereof.

The foxe is their common enemye, for with singuler crafte and subtiltie, he setteth vpon them and surpriseth them. Whereof Ælianus giueth this testimony: *Vulpes sic otidas venatur, vt & sese auertens, & in terram abiiciens tanquam auis collum sic caudam extendat: eæ autem hac* [47v] *insidarum instructione seductæ, ad illam tanquam ad suam gregalem accedunt, illa vero se vertens nullo negotio capiat.*[68] The craftie fox doth hunt the Bustard after this manner; first he turneth his head from the fowle and cowcheth close to the earth, turninge vp his taile to the viewe of the fowle, wherewithall the seelie creature is deceiued, for hee thinketh it to be the head of his Companyon, and so commeth neere vnto it till he is within the foxes reache, who easilie turninge about taketh the birde for his dinner. They are much afraide of the barkinge of dogges as of the dogges themselues, for they knowe well ynough their oune ponderous heauynes, and before they can vse their wings many tymes the nimble dogs are within them and take them: wherefore at the barkinge of dogges they flie away and hide themselues either in Marshes or bushes. They are not afraide of any fowle, no, not the Eagle, and by reason they keepe vpon the earth their quantitie and bignes maketh them terrible to others, yet they harme none at all. They loue horses accordinge to this olde sayinge, *Attagen ceruum amat, perdix damam, Otis equum.* The Godwitt loueth the Hart, a partridge the fallowe Deere, and a Bustarde loueth a horse. *Equum ubi aspexerit, statim gaudio ad ipsum aduolat.* As soone as he espieth a horse he flieth vnto him.

This their loue vnto Horses is the cause of their ruyne: for by the traynes which are made by colour of them, they are vnawares drawen into their netts. Which Oppianus describeth on this manner. *Qui perdicum in Ceruos amor est, idem Otidum in Equos. Quamobrem huiusmodi industria falluntur: Retia aliquis prope fluuium aut stagnum idoneo loco erigit, angustoque per medium transitu relicto quo eques vnus transire possit, equum auibus ostendit. Sequuntur illæ statim pennis omnibus expansis donec equus ex illo loco angusto recedat, ipsæ verso inclusæ omnes irretiantur.*[69] Suche is the loue of Bustards to horses as is the loue of a partridge to a Hart, whereby they are deceiued on this manner. The fowlers plant their netts against a Riuer or a poole of water in such sort as they leaue a litle lane or passage for a horse betwixt them: then they shewe the horse to the fowles, who instantlie make toward him with spredd wings vntill they are within the netts, who by a devise is drawen furth whiles the fowles are ensnared and loose their liues. Whereupon I may remember that olde Hieroglyphicke, *Otis auolat viso equo,*[70] for they pictured a Bustard flyinge to a horse to signifie a man that in good hope of [48r] defense repayreth to his friende and Patron, and so is deceiued and betrayed by him. In like manner they figured this fowle flyinge to a horse, to signifie a man of weake witt or force, that yeldeth to another man more potent and expert. When the feathers of Bustardes are wett with much rayne, and there be but a litle winde stirringe in the aer, they maie be taken by the hand of man, before they can raise themselues and flie away. Also I haue reported vnto me that there be Greyhounds which by a windinge and turninge of their bodies in a wonderful nimble and strainge manner doe gett within the Bustardes (who stand and wonder at the play of the dog vntill they haue not tyme to descrie him and flie away) and so take them, as the small Norfolke Tumbler taketh the Conye. I doubt not but there be manie other wittie inuentions, whereby they fall into the hands of Fowlers, but these are the most principall and worthiest our knowledge. And so I will proceede to their vses naturall, artificiall, and Ciuill.

The naturall vses of this birde is the meate and foode it affourdeth to the tables of greate men: Simeon Sethi, Xenophon, Demetrius, Constantinopolitanus, and Bellonius doe all agree that the fleshe of Bustardes is sweete and more nourisheable then a Cranes but lesse then a gooses bycause the fowle is bigger and the fleshe blacker: by reason of the continuall feare it liueth in. Yet if it be well digested it breedeth good bloud, and is a verie stronge kinde of foode. Onely Pliny, mistakinge *Otis* for *Otus,*[71] a Bustard for a horne owle, dispraiseth the fleshe thereof: bycause the marrowe turned out of the bones stinketh or smelleth vnsauorlie. But there are none which knowe Bustardes that deny them to be very good meate, especiallie if they be hanged vp dead three or foure dayes before they be dressed, and then eaten at dinners in the Sommer, and at Suppers in the Winter.

The artificiall vses are the medicines, which are not many. ffor Almightie God hath made more familiar and domesticall Creatures of more vse and benefitt then these wilde and vntameable. The fleshe of Bustardes is forbidden to be eaten of them which haue the fallinge sicknes, and their fatte was vsed amonge the Phrigians and Licaonyans for a remedy against the sorenes of womens breasts when they were with Childe, as Pliny writeth.

[48v] The Ciuill vses are also not many. ffishermen bayted their hookes with their feathers bycause the spotts in the water seeme like browne flyes; the quills make as good pens to write withall as doe a gooses; the egges broken vpon haire or wool dieth them blacke, as doe a Crowes mixed with wyne.

[XII]

The Bald-Buzzard.

There is some difference amonge Writers about this fowle, some makinge it a kind of Hawke and some of the kinde of Buzzardes. Gesner and Aldrouand thinke that our Englishe Bald-Buzzard is the Kyte of the fennes which they call *Miluum Palustrem.* Dr Turner maketh it the Ringetayle. They which will haue it a kinde of Hawke reason from Aristotle, *Subbuteones appellari in accipitrum genere qui latiores sunt.*[72] They call those broade Hawkes which are Bald-Buzzardes and also from the quantitie bycause it is lesse then a Buzzard. But the breadth of it to be more then a Hawkes is not reasonable: for some kindes of Hawkes are greate and some lesser: and there is not any difference gathered from the quantitie but from the nature. Besides it is obiected that it is a more generous fowle then the Buzzard which is easilie beaten from her bootye by a smaller bird: but this will fight eagerlie with Hawkes and Kytes for the prey: therefore it is not thought reasonable that [49r] it shoulde be ascribed into the ranke of Buzzardes. All these arguments may proue a disparitie of kynde but no absurditie of name: wherefore I will not trifle out the readers pacience to aunsweare these obiections, which I coulde doe with a wett finger:* but will describe him and so leaue thee to ranke him at thy pleasure, for I am sure this is his place in the Alphabet of my proposed methode.

The Greekes call him *Hypotriorchos, Gypotriorchos,* and *Gypaetos,*

* *with a wett finger* easily (Tilley)

a small Eagle: from hence the Latynes call it *Subbuteo,* the Italians *Barello* and the Frenche *Hobreau.* They are in leingth about two foote, the beake but short, blewishe at the toppe and blacke downewarde; the nostrills wide and smooth. The vpper part of the beake is very crooked and sharpe at the ende: and from the crooked ende hange downe two sides which close in with the lower part, which is of colour like the vpper, and hollowe in the middle, blunt at the end: the palate of the mouth within of a horne colour: the tongue very broade, the eyes blackishe and the eye liddes of a pale earth colour. The Crowne of the head pale Chesnutt, and ashe colour, and so descendeth to both sides of the throate: and from the Temples about the Chinne, necke, and throate. The feathers are white, which diuersitie of colour vpon the head maketh it seeme balde: and so is tearmed a Bald-Buzzard. The Chesnutt colour of the head compasseth, as it were, in the spott about the eyes and openinge of the mouth. Round about the necke is a ringe consistinge of white and redd feathers: the ground of the backe, wings, and tayle a russet or ashe colour; but on the ridge of the backe and typpes of the wings are some feathers of Chesnutt, yet the winges are darker then the backe. All the inside of the winge feathers, and the ten taile feathers, exceptinge the two middle-most, are spotted with browne and redd spotts. All the breast feathers to the middle of the belly are marked with a longe browne spott, and are also white at the endes. The thighes to the shankes are couered with iron colour and spotted darklie blacke: the legges short and couered with scales to the clawes or feete: the feete are almost as longe as the leggs, which is very longe in comparison or naturall proportion: for the legge is about eight ynches, and the feete [49v] as much and the tayle so much likewise. The talants and clawes very blacke, crooked, and stronge; vnder the spurre or heele was a hard bunch of callous fleshe. And thus much for the description.

It is in quantitie inferiour or lesser then a vulgar Buzzard which causeth the name *Subbuteo,* yet in qualitie more worthie and spiritfull: it lyeth aloft in the aer, to hunt small birdes, and therefore Bellonius compareth him in the aer killinge small birds, to greate fishes in the Sea, killinge small fishes.

Grandibus exigui sunt pisces piscibus esca.[73]

So take the fishes greate:
the smaller fishe for meate.

So the small fishes hunted by the Dolphin, and other devourers, for their more safetie forsake the middest of the waters, and expose themselues to a perill of fowles vpon the toppes and creame of the Seas, choosinge rather to fall into the prey of birdes then their oune most vnkinde generation: and birds hunted by these raveners doe fall downe into the power of men and dogs, beneath vpon the earth to escape the tallants of Buzzardes flyinge in the aer.

They keepe in the highest and thickest woodes vntill they growe hungrie, then they flie alofte vntill they finde a prey. They obserue Falconers and make after them that haue doggs. ffor they knowe that partridges, quayles, larkes, and such other small birdes that lyve beneath vpon the lowie earth are sprunge and terrified by the spaniells. Therefore hee awayteth aboue head with a wakinge and neuer winkinge eye that when the birde riseth from the dogge beneath she may fall into the clawes of the Buzzarde aboue.[74] Wherefore it is obserued, that if these poore persecuted vnderlings shall perceiue this their sworne and vnreconcileable enemy over their heads, they sitt still and stirre not, sufferinge themselues to fall into the mouthes of dogs, and to be taken vp by the hands of men, rather then to giue their liues to their naturall foe. Wherefore those that see this bald-Buzzard hoveringe for meate make vse of her, as if she were a hauke: for they carry abroade their dogs and gett much game bycause [50r] the fowles dare not stirre from the earth for feare of their cruell foe watching in the aer. And this is the naturall propertie of this Bald Buzzard, that he will not feede but vpon that which himselfe killeth, and he disdaineth to take a bird sittinge on the tree or vpon the earth: but flying in the aer. They fight with those that wolde preuent and take away their game. There was a Combate betwixt a Bald-Buzsard and a Ringtayle. It is one of the best pastimes that a falconer can beholde to see the two spoilers spoile themselues for a larke: this is more swifte of flight, althoughe the Ringtayle be stronger. The larke outflieth the Ringtayle and so escapeth: but if the Bald-Buzzard be at hand, she falleth into his clawes. Then beginneth the Ringetayle to buckle and contende with this Buzzard for the larke: they fight fiercelie, and in that contention many tymes fall downe to the earth and part not vntill the Falconer cometh and taketh them both vp: so for one larke they lose two liues. Such is the violence of wrath, want, and couetousnes, that in revenge of a passion, or for recovery of a penny, many tymes men lose their liues, and their whole estates; and worthilie are such exemplified in these two Buzzardes whose posteritie may take them into their armes with this subscription, *Ex vindicta perditio*: perdition accompanieth revenge.

Two Buzzards fought and died for one poore birde:
Two Brothers slayne for one ill placed Worde.

I haue not reade or hearde whether they be tamed and made gentle for hawkinge, but certeinelie the opinion of men is, that they were not vnfitt for this sporte. Yet seinge it neuer eateth any meate but that which itselfe killeth, therefore it were ouer costlie to feede. And peradventure if it were tamed it wolde be like the Souldiour of Antigonus,[75] who was most valiant while he was a Leper, but beinge thereof cured at the charges of the Kinge, neuer wolde fight more: whereof vpon demaund hee gaue this aunsweare: *Leprosus dum fui vitæ pertæsus eram; idcirco eam minus faciebam: libenter talem vitam pro morte comutaturus; Curatus, non iam onerosa est vt prius pluris ergo facienda nec indiscrimine bellorum ponenda.* When I was a Leper I was weary of my life, and wolde haue ben glad to haue exchainged such a life for a noble death, therefore I fought valiantly: but nowe beinge cured, I haue no such cause to accompt my life a burd[en], and therefore I will neither take so much paynes nor adventure so many perills [50v] of death as before. So this Buzzard is nowe forced for hunger to hunt for foode, but peradventure if it were tamed, it wolde neither kill birde in the aer nor in the earth. ffor it is impacient and will not longe tarry ouer the heads of huntinge dogs: but flie away if it be not satisfied. And so much for a Bald-Buzzard.

[illustration on p. 82]

[XIII]

The Buzzard.

Aristotle reckoneth this idle fowle amonge Hawkes, beinge ledd thereunto by the externall shape and greatenes of the bodie. But hee is iustlie crossed by the late learned writers, because it is a cowardlie and slouthfull bird, vpon whome is deseruedly affixed that Terentian interrogation, *Nullane in tam magno corpore mica salis*:[76] there is not one dramme of goodnes in such a bodie of greatenes. Wherefore I will rather rainge it among Kytes: of whome the frenche make many kindes. One whereof they call *Boysart.* It is called in Latyne *Buteo* and *Triorchis,* this latter name is giuen it because it hath three stones, which no

other fowle hath and by the same similitude there is an hearbe or plant *Triorchis,* dogstone or ragwort, which hath three rootes, and one of them like a mans genitall part. And one Festus assigneth the originall of the latine name, *Buteo propter vastitatem hiis locis quibus viuit,* for the vastitie* or evill lucke it bringeth to the places wherein it liueth: but I professe I knowe not what he meaneth hereby. Albertus for *Buteo* calleth it *Buteus.* The Italians *poiana* and *Villana,* because it haunteth about Countrey houses and small Villages, and sometymes *Aieta.* The Spanyards and portugalles [51r] *Gauia.* The frenche *Buysard, Busard, Busant, Boudree,* & *Goiran.* The Germans *Bushard, Bussahrn, Buse,* and *Busshen*: and in Belgia *Brobuxen*; in Saxony *Rüttelwye*, that is, a redd kyte; in Heluetia *Masshuw* and *Masswy,* a Kite of the Fennes or Marishes. And thus much for the seuerall names.

The quantitie of this fowle is æquall to the Kyte and the colour inconstant, beinge sometymes browne, ashecolour, and cleane white: So their quantitie alsoe varieth. And therefore Gesner obserued three seuerall kindes in Heluetia, euery one bigger then another: which kindes are here to be seuerallie described.

This first is a Buzzard of Italy, beinge a foote and a halfe longe from the beake to the extremitie of the taile: the beake thicke and coloured a blacke blewe, couered with a membrane about the Nostrills of an earth or clay colour, the wyde† or openinge of the mouth beinge a pale earthie colour, the head flatt like a Falcons fashioned triangular: The tongue broade, thicke, and blunt, the eyes smooth, bright, and cherefull:

* *vastitie* desolation
† *wyde* width

the iris beinge black and white, the necke short, thicke, and roughe of feathers: the whole backe from the necke to the taile of a darke iron colour: the taile broade, a spanne longe, and spotted blacke goinge crosse, the belly white full of longe iron colour spotts, the leggs a pale clay colour and three fingers longe, the feete and clawes blacke. Gesner doth describe a female Buzzard, and her younge one in this manner: which I will relate because he saieth it was brought out of Sauoy. The beake was short, crooked, and blacke, and the colour of the forehead compounded or mixt of a greene and yellowe: the feete yellowe and the leggs couered with feathers midway. The backe browne, hauinge some rednes at the feathers ends; the inside of the feathers which lye couered white; vnderneath them are many short, thicke, and softe feathers. The breast and belly white with blacke spotts through their middle: and the feathers of the head browne with a litle white at the endes or brymmes: the greate feathers of the wings are blacker then the other which are browne, and all the quilles white withinside: the leingth was about two foote longe, the tayle halfe a foot longe, the necke short like a hawkes. The weight of the body about two pound, æquallinge a common henne. The Chicke or younge Buzzard was of an Ashecolour, the beake, feete, and eyes yellowe. And so much for the description of this first kinde.
[51v]

The Second sort of Buzzards both Frenche and Italian

The wings of two or three colours withinside white, and fyve of the longe feathers without blacke, the other browner. So to a man that beholdeth it flyinge in the ayer it seemeth white because it is white vnderneath, but to them that see it sitt on the grounde, it is an ashe-colour browne; yet the belly feathers which are white haue in euery one of them neere the stalke a blacke spott at the ends: and the blacknes of the longe winge feathers haue notches in them like the diuisions on the edge of a sawe. The leggs are couered with browne feathers, the talants are not very greate but crooked ynoughe, the taile like a God-witts, with crosse spotts thereupon. The leggs short and not round, couered before and behinde with spotts like tables and on the sides with scales like fishes: the beake short, blacke, and crooked, at the ende: the openinge of the mouth [and] the nostrills yellowishe. It is descerned from a Kyte because it is lesser: and the taile is whole, not forked. And when it flieth it flappeth the wings [52r] more frequent. And so much for the description of this second out of Bellonius.[77]

The third Figure.

[illustration]

This Buzzard was both described and dissected by Aldrouand. And therefore for varitie both of Gods workes and mens witts, I will relate this also, and so proceede to other parts of this History. It differed not from the former in any thinge except in these particulars followinge: the back was altogether of a rustie yron colour, hauinge a litle white at the feathers ends: so was the breast, belly, and necke: but inwardly towards the rootes of the feathers they were of a whitishe ashecolour: so as if a man moue the feathers against the haire (as wee saie in prouerbe) and turne them out of their natural order, they appeare all white or full of white spotts. The head neither very round nor very playne, the leggs to the hammes couered with pale yron coloured feathers, the taile of the same colour, adorned with browne spotts, [52v] equally distant one from another. And this varietie of colours hath our Almightie Creator put vpon these seueral fowles not onelie to shewe his infinite power and wisedome, who can by his worde thus tincture nature in an admirable manner that wee might more zealouslie praise his hand, but also to shewe the ages of these birdes, for those which in youth are of a pale ashe or watry colour, in their age are more blacke, red, rustie, spotted and partie coloured. And so much for the diuersitie of Buzzards.

A Buzzard flieth but a small or short space, for she is constrayned to keepe her wings in perpetuall motion: therefore it loueth not to stirre, but out of her sluggishe disposition abideth perill of strokes before shee arise. Whereupon the Germanes to expresse an idle person that is no ravener at his worke haue this prouerbe, *Du sitzest wie ein Busshart.*[78] Thou sittest like a Buzzard. This is not a fault in the disposition of this fowle as if it were afraied to flie from a tree to a bird or other bootie that cometh neere it, but onelie out of slouth and vnwieldiness to remove; therefore it suffereth much hunger and feedeth vpon wormes, field mice, and such other imperfect insects. So Oppianus writeth: *Accipitres nonnullos pigerrimos esse & ad volandum ignauos adeo vt ab aliis nutriri desiderent & sero tandem ad venationem procedant: solisque ranis insidientur.*[79] Some kinde of Hawkes are most slouthfull and vnwillinge to vse their wings, so as they wolde haue other to feede them: for they sieldome hunt, and then also they are contented with frogs: which is not verified of any except these Buzzards who are so idle to prouide and keepe their meate, that without resistance they suffer Bittours and other cowardlie fowles to robbe and take away their foode from them: whereof Athenæus giueth testimony out of these verses of Simonides.

ἐρῳδιὸς γὰρ ἔγχελυν Μαιανδρίην
τρίορχον εὑρὼν ἐσθιοντ' ἀφείλετο.[80]

The Hearon did finde a Buzzard eatinge eeles,
And takes them from her in spite of her heeles.

Whereby is noted the slouthfull pusillanimitie of this fowle, who giueth place not onely to Hawkes and other raveninge birdes but to Hearons and such like weaklings that haue but little stomacke. Wherefore it is [53r] much wondred at which is written by Festus, that there are some kinde of Buzzardes which by force and violence take away the prey from Haukes.[81] Surelie such haue neuer ben knowen in this Europæan worlde: or if at any tyme such a thinge haue happened, the Hauke was full, and so listed not to resist, or ells it vsed deceipt, where it dared vse no violence: for wee see many tymes that a small bird doth make it flie away for feare. And therefore in Italy they call a fearefull person *Poiana,* a Buzzard. And hence it cometh to passe that they dare not approache Cities or greate Townes: where are store of people, and therein the boldnes of kites seeke their prey: but abide in the Countrey farre from the popular multitudes of men or of fowles. They eate wormes myce frogs todes, snayles scolopendrayes* butterflies and such like; yea, Gesner saieth hee found in the mawe of a Buzzard a whole mole and many other insects as Serpents, eeles, and such like. Bellonius addeth that they also eate some kinde of hearbes as Wood-rowell,† goose grasse, hony suckles, and such like: which some suppose they doe not for hunger or necessitie of meates but for a secreate sympathy or loue they beare to these hearbes. ffor it is not true that they eate Serpents, toades, and frogs because they hate them, but for necessitie of meate, yet this is true, that the Hauke, the Kyte, and the litle Vultur are enemyes to the Buzzard. They are easilie taken by the bayte of a mouse and is ensnared or entangled with the lyne: so it is not able to ridde it selfe but the fowler cometh and easilie taketh it away.

Some may wonder vnto what they are to be applyed when they are taken, for here in England they are neuer eaten that I haue heard of. Pliny wrote hereof in this manner: *In Balearibus Insulis Buteonem etiam accipitrum genus in honore mensarum esse*:[82] In the Ilands Bale-aryes they much respect the Buzzard (a kinde of Haukes) for meate at their tables. There are no Nations in Europe more delicatelie fedd then Fraunce and Italy. And yet Bellonius saieth that in Aruergne or Lor-rayne, they make greate accompt of Buzzards. And in Italy (saieth Aldrouand) they pull of their feathers and sell them in the Marketts in the wynter tyme when they are fatt even [53v] [as] Pulters sell Capons. *Dulcissimus & boni saporis est* (saieth Albertus),[83] they are very sweete and of a good rellishe. But I thinke in greate extremitie of famyne we shall neuer be persuaded to eate them, especiallie seinge they feede vpon vncleane creatures worse then Catts and dogges. They are verie lasciuiouslie venereous, as may appeare by their three stones. And for this cause Agathocles the Tyrant was surnamed Buteo, for in his minoritie hee was a Sodomite, and abused boyes and younge men: but in his full age he chainged that vnnaturall lust from men to women. I doe much wonder at the Authors who ascribe vastitie vnto these fowles, as if when they liued they brought depopulation and desolation. When Fabius was Admirall of the Romanes, a Buzzard came and sate in the sterne of his shippe after which tyme hee fought very fortunatelie against his enemyes. And then hee added to his name *Buteo,* saieth Liuy, and was called M. Fabius Buteo. And Pliny: *Triorchæ Accipitri principatum in Auguriis Phoemonoe dedit.*[84] The Augur gaue the first

* *scolopendrayes* centipedes
† *wood-rowell* woodruff or wood-rose

place vnto the Buzzarde in soothsayinge aboue all birdes: and thereupon relateth the newly recited History of Fabius.

The vses medicinall of this fowle so many as I coulde learne are brieflie these. Marcellus prescribeth a weake man in venereall causes to eate the stones of a Buzzard sodd in hony and runninge water, and this hee must doe three daies together fastinge. And so my Author promiseth all good prosperitie in Venus Courte, whereunto agreeth John Baptista Porta and others. Let the Venereall Dames followe Lea[h] in this action rather by naturall Mandrakes and such inventions as are here related, then by defilinge their marriage bedd in bringinge straingers to their dishonor without tarryinge the course and returne of nature: or helpe of naturall meanes. ffor I wolde rather wishe my arme without streingth to guide my penne then to encourage and instruct wantons to abuse the benefits of Almighty God by my writings. Yet for feare of abusinge good medicines to euill purposes, I must not conceale either Gods mercies for the soule nor natures vertues for the bodie, hopinge out of a charitable devotion, that all men will rather imitate Iesus by drawinge good out of evill, then sathan by turninge good into evill. Unto these I wishe the punishment of Agathocles and vnto the other the honour of Fabius. And so I take my leaue of this Buzzard.

[54r]

[XIV]

The Bittour or Astrean Hearne

[illustration on p. 87]

This Bird the Greekes call *Oknos* and *Phoix* bycause it is fabled that Oknos and Phoix were slouthfull and vnthriftie seruants, and were metaphorphized [*sic*] into this bird: and so they are called *Asterxai* bycause of their spotted feathers like starrs. The Latynes thereupon call it *Ardea stellaris,* and by reason of the greate voice *Taurus,* a Bull, and *Botaurus quasi boatus Tauri,* the Lowhinge of an Oxe, from hence come *Butora, Butio, Butorius,* bycause of the voice

Inque paludiferis Butio butit aquis.[85]

And in ffenne waters not in rockes,
The Bittour roareth like an Oxe.

ffrom the voice arise the names thereof in other nations, as the Italians *Trombono* and *Terrabuso,* in France Heron *paresseux,* and in litle Brittayne *Gallerand.* The Germanes call it by many names expressinge the nature thereof, as *Vrrind, Meerrind Masskuh,* bycause of his Oxelike voice, and *Rortrum, Rordump, Rorreigel, Moszreigel,* a Hearne of the fennes, or a trumpet soundinge Hearne, or a reede [54v] soundinge Hearne, bycause it lyueth amonge reedes: The Frisians call it *Rosdam pyttouer, Luyend rynd,* and *Lorrind,* The Saxons *Wasserochs,* a water Oxe, the Austrians *Erdbuell,* bycause he thrusteth his beake downeward to the earth or into a reede when he roareth like a Bull. So at Aushburgh* *Hortybel* and *Pickart,* bycause in fightinge it pecketh at the eyes: in Holland *Pittoor,* in other parts of Germany, *Rordummel, Domphorn,* and *Dompshorn*: The Turke *Geluae,* the Polonyans *Bunk,* and the Ilirians *Bukacz.*

The writers of our tyme make three kindes of theis Bittours or roaringe birdes whose figures and descriptions hereafter followe. The one is greate, the other is lesser. The thirde a Crested kinde which about the Sea Adriatique is called *Quaiotti,* and vnto these Aldrouand addeth

* *Aushburgh* Augsburg

a fourth with a ringe about his necke of white feathers hauinge leggs somewhat smaller and longer, the taile also beinge shorter. In other thinges, they resemble no other fowle so much as they doe Hearnes: and therefore cannot be ascribed to any other kinde. The Crested Bittours or *Quaiotti* which liue about the Sea Adriatique are hatched with plaine heads, but as they growe in age, so the tufts of their longe feathers growe out backward, beinge for the most part white exceptinge their tipps or ends which are blacke. Their necks partie coloured, their backs a light browne, and the neather part of their wings white. But wee will not trouble the Reader with any further labour about the difference of the kindes least wee blemishe the particular delineation of the generall: whereunto I will nowe bend my penne and paper.

The Bittour very like a Heron but with shorter leggs, the necke longe and full of feathers, the beake longe and sharpe, the head couered with very blacke feathers, the residue of the bodie browne and pale, sett ouer with blacke spotts. The Clawes or feete very longe, for the middle clawe of one foote and the spurrs of the same are a foote distant, especiallie the spurre which is halfe a foote longe and verie sharpe, wherefore they vse to sett them in handles of siluer to picke their teeth withall. The inside of their Clawes are sharpe like the teeth of a greate file, wherewithall they [55r] catche and holde the most slippry eeles: wherein Almighty God hath mercifullie prouided for the poore fowle to take her foode and sustaine herselfe: her taile is very short, her whole height stretched out is about fourtie ynches, her beake a hand in leingth and an ynche in breadth, beinge browne aboue and redd vnderneath, round within, made hollowe with three longe furrowes or small channells: the vnder chappe shutteth within the vpper like a knife turned into the hafte; the gape or stretch of his mouth almost two palmes wide. The eye lidds not round nor couered with feathers but bare and naked. It hath broade eares vnder yellowe feathers. The brownishe or yron colour thereof, so spotted as aforesaide, hath longer spotts or starres on the breast and the rumpe: the feathers are all white at the rootes. The longe quills of the wings very thicke, and foure and twentie in nomber: besides these there are foure other on a side which make the coniunction of the wings to the body; the hinder parts to the feete are of a lead coulour. By reason of the greate voice it needeth a stronge and wide arterye or throate-bole; wherefore it is contynued without divarication, not separated nor rugged as in a Swanne: without any Larynx at all: and insteede thereof God hath recompenced it with a more easie passage, makinge the externall parts like other birds, but the internall part of the

artery a thinne and strange membrane or skynne, which is one halfe æquall part of the *aspera arteria.* And also the circles on the outside are very thinne, and farre distant tyed together with such a thynne stretchinge skynne as may easilie extende itselfe in the roarings of the birde. It wanteth a bagge or throate, to convey downe the foode from the *aspera arteria,* and insteede thereof it hath the wider Chappes; their Mawe is not like a birdes but like a Dogges. And thus much for the description of the lesser kinde of Bittours.
[55v]

The larger or greater Bittour is thus described by Dr Gesner. It is in height three foote, beinge stretched out in leingthe. It is a bastard betwixt a Bittour and a Heron, coniectured to be the same which Oppianus calleth *Elaphis.* The feete or leggs sixteene ynches longe, the beake about tenne, the Iris of the eyes yellowe. The necke very narrowe and about sixteene ynches longe, whereof the feathers are coloured a pale redd and mixed with some blacke which in the lower part next the winge or shoulders are longer, like a Capons, beinge of white and browne colour. The backe and wings browne, and vnder the wings redd, but vnder the beake and eyes white. The beake and leggs yellowe, the feete and clawes browne, the Crowne of the head blacke, and the belly redd. The tongue very longe which hee putteth into the water as a baite to allure fishes to bite at, and so he taketh and eateth them. ffrom whose example I thinke men haue learned to baite hookes and drawe out fishes with an angle: so that as the lesser Bittours fishe with their Clawes, this performeth it with her tongue, and therefore may more easilie atteyne his prey. The colour in the Italian birds is most comonly yellowe, and thereupon they call it *Ruffey*. They abound most in Holland and in fenny places, beinge not alwayes of one constant colour. It is an idle birde restinge by ditches and watery Marishes: snatchinge vp the fishes [56r] which they see swymminge. But howe it commeth to passe they call it *Oknos* I haue shewed already. Howbeit they call it also *Phoix*[86] which may be bycause the wife of Oknos was so called that consumed her husbands earninge. Like as it is saied an Asse consumed the rope of haye which Oknos did wynde out of a heape as fast as he layed the same behinde him, so this birde lyvinge and sittinge idly on the banks eateth vp the fishe that swymme in the waters. They eate not onely fishe but frogs and water snakes. They builde neasts not farre from the waters, either vpon trees, if any be neere, made of stickes, or in their defaulte vpon drye lande amonge reedes. Their egges are vncerteyne, for Bellonius saieth they lay but three or foure, and Gesner affirmeth he sawe a dossen in a neast. ffor it is a slouthfull birde, and suffereth a man to come to her nest, and then riseth not to flie, but to hide herselfe in some reedes, or dyveth into the water: Wherefore it hath ben called *pigra auis*. And Alciatus maketh vpon it this Embleme.

Ignaui Ardeolam stellarem effingere serui
Et studia, & mores fabula prisca fuit:
Quæ famulum Asteriam volucris sumpsisse figuram
est Commenta: fides sit penes hystoricos.
Degener hic veluti qui cœuet in aere falco est,
Dictus ab Antiquis vatibus Ardelio.[87]

The ffables olde an idle seruant paynted,
Asteria changde from mans shape to a fowle:
And fayned a Bittour of slouthfull manners taynted,
A sluggishe man and manners to controwle.
Belieue then they that list, this base declined mate
shoulde suppe aloft like falcon, but in ditch he sate.

And for this cause Appolonius blamed the Citizens of Tarsus, *Quod iuxta Cydni aquas otiantes, tanquam fluuiatiles aues sederunt,* sittinge idly by the ryver Cydnus as water birds, meaninge these Bittours. The reason of their slouth is bycause of the difficultie [56v] of their flight, for they cannot flie vnlesse first of all they leape. It is a subtile and industrious birde, ffor hee knoweth in what waters are greatest store of fishes, and there he sitteth shrinkinge in his longe necke as if he were dead: but assoone as hee espieth a fishe in his danger, hee snappeth him vp without gyvinge him warninge. Albertus addeth moreouer that it is a cruell bird and full of reuenge, for if the fowler haue ensnared him, hee must lay holde on him very warily, otherwise hee will reach him in the face or bare hand with his beake, a wound more hurtfull then the birds body is beneficiall. Ælianus writeth thus of them: *In Ægipto mansuescit atque adeo præclare humanam vocem intelligit, vt si quis huic conuitium fecerit vel appellauerit seruum, ex ea contumelia irascatur: vel eandem ipsam vocauerit pigram, & sic dolenter tanquam ignobilitatis, & segnitiæ arguta indignetur,*[88] that is, They growe tame in Ægipt, and come to vnderstand mans language, for if you call them slaues or sluggards they are angrie and moued with indignation at suche ignoble tearmes. So Elianus.

The voice of this fowle is most admirable, ffor fasteninge his beake in the waters or in the earth he roareth like a Bull, which is vsuall with him in the Springe when he is stirred with lust for procreation. And at the sound thereof cattell are saied to be moued as with the voice of a Bull, for which cause they are also called *Boningi* and *Bubices.* Their fleshe is good for meate: and the vses are the same which are of Herons. And so I will forbeare to entreate of them in this place, referringe the Readers to the historie of those fowles.

I finde the Bittours giuen here in England for Armes of Gentlemen.*

Dale. Gules. 3. Bittours argent membred. Or.
Dale. of Bristoll. Sab. on a Cheueron Or. seauen Torteaxes betwene three Bittours risinge Argent.

* Heraldic terms are defined in Appendix II

[57r]

[XV]

The Blackbird or Owsell or Blackmacke

[two illustrations on p. 94]

This birde is well knowen both in Citie and Countrey beinge desired and enterteyned both aliue and dead: I reade not of the Hæbrews worde for this birde, belike they knewe it not, and so had no name for it: Syluaticus, Aristotle, and Albertus haue many strainge names for it: but out of what language I knowe not, such as are *Cosefos, Cossifos, Kepsos, Pro Archi, Alfia, Echus, Edulcus, Ethida, Fastozoz, Farrakoz, Cokoylos, Folkynos, Chiricos,* and *Focoton.* All these strainge names I doe but relate leavinge their application to the iudicious Reader. At this day the Greekes call it *Kottiphos* as in olde tyme they called it *Kossyphos.* The Latynes *Merula,* of the similitude it had with the Tanagræan Cocke, whereof one kinde was blacke and called *Merula,* for Plautus calleth blacke *Merulum,* or as Isidore saieth, *medula,* of his modulation or singinge voice, and not as Varro, *merula, quasi mera volans.* Some call it *Nigrettus* of the Colour, which worde wee translate and call it a *Blackbird,* or *Black-macke.* The Italians *Merlo.* The Spanyards *Mierla,* the Portugall *Melroa,* the Frenche *Merle,* the highe Germanes *Amsel,* the Dutchmen, *Merl, Merlaer, Meerel,* and sometyme *Ein Lyster.* The Illyrians *Kos,* and the Turkes *feluek* and so much for his name.

There are diuers and sundrie kindes of Blackbirds or Owsells or [57v] Black-mackes, for I doe purposelie vse all these wordes beinge his seuerall appellations in our language. Wherefore after their seuerall figures, I will adde their descriptions. And doe nowe beginne with this vulgar and best knowen bird so called by reason of his coulour, which also chaingeth as it doth in Crowes and ravens. In the winter they are more yellowe or reddishe which caused Naeuius to write of one of these birds (*Coloris sandaricini,* a browne sand colour or bright Chestnutt). So Aristotle telleth of this kinde that be white about Cyllene in Arcadia, and in his tyme that kinde was thought to be proper and peculiar to that Countrey.[89] But since those dayes it is found otherwise, ffor England, Norway, and West India doe affourde the like. And Aldrouand sawe

one all white in Italy, and before him Varro. *Solent poni Gallinæ rusticæ in ornatibus publicis cum psittacis* [&] *merulis albis, item aliis id genus rebus inusitatis* (saieth Varro). They were wont to adorne their publique shewes with Countrey hennes, parrotts, and white Owsels or black-mackes, and other such rare and vnvsuall sights. To this vulgar kinde are found browne,* which liue amonge rockes and their beake is not yellowe. The beake is commonly yellowe or of a saffron colour, and so are the feete, yet both chainge, especiallie in wynter, and in olde age, but onelie in the Cocke or male kinde. The vulgar female is not so blacke as the male, but more browne, and sieldome is the beake so yellowe, but browne or of an earth colour: the breast and throate speckled with white and browne. And so much for this kinde.

The whiteheaded Blackbird.

[illustration]

[58r]

The white headed Blackbird.

This birde they call in Greeke *Leukokephalos,* a white head, bycause his head is all white exceptinge three small lynes behinde the eyes. The beake and the Iris of the eye of an earthie colour, the taile and belly blacke, the breast and wings blacke with some white spotts and some of the longe feathers in the wings white and the feete browne. All which differences well considered, doe make this a second or other kind.

* *browne* a brown kind

This maketh a thirde kinde for they are partlie blacke and partlie white, the Male more white; and the female a more deepe and pure blacke: and their taile whollie blacke. The beake of the Male very redd, and so are the feete, but the females both beake and feete are a pale yellowe.

[illustration]

This is the figure of a white birde of this kinde, all whose feathers were white tendinge to a litle browne, but his beake very redd, and his feete and leggs of an earth colour.

[58v]

[illustration]

This fifth kinde Gesner calleth *Birckamsel* and *Birckamsslen* and *Hagamsslen,* bycause it keepeth in the Mountaynes and therefore called *merula montana,* a Mountayne blackbird. The quantitie of the body is a litle inferiour to a thrushe, the head, beake, and wings blacke, with a litle yellowe, the breast spotted with feathers blacke and yellowishe,

the taile blacke, and the leggs like a colour compounded of a skye colour, and a yellowe, the belly blacke with some ashe colour, feathers: The beake and clawes blacke, the inner side of their mouth and their tongue of a clay colour: The Male is somewhat blacker then the female, and hath a breast more spotted and redd. In the winter they chainge colour and growe browner. They are a gratefull meate at table. And so much for this kinde.

[two illustrations on p. 95]

This kinde is called *Merula torquata,* a Black-macke with a ringe about his necke, by the Germanes *Ringamsel* and *Waldamsel,* a Black-bird of the woodes of the bignes of a thrushe. Upon the throate or breast before are white feathers like a halfe ringe, two fingers broade ascendinge vp to the [59r] wings or shoulders: the other colour a darke browne. The longe feathers of the wings on the belly are a litle white at the typpes, the beake about the nostrills, and vp to the head blacke, but yellowishe on the sides, the leggs a brown redd, and the clawes browne. And this is the description of the female. The Male is of a blacke colour, excepting his ringe and his beake, which is of an earth colour. The Frenchmen call him *Merle au Collier,* they are good meate and in all other thinges resemble the vulgar blackbird. They abound most in Morienna and the hills of Sauoy.

[illustration]

(7) This bird is called *Merula bicolor,* a two coloured Black-macke, bycause the whole body is couered with two colours, that is to saie with a darke browne and a bright earth colour. This birde is lesser then a vulgar black-bird, the head browne distinguished with small whitishe prickes or lynes: the beake shorter then a Blackbirdes coloured redd earth, which is more deepe on the backe and taile, but paler on the breast and belly. The longe feathers of the wings browne, and their tippes white, their feete very short, their clawes longe and redd, and the taile shorter, then a vulgar black-birds.

[59v]

[illustration]

(8) This for the proportion of the body is most like a Black-bird, beinge about halfe a foote or eight ynches longe. The beake, head, & backe are blacke, but the taile paler or white, the feathers ends beinge white and full of Ashecolour spotts drawen one crosse another; vnderneath the beake vpon the breast and belly runneth a redd lyne. The forme of the taile most like a Hawkes trayne.

[illustration]

(9) This kinde is lesser then the vulgar blackbirds and yet bigger then a sparrowe: the head of an Ashecolour, the eyes blacke enringed about with a golden circle: the beake thicke, stronge, and sharpe beinge blacke at the ende; the breast of a sadd Ashecolour: and the belly more white or bright. The taile all white except two middle feathers which were of Ashecolour, and the backe next the taile of a darke or sadd [60r] chestnutt, the quills of the wings white next the backe, and the longe feathers of an Ashecolour.

[two illustrations on p. 98]

(10) These two are called *Merulæ roseæ,* rose coloured black-mackes, bycause the breast, backe, and vpper part of their wings are of a rose or freshe colour, the head tufted blacke and the wings and back blacke, the longe feathers a sadd or pale Chessenutt, the beake redd or of fleshe colour, in the sharpe,* but blacke neere the head: the leggs of a saffron colour. The Male is of a more liuely colour and beautifull then the female; for her head and wings are not so deepe a blacke: They live in highe wayes and dunghills and growe very fatt: wherefore they are much desired and commended at the table.

[illustration on p. 98]

(11) This is a Black-macke of Brasilia, and is brought by Marchaunts out of that Countrey. The body is bigger then the Vulgar hauinge nothing blacke vpon it except the [60v] winges and the taile: and a fewe blacke mane feathers. The other parts are more redd, then the dye of any scarlett, for no arte of man is able to expresse so perfect and deepe a colour. The feathers are all redd at the bottome, the feete and legges are browne or blackishe ashecolour: the taile very longe, the beake crooked beinge browne on the outside, and of an earth colour in the inside, the clawes short and crooked coloured like the leggs.

[illustration on p. 98]

(12) This is a Blackmacke without feete called *Porphyromelanos* by-cause his head, belly, and backe are a pure scarlett colour: and the other parts blacke: the breast and forepart of the backe is besett with greenishe half Moone circles: the beake recurued being blacke at the ende and white in the vpper part neere the head. It is doubted whether they want feete by arte or creation, seinge it hath nothinge where-withall to hange by or cleaue to trees, to rest vpon as haue the birds

* *in the sharpe* toward the end

[Merulæ roseæ]

[*Black-macke of Brasilia*]

[*Blackmacke without feete*]

of paradice. The Duke of Florence gaue one of them dead to Aldrouand, and therefore he examyninge it with all diligence doeth not resolue that all of that kinde doe want feete, but rather concludeth out of Aristotle that all Creatures which haue bloud are knowen by foure notes or marks which (saieth hee) doth moue them to the actions of their life, as beasts haue foure leggs and birdes haue two wings and two leggs (or els like the bird of paradice) some haue nerves in steede of their leggs. So hee leaueth the matter. And I dare not conclude otherwise, seinge I neuer sawe nor reade of this bird but in this Author. But yet in his History of swallowes he dissenteth from Aristotles before expressed opinion. And therefore hee and wee haue as great reason to believe Black-birdes as swallowes without legges.

[61r]

(13) This is the last kinde of Black-birds called *Merula saxatilis* and of Gesner *Cariocatactes* or *nucifraga,* a nutbreaker. So the Germanes call it *Nussbrecher* and *Nussbicker* and *Nusshæher,* the frenche *Cassenoix,* a breaker of nutts. And the Italians *Merle alpadic,* a black-bird of the Alpes. It is bigger then a vulgar one, and spotted like a stare, beinge blacker about then beneath except in the wings which are a deepe blacke euery where besett with white circled spotts like halfe moones, lesser on the head and bigger on the winges and backe then on the taile. The greate feathers of their winges are blacke and white at the ends. The taile blacke aboue, iron colour beneath and the legges browne. A pleasant bird to beholde by reason of the varietie of colours. And thus much for their seuerall kindes and seuerall descriptions. Nowe it followeth that wee proceede to the handlinge of their seuerall natures and other accidences.

The first thinge memorable in them is their voice-singinge whereof Elianus writeth, *Cantu merulæ valent & se ipsas oblectant amœnitate,*[90] Black-birds excell in their singinge voice and delight themselues with the sweetenes thereof. One Pantheus of Verona hath devised a newe proper worde to expresse their singinge which he calleth *fringulicire quasi fremitum gula ciere.* Wee are not much beholdinge to him for it, for euery bird doth the like: but in my opinion if he had saied *frindulciere fremitum dulcem ciere* hee had come neerer their sweete voice. Another poet describeth their singinge after this manner.

Et merula modulans, tam pulchris concinit odis
nocte ruente tamen carmina nulla canit.[91]

The tuninge blackbird sweete songes doth singe in light,
but silent, noteles, sitteth all the night.

[61v] Albertus writeth that he knewe a black-bird that had distinctlie learned nyne seuerall musicall straynes, whereof he grewe proude, and of his oune accord wolde tune them orderlie, in the presence of straingers to deserue their commendation.[92] They learne one of another in the woods and fieldes, but enclosed in Cages they learne by the voices of men, or by the sounde of musique. They learne and imitate more willinglie if they be fedd with fleshe. As they chainge their feathers, so they chainge their voices and in wynter they singe not at all, neither is their voice any other then a chirpinge. In the springe they beginne and contynue till the autumne, be ended; but with this difference, ffor first they singe all the day, and afterward onely morninge and eveninge. Of their springe songe thus writeth Theocritus.

εἰαρινοὶ δὲ λιγυφθόγγοισιν ἀοιδαῖς
κόσσυφοι ἀχεῦσιν ποικιλότραυλα μέλη.[93]

Sweete soundinge songes in springe,
The black-birds tune and singe.

They feede like vnto thrushes; they delight in woodes and trees as especiallie Myrtle, bay, C[y?]pres, holme,* birche, hasel, and such like, bycause they eate of their tender buds and sprigges. Also elder berryes, grape-stones, ashe, and seruices.† I haue also reade, that they will also eate some kinde of plants as the small rough Cedar, water holme, *myrta cantha,* wilde sage, and groundsell. Also they eate wormes and locusts. But for asmuch as they are excellent good meate when they are fatt, in auncient tyme they vsed to diett such as were leane and taken aliue for the delicacie of their fleshe. They made litle houses which they called *Testudines* couered ouer with tyles as an Oyster or Lobster with shells, and therein they put thousands of thrushes and blackbirds which

* *holme* holly
† *seruices* or service, sorb apple *Pyrus domestica*

had ben taken with netts. They made certeine pipes to come and bringe water amonge them; least by open standinge it shoulde growe filthie and hurt them. They made vnto it a lowe and narrowe doore, such as were made for the caues wherein Bulles were wont to be bayted. The windowes also were small, and in such places where were no trees in sight least by beholdinge the trees, and birds at libertie thereupon they shoulde pyne away and growe leane, leavinge them no more light then whereby they might see their meate, their water, and their roosts. And therefore withinside they made many pearches fastened in the wall: and there they sate, which they placed in degrees one aboue another: like the seates of a playhouse so as they might easilie and with delight leape from one to another: and beneath vpon the earth, not neere their pearches they layed their meate and drinke.[94] Their meate was chopped entralls or corne or figges cutt small, the smaller corne doth feede them [62r] best of all. They beginne to sett them with a thinne and small proportion, gyvinge water ynoughe, and so encrease the proportion till twenty dayes, and so kill the fattest. But they ioyned a greater roome wherein they haue more light, and into that house they did suffer them to flie, and there they made their choice of the best: beinge so roosted that a man might reach them with his hand. And after the same manner did they keepe their turtles and quailes, alwayes hauinge a respect least by takinge some to kill, the other shoulde be made more wilde by the trouble and vexation. And thus much for such as are kept close. But those which are wilde and at libertie are fedd as is before rehearsed.

When they builde and make their neasts, they gather small sprigges and fashion them like a dish round and sometymes longe, which they compound very artificiallie, layinge within side mosse or feathers which may be softe both for the safeguarde of their egges, and also for the ease of their younge, wherein they plaster not with earth as doe swallowes and other like birdes. They beginne to lay before other birdes but their first broode seldome come to good: by reason the colde killeth them. They lay againe before June, and those they breede vp, feedinge them with wormes or corne: so that it is true which the Philosopher noted: *Pariunt bis in anno.*[95] And for the most part they lay fiue or sixe egges. Langius writeth that the Magitians of Persea did take sage, and couered the same in warme dunge, wherein they suffered to putrifie vntill the Sunne and Moone grewe opposite, and out of that putrefaction they ingendred a Creature like a blackbird, which they did burne to ashes. And then they wolde take some quantitie of these ashes and cast into a burninge lampe, by reason whereof the house did appeare full of the shapes of lyvinge and movinge serpents. Marsilius and Gaudentius Merula doe affirme the same thinge and adde, that it must be putt in a viall couered in horse dunge when the Sunne entreth into Leo.

The disposition of this bird is very gentle, and friendlie apte to learne and imitate the sounds of their voices; and doubtlesse if their beake were crooked and their tongue broader they wolde speake more formally then parrotts. Philostratus sayeth, that he knewe a yonge man which had taught a blackbirde to speake. Belike it was one of the Schollers of Appolonius, the Successor of Simon Magus, [62v] who did many strainge feates and prankes by the helpe of the devill: yet neuerthelesse they take vp tunes and notes, wherein are not any of these three letters, D. R. T., for men that haue lost their teeth or such whose tongues cannot reflect from their teeth can hardlie speake any of those letters. They loue to washe themselues and picke their feathers with their beake; they leape aswell as they flie, for their flight is not longe and vnequall, onelie it is sufficient to saue it selfe from the hand of man, whereupon came the Prouerbe, *Merula riuum praeter uolauit,* or as the Italians say, *Egià di là del rio passato e'l Merlo,* the blackbird is passed over the ryver, to signifie a man that is escaped danger. Likewise they loue woodes and solitary places. Whereupon the Auncients paynted a blackbird to figure a melancholy man who delighteth not so much in any thinge as in woodes and waters. They loue one another, and lyve by couples like married persons. It was therefore a Prouerbe, *Merula ad merulam*: when like goeth with like, as *formica formicæ chara,* One Emmett is deere to another. They loue thrushes also as if they were brothers, or at the farthest Cosons Germanes. They loue the litle Rubecula, or Robin-red-brest; they will followe it in the day tyme and it will lodge neere to them in the night. They are afraide of all Hawkes, for if they see a Hawke they will sitt so still that a man may take them with his hand, orells come neere vnto them to kill them with arrowe, gunne, or piece: They are also afraied of the Crex or Dakerhen and the horne owle. *Crex merulam impugnat nocetque etiam ipsi & pullis.*[96] The Dakerhen fighteth against the blackbird and hurteth her and her yonge ones. And they saie, that if this bird here the Horne-owle crie, it instantlie flieth vnto her as it were to revenge some notable iniury. They die if they eate a kernell of a pomegranate, saieth Ælianus, and so doeth the falcon gentle, the Seagull, the Turtle, and the Vulture, whereof no philosopher coulde ever yelde a reason.

They are simple that cannot tell howe to take them, for they are taken with netts and baites like fishes, for if a baite be putt vpon a hooke, especiallie a worme wherein the hooke is couered, hee will swallowe it like a fishe, and so may be drawen by a lyne as a fishe with an angle. In the night tyme they are taken by torchlight, if they bee remoued out of the hedge or tree wherein they lodge; for they will flie to the light, and so are taken in boughes nointed over with birdlyme. If a litle pitt be digged in the earth and a worme or greene bay leafe or berry [63r] fastened in the same, over which they sett a small boorde or a tile so artificiallie, as it falleth downe vpon the bird when she comethe to eate the baite: and so is it inclosed in the pitfall till the fowler come and take her furth: which caused Horace to compare foolishe Poets to Fowlers huntinge after these birdes.

Hic dum sublimes versus ructatur & errat
Si veluti merulis intentus decidit auceps
In puteum foueamque.[97]

This man deceaued doth belche out verses highe,
As fowler falls in ditche whiles he a Macke doth eye.

The reason why this birde is so much hunted after, is because their fleshe, especiallie their breast piece, is so acceptable, as is witnessed by Horace in these elegant verses.

Et leporum auulsos ut multo suauius armos
Quam si cum lumbis quis edit, tum pectore adusto
Vidimus & merulas poni, & sine clune palumbes.

Wee sawe the shoulders rent from side of Hare
As sweeter meate then when with loynes tis drest:
Then blackbirde brawne was serued schorcht and bare,
And rumpeles ringdoues much praised at a feast.

It was accompted a modest aunsweare in Nicostratus[98] when one beinge asked what shoulde be prepared for his diett, nothinge, saied hee, that is costlie nor base, but Conyes, Duckes, thrushes, and black-birds. Some greate Phisitians disallowe the fleshe of these birds bycause they feede on wormes; the tast of the fleshe beinge somewhat sharpe, increaseth melancholie, yet Galen and the Salernitans praise it amonge meates of the second degree. They are saied to be the best that are taken in nettes or ginnes or by the Horne-owle. And in France they dresse them fillinge them full of marrowe and the fattest newe cheese lardinge them with the fatt of bacon and ginger, as Gesner learned by relation of a Frenche Cooke.

These birdes besides their wholesome meate at table which they supplie with delight doe also minister phisicke vnto a sicke man, for their fleshe is astringent, and prescribed by Hippocrates against the loosenes of the bellye. And Plyny praiseth it sodde with the sprigges of myrtle for such as are sicke of a bloudy flixe. Another saith they are to be eaten of such as are sicke of the pestilence or excoriation in the gutts. By the [63v] blacke colour Rhasis and Baptista Porta doe praise it against Melancholy: bycause many other such birds of this feather are vsed against that disease: so spotted herbes and beasts of a spotted colour doe cure the spotts in our humane body.[99] The dunge of black-birds mixed with vinegar take away freckles from the face: but, saieth Haly, then must the bird be fedd with rize.* A dissolued black-birde in olde oyle easeth the cricke in the necke; and the ache in the hippes. And the olde Magi made an amulett of the feete of a hare and the head of a blackbirde bound to the left arme to make men bold and fitt to enterprise greate and waightie matters.

The Coates giuinge black-birds are these.

Anslaye. Arg. Fesse. Gules. betwene sixe black-birdes proper.

Powell . Arg . a Cheueron sa: betwene three blackbirds proper.

Starden . Arg . a Blackbird proper, within a border engrailed Sab.

Stowe of Oxen. a Cheueron Gules betwene three blackbirds proper. [64r]

[XVI]

The Birdes of Paradise.

[space for illustration blank]

If all the worlde conspired to beholde a miraculous worke of God sufficient to stoppe the mouthes of Atheists, Heathens, and prophane persons that respect not a celestiall spirituall life wherein our conversation is aboue the common reach of men, then lett this little bird haue the attention both of mindes and eyes: that at the least grace may be as powerfull to keepe men of religion from the pollutions of the earth as is nature to supporte and sustayne one of these Creatures aboue in the ayer: for while they are aliue, they are neuer founde or seene vpon the earthe of this worlde. Therefore I will diligentlie collect and expresse all the obseruations of writers vpon this eminent and almost supernaturall bird.

* *rize* the seed or a concoction of rice

In Ethiopia and East India from whence our Authors haue fetcht their descriptions, they are called *Manucodiatæ,* that is in our language, *The Birds of God,* bycause they neuer see them till they fall vpon the earth, and doe belieue that they come from heauen, for neuer man founde any originall place of their generation. And moreouer bycause of the rare elegancie and colour of their feathers which no other fowle or earthlie Creature can æqualize or paralell, they are therefore called [64v] *Birdes of Paradice.* And by this name I must handle them bycause that hereby they are best knowen vnto Christians. Some haue written that it is belieued they liue in the Paradise which Adam lost, alway aboue in the ayer, and are susteyned with the dewe of heauen, and therefore are called the Birds of Paradise, in the which they die not, but in their age are carried into another Clymate, and so fall downe dead vpon the earth. If this earthlie Paradise did stand and abide since Noahs floude, I wolde belieue it, or if the fiction which Ariosto maketh thereof in his 34 . Booke . stanz . 50 . of Astolpho the Englishe Dukes voyage were true, who writeth thus.

This Hill nighe toucht the Circle of the Moone;
The toppe was all a fruitefull pleasant fielde
And light at night as ours is here at Noone,
The sweetest place that euer man behelde
There wolde I dwell if God gaue me my boone;
The soile thereof most fragrant floures did yelde
Like Rubyes golde pearles saphirs Topas-stones,
Chrisolite Diamonds Iacinthes for the nones,
The trees that there did growe were euer greene;
The fruites that thereon grewe were neuer fadinge;
The sundry coloured birds did sitt betwene
And singe most sweet the fruitfull boughes them shadinge.[100]

I say if these things were true in a corporall and literall sence, then wolde I alsoe subscribe to their opinion that affirme these birdes to be bred in Paradise. But for as much as the sinne of man hath brought a desolation vpon that faire and delicious garden I will neuer be Author nor Abettor to such an opinion as fauoureth heresie, as if Paradice had ben in the aer and not vpon the earth.

There be also other birdes which be called birds of Paradice, as the Lapwinge[101] and the Goldfinche in Italy are called the birds of Paradice. So in Ægipt they haue certeine birdes but [65r] litle lesse then Dawes, being of a browne redd colour, which they call *Birdes of Paradice.* And

Aldrouand writeth that hee had read a description of a voyage in Italian made by certeine Merchaunts, wherein they affirme that passinge ouer a great river called Phison in Africa they sawe many beautifull birdes which the people of that Countrey called birds of Paradice, by all which is apparaunt that the name of or denomination of these birds argueth not that they are bread in an earthly or aereall Paradise, no more then Lapwinges and other the last recited fowles: *Exoticæ aues statim aues paradisi dici coeperunt.* Strainge and rare fashioned and coloured birdes are soone tearmed by the name of birdes of Paradise, say Aldrouandus and Gesner.

But this of which I entreate is none of them, but that which is most properlie so called, being also tearmed *Apos Indica,* an India bird without legges. Bellonius fancieth the olde fayned Phoenix to be this bird of Paradise, and compoundeth it of two or three other birdes, without auctoritie of any good writer, or proufe of his oune experience. And therefore I will passe it ouer as a fable, and not worth the labour of confutation. It is a Maxime with Aristotle that there are no birdes without feete, and therefore those kinde of birdes haue troubled the writers, some affirminge and some denying it to be a birde bycause it wanteth feete; the Aristotelian marke of a fowle. But it appeareth most playnelie that Aristotle was deceaued in this, bycause hee neuer sawe a birde of Paradise. And if it had happened him to beholde it, hee wolde haue chainged his Axiome, and made the feathers and the winges to proue it a kinde of birde and noe insect or other kinde of Creature. There is a difference betwixt Scaliger and Cardan about their quantitie and size of their bodies. Cardan affirmeth that they exceede not a Swallowe. Scaliger on the other side affirmeth that a Captayne of the Gallyes about Iaua Maior sent him one as bigge as a pigeon, or a sea pye, but I haue no picture but this followinge description of it, whereof I will not defraude the Reader.

The quantitie and bulke of their body differeth, but in this it [65v] agreeth with other:[102] It wanted legs, and insteede thereof the Creator gaue it longe stringes or nerves in the taile, by which it is supported when it resteth on a tree by windinge the same about a boughe. The head like a Swallowes about the bignes of a walnutt, not round but somewhat flatt. The winges and taile stretched out to their leingthe are as longe as a Hawkes or a Kites, which is an admirable gifte of God, who hath framed those feathers so large that they might be spread vpon the more aier for their support, and longe abode in that region. The quills of their feathers are very small, like as is the body, resemblinge

a Peahens, for they are not oculated* like a Peacockes. All the longe feathers growinge both on backe and belly doe stretche backwarde and make the taile, wherein they differ from all other kindes of birdes whatsoeuer: whose tailes are distinct from the feathers of the body. Againe their wings are euer stretched furth, neuer contracted and drawen together: but as by nature it is made to be supported in the aer, so without paine or distention of their wings they are moued vp and downe at their owne pleasure: yet these winges stand immoueable. The two nerues are ioyned to their backes as it were growinge out of them about three hands breadthe in leingthe, beinge neither round nor square, nor thicke nor thinne, but of a middle forme betwixt round and square, and in bignes like a shoemakers threede; and these two nerves serue in steede of legs, althoughe they growe vpon their backes. The inwarde parts of these fowles are always verie fatt althoughe they neuer taste of earthlie foode. And thus much for these figureles bird[s] of Paradise, described by Scaliger, where the colour which is the most principall part is forgotten. And therefore I will proceede to the other: whose kindes are fiue. And here followe described in order.
[66r]

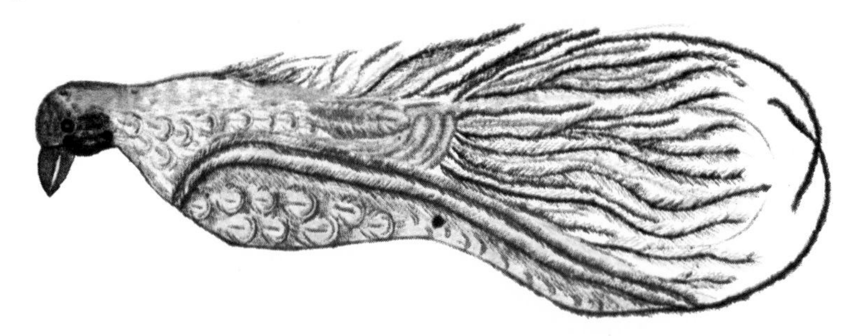

This birde is sett in the first place bycause of the beautie of it which exceedeth all the residue. The quantitie of the bodie is æquall to a swallowe, and so is the forme of the forepart: The compasse of the feathers of a different colour, but very beautifull and pleasinge to beholde: the head like a swallowes head, and greater then the head of so small a birde, the feathers thereof from the foreparte of the Crowne to the beginninge of the beake, are short, thicke, harde, and roughe but of bright clay colour resemblinge the sunnebeames shininge vpon goulde: the other feathers vpon the chinne and cheekes of a blewishe greene-colour, such as is the colour of a Drakes necke, held vp against the light, and the feathers are shorter, softer, and more slender: the

* *oculated* having eye-like spots

beake longer then a swallowes. The wings and the taile spredd out are like a Circle or a Wheele, they are but thinne, and their colour betwixt a browne and a bright redd colour; these feathers are all immoueable and like a darte in a piece of fleshe, so doe they stande fixed without alteration or motion. About and vnder their longe feathers are growinge lesser which support and fill vp the spaces of the greater: coueringe their rootes beinge parted like leafes some redd, scarlett, saffron, and golde coloured with a wonderfull and vnvtterable beautie throughe the mixture and disparitie of those colours. On the brest the feathers are most bright yellowe by the space or breadth of two or three feathers: the other part of the belly and on the sides are diuided into yellowe and redd except [66v] the backe which is of a bright fleshe or pomegranate colour. The two nerues fixed to the backe are somewhat blacke. And this is the description of the first kinde.

The second Figure.

[illustration on p. 110]

This bird was shewed to Aldrouand in the yere 1577 by one Cauallerio, a Knight and greate Antiquary at Rome: it differed from the former bycause it had two very longe feathers growinge vpon the rumpe. The head was white full of yellowe golden lynes or spotts. The eyes yellowe, the eyelids red, the beake betwixt a yellowe and a greene, beinge two small ynches longe and the vpper part somewhat crooked: the tongue redd, longe, and sharpe. It was reddishe vpon the breast, but the belly, backe, and winges were white: and yet the brimmes and tippes were of iron colour, and the backe was in the foreparte a yellowishe white, and in the hinder part next the rumpe of a rustie white colour. The leingth or breadth of the wings about fyve palmes, and therefore it farre exceeded the other: The taile feathers were white next the backe, and the residue of a rustie yron colour. All the feathers were longer then in the other, and the two first spoken of were longer then the residue by two handbredthes. It wanted the two nerues or stringes which the former had: wherefore some coniectured it to be a female. But Aldrouand iudged otherwise, that by the age of the birde, or by some accident of the iourney they were lost and taken away. But it may be those two feathers serued also insteede of them: and that in their youth they have no stringes but feathers, which in their age grewe

naked and weake, and so are reputed for nerves which in truth are feathers. And thus much for the second.
[67r]

The thirde figure.

[illustration]

This figure is called *Hippomanucodiata,* a horse-birde of Paradise, because of the leingthe thereof, for it was a foote and a halfe longe, and the breadth was two palmes when the wings were foulded vp. The vpper part of the beake was three ynches longe and very crooked. The necke and belly was of a chesnutt colour. All the residue of the body a pure white: The Crowne of the head an iron colour, and next about and vnder it yellowe and after the yellowe greene: vpon the backe, the quills did stande out two or three ynches. And it had but one stringe vpon the backe which was verie softe and flexible.

The fourth figure.

[illustration]

[67v] This birde from the ende of the beake to the typpe of the wynge was a foote longe. The beake was very longe, blacke, and crooked. The feathers of the necke and wings blackishe and so was the head, except about the Crowne where it had a tufte of bristles like a Peacockes crest of a yellowe colour, standinge three inches highe and very stiffe. And these are the different markes of this fourth kinde from all the precedent birds of paradise.

The fifthe figure.

[illustration on p. 110]

This fifth and last was taken by Gesner from the picture of a birde of this kinde at Norimberga with this followinge description. This Indian leg-les birde was of the bignes of a thrushe, yet of an vnspeakeable levitie* hauinge very large and wide wings, pervious and easie to

* *levitie* lightness

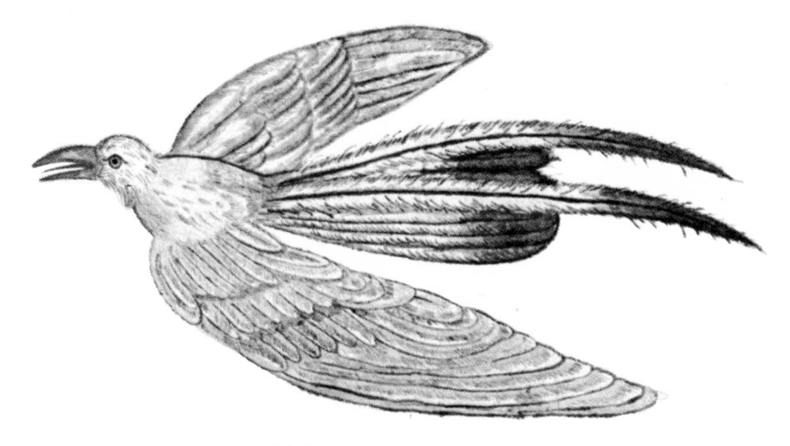

[*The second Figure.*]

[*The fifthe figure.*]

see through. The two longe feathers were like bristles; and they were blacke, thinne, and as harde as horne. It hath no feete but flieth perpetuallie, vnlesse it happen to stay itselfe by those two longe griestlie feathers vpon a tree. The beake was very small and the vnder part crooked; and not the vpper part as in all the former. And therefore this is the description of another distinct and seuerall kinde. And so wee will proceede to other parts of their History.

[68r] I haue read in the Ethiopian History written by Luys de Vrretta[103] that there are greate store of these birds in that Countrey which they call *Camenios,* that is, flyinge Chamelæon. And that the bodie of this birde is no bigger beside the feathers then the knuckle of a mans thumbe or finger, and lesse then the bodie of a Nightingale. And

because of the rare colours of the feathers, and for that it neuer lights on the earth till it dye, they adore it as a thinge divine. It sleepes in the aër and feedeth on flies and the dewe of heauen. It must needs sometymes rest vpon trees which it doth by the benefitt of the longe stringes or sinewes growinge vpon the backe.

To ascribe vnto it nothinge but aereall foode is an absurde thinge, and against all humane reason. *Ex iisdem nutrimur e quibus constamus.* Wee are fedd by the same thinges whereof wee consist, but if it consists of water and earth out of which Almighty God made all fowles at the beginninge, it must necessarilie be fedd also out of earth and water; and the more it flieth the greater is the necessitie of nature and of motion, whereby the spiritts weakened neede a more continuall supplie. Moreover the dewe falleth onelie in the morninge, and when the aër is voide of winde, the rayne also falleth but sieldome in those whott Countreys, and therefore it must needs haue other foode besides the deawe. And whereas the beake is crooked as wee haue shewed in the description like to a bird of præy, and therefore *non est calceamentum vbi non est calceatio,* there shoulde neuer be a shoe if there were not a foote: and there shoulde not be giuen to this bird a beake so greate, so stronge, so crooked, if it were to be exercised, onelie vpon the aër and deawe of heauen. Therefore I conclude bycause it neuer toucheth the earth that insteede of drinke it sucketh in the deawe, and the other foode are the flies and insects it meeteth in the aër: and peradventure the fruites of some trees. ffor by an vnavoideable necessitie of nature it must rest: no sublunary bodie can liue in perpetuall motion; yf it be graunted that they liue aboue the cloudes, then they want the benefitt of the deawe: and therefore they must be in a turbulent motion by reason of the windes, which wolde speedilie destroy them, if sometymes they did not fixe themselues to trees and there take their sleepe and quietnes. And bycause they are heavye, they fall on the ground when they die: wherefore their sleepe is very short which they take in the aër: orells they take none at all, [68v] for otherwise they must needes fall downe and die whensoeuer they sleepe, except they support one another when they sleepe, that is, the wakinge birdes those that sleepe; as the stronge cranes doe, those that are tired with longe flyinge. And I am verie inclineable to this opinion seinge they lyve male and female in a wonderfull charitie and love one of the other. And also my Spanishe Ethiopian Author doeth constantlie affirme they sleepe in the aer. Hee further saieth that the people of the Countrey haue many tymes assayed to take them aliue by hanginge lymed threeds, canes, or reeds in the aer, whereunto it happeneth that their feathers cleaue; but before they can reache the birde so entangled it is dead, as if it had touched the earth. The greatest wonder is about their generation and hatchinge of their younge. ffor the Ethiopian writer affirmeth the performance of that naturall worke on this manner: when nature enclineth them to the worke of generation, the Male binds himselfe by his backe sinewes vnto the female, and so flyinge both together they engender the eggs. And afterward when the eggs growe ripe, and the tyme of layinge is come, the females couple themselues to their seuerall Males and lay their eggs in a dint or hollowe place vpon the Males backe which is their nest prouided by nature. And there shee sitteth and hatcheth her younge who are likewise carried by the Male on his backe vntill they be able to flie, and the damme procureth them foode. So Luys de Vrretta. But Aldrouand calleth this *explodendam opinionem,* an opinion to be abhorred as contrary to nature and necessitie. ffor, saieth hee, I haue handled and narrowlie searched fyve of these birdes, and neuer founde any such hole in the backe of the Male. Therefore hee proceedeth to confute another opinion f[a?]r [more] improbable then this: for hee saieth that some haue written that the female hath such a cavitie vnder her winges wherein she layeth her egges and keepeth them till they be hatched: which must needs be a verie ridiculous conceipt not worth the confutation.

What then, doe they builde their neasts and lay their younge till they be able to flie, for neuer any mortall founde either egge, neast or younge not able to flie of these birdes of paradise. He aunsweareth, *In Arboribus nidulari & in propriis nidis incubare,* that by the benefitt of their sinewes aforesaide they builde in trees and therein haue their younge. And this, he saieth, agreeth with scripture: which testifie that fowles breede vpon the earth; the which sayinge I remember not: but onelie this is affirmed [69r] by the prophet Dauid Psal. 104, 16. 17. The high trees are satisfied* euen the Cedars of Lebanon which he hath planted, that the birdes may make their neasts there, and the storke dwelleth in the firre trees: which is but a pore proufe that therefore the birdes of paradise builde neasts in trees.

In such varieties of opinion the wisest labour through want of experience and knowledge of a litle bird of heauen; therefore wee may easilie be deceiued in the Angelicall nature, and much more in the Diuine; if hee onelie which best knowes himselfe had not revealed him-

* *satisfied* rather, are "full of sap" (A.V.)

selfe and his Angells vnto vs: wherefore I will leaue this inextricable quæstion about their generation to the further discussion of Trauailers and industrious Readers wherein I professe that in naturall thinges, it is euer best to avoide miracles, and miraculous imaginations. And therefore althoughe no man euer founde the neast of these birdes, yet it is not presentlie to be true that they lay and hatche their younge vpon the backs of their husbands.

These birdes are founde in Arabia, Ethiopia, and the Mountayne Amara[104] in the Ilands Moluccaes, where the Lordes of the Countrey doe reuerentlie respect them: accomptinge their feathers a very riche Iewell vpon a superstitious opinion, that if they weare them in battell, they are as good as Armour of proufe to keepe them from wounds and hurt: although they marche foremost and in the greatest perill. And hereunto I may adde the wordes of Bellonius: *Sunt elegantissimæ & simul ad Gallinacei crassitiem coniunctæ, omnes tamen ab exiguo corpore prodeuntes pellem duntaxat retinente. Nam Arabes, qui eas vendunt, carnes eximunt: Illi ergo plumis in hunc modum exornati Diui Michaelis picturam quodammodo referunt: At non perpetuo incedunt isto ornatu; verum duntaxat, dum Imperator in bellum proficiscitur.*[105] There are certeine Indians called Ianissarai that delight in those feathers: ffor they are as thicke and stronge as some Cockes feathers: yet when they are plucked of from the fowle they bringe away the skynne with them: ffor the Arabians that sell them doe first separate them, the fleshe and skynne. Those Indians adorned with those feathers doe seeme like the picture of St Michael [69v] which they carry about in Fraunce. And therefore they doe not weare them at all tymes; but onelie when their Emperour goeth furth in person to make warre.

There are two Embleames vpon this bird. One inscribed thus, *Sine pondere sursum.*[106] The bird flyinge with her beake vpright to heauen, and so dyinge in the aer, her body falleth downe: So Alexander Farra, a Noble gentleman of Alexandria in Italy, pictured his care for the saluation of his soule, as it were imploringe the helpe of heauen, that when his body shoulde fall into the earth, like one of these birdes of paradise, yet his soule without the ponderous waight of sinne might ascende vpward to heauen. So Aldrouand vnder the signe of this bird, wrote in his garden, *Sic animus petat alta:* ffor as this earth is death to this bird, so is the loue and enioyinge of this worlde death to the soule, when it falleth from God aboue, to the base and transitory thinges here beneath.

Havinge read of sundrie birdes in the Ethiopian and Indian History, written by Luys de Vrretta and Ramusius,[107] I thinke this place very fitt to expresse their collections, bycause they haue not described them thoroughlie with all their abilments [*sic*] of nature, but onelie noted some rare and strainge proportions and qualities adhaerent to them, as the wonderfull worke of Almighty God: by admiration whereof wee that are his reasonable creatures for whose sake all these thinges were created, might be stirred vp so much more to magnifie his Greatenes and goodnesse aboue the common sort of men. As these fowles doe differ in their rare shapes from the common formes of other birdes: so must wee singe vnto his Maiestie newe songes of Magnificats: for the newe reuelations of olde Creatures, whose demonstrations were lost in the losse of paradise and are nowe recouered againe in the tyme of our Redemption: wherein I desire the Readers to stay themselues from scornefull detestacon* of their narrations, because their rarities may seeme incredible to them that haue not well scanned the power of God, nor resolued of the varietie of his workes, believinge that all the worlde is in Englande, and that there [70r] can be nothinge vnder the cope of heauen which is not visible at home in our oune nation. So was wyne strainge to our forefathers. So Camells, Elephants, parrotts, peacockes, and such like vntill they were brought over from other Countreys. But nowe wee belieue and admire them as the rare workes of the Diuinity. And so I doubt not in tyme to come, but that some of these shall growe more credib[le?], familiar and better knowen to vs, and our posteritie.[108] And so to their Historyes.

They haue a bird in Æthyopia of the bignes of a thrushe, hauinge a longe lifted vp necke, and all his feathers of chaingeable and beautifull colours, beinge crested on the Crowne like a Cocke, and so bearded vnderneath. And from his crest springe vp fyve or sixe feathers, like the feathers of a younge hearon beinge wonderfull faire intermixed with the rarest colours in nature. The Ethiopians call this birde *Suhayo*.[109] And these feathers are giuen by the Emperor of that Countrey vnto other Potentates and Princes, for presents of worth and rare guifts. The Turkes and Persians weare these feathers in their Turbants like the feathers of the bird of Paradice, and giue fyve or sixe Zequies,† that is, Frenche Crownes a piece for them, bycause their luster is so orient, that a Noble man taketh not himselfe better adorned with any kinde of vesture, then with one of these feathers. And therefore I haue placed it in the next place to the bird of Paradyce: for

* *detestacon* detestation

† *Zequies* Sequins or Zecchini, Venetian gold coins worth about eight shillings

peradventure the feathers hereof are vented* amonge vs for feathers of the Manucodiate.

The same Authour relateth that there be birds in Ethiopia which haue no excrementary or hole behinde: but they haue a hole open vpon their backe insteede thereof out of which alsoe the female shutteth† her eggs that bringe furth and contynue their kinde. They are alsoe Apodes, feetelesse, and lyve perpetually in the water.[110]

They haue also another vncleane bird which they call *Cacancello*. I say an vncleane birde bycause it feedeth vpon the dunge and excrements of other birdes, therefore it followeth them at the heeles that it may devoure them so soone as it falleth from them. Dionisius Colan is very mannerly in comparison hereof. And so were the [70v] first flatterers of the worlde, who did but licke vp the spittle of their friend and framed themselues onely to *Ait, aio, Negat nego*. But nowe the flatterers of our tyme exceede all the parasites of the former ages, for they licke vp the filthe of greate mens shame, and glory in this to folowe them at the heeles beinge ready prest to take vp all beastlie and inhumane actions which their Masters lett fall least their shame shoulde make them odious. Such knaues, saied a greate Lord, are necessary and our turnes serued by such, like vs best; bycause then wee can turne them of like knaves; the reason is bycause they are groomes to bad mindes, and receiue for advauntage and filthie lucre, the dunge of their Masters lewdnes into the close stoole of their oune breasts and consciences which they neuer empty till they and their Masters be buried in hell fire. And so much vpon occasion of this strainge filthie fowle decipheringe more foule filthie men.

There are another kinde of devouringe birdes in Ethiopia, which they call *Catalinitas*:[111] the people of the Countrey take them for as greate a punishment as Locusts. They flie by flockes contayninge innumerable multitudes and eate vp all the greene and fruites of their trees. The Priests and Fryers of the Countrey together with all sorts of people, men and women, doe coniure and cast out many maledictions against them vntill they flie away. And so they holde opinion that these kinde of excommunications (such as are vsed in Spayne against Locusts) doe expell and driue them away. ffor in whatsoeuer nation are Priests and Fryers of Rome: there are also regnant many magicall and superstitious vses of and against other good Creatures of God.

They haue another birde (saieth Luys de Vrretta) which they call

* *vented* sold
† *shutteth* lays, produces

Rocho, or *Ruc* in that part of Affricke wherein is the Iland of Madagaschar. It is in forme like an Eagle hauinge a longe crooked beake and crooked clawes. The feathers coloured like the Eagle but much greater and longer: ffor (hee writeth) that the feathers of his wings are twelve paces or yardes longe: but the whole breadth of the fowle with displayed wings from point to point is thirtie yardes. And all other parts of the bodye are aunswearable in proportion: so that this is the greatest amonge all fowles, so farre excedinge the Eagle as an Elephant doth [71r] a Lion. Besides such as is the monstrousnes of his body, such alsoe is the fiercenes and streingth of all his parts, so as it seemeth vtterlie incredible which my Authour relateth, for he saieth that it taketh vp an Elephant into the aer by the gripe of his talants, and so letteth him fall downe againe wherebye hee is dashed to pieces or slayne. And then the birde feedeth vpon the flesh of the dead Elephant. Also hee reporteth that hee taketh vp a Cart laden, as it goeth, or a shippe laden with merchaundize as it saileth, and so casteth them downe againe, to the destruction both of men and cattell. It is to be doubted whether this bee a fiction or an imposture of deuilishe arte, or the devill himselfe: for no man can tell from whence it commeth or whither it goeth: yet it is belieued of many wise men that it is a fowle, bycause it feareth Gunshott and flyeth away from the same, the poore people of Madagascar hau[ing?] no other defence for themselues but to shoote of their ordenance, when first they espie it.

There is in Ethiopia a goodly flower, no where els in all the worlde to be founde: they call it *Ghoyahula,* it is like the flower of the Sunne, but the leaves thereof are like to Iuy: they are infinite in nomber, of an admirable beautie and sweete sauour, so as it smelleth a greate way of. And beinge layed amonge clothes, there is neither pomander, muske, or Cyuet that giueth them so sweete a perfume. About this flower there keepeth a birde of as faier a colour as the flower, called *Supiniminis,*[112] which attendeth pruninge, dressinge, trymminge, and defendinge it from the iniury of flies, weavills, wormes, mothes, or any other fowles. ffor if any dare to approache this flower, the *Supiniminis* is at hand to giue it a mortall pecke. But when a birde (that is more then her matche with whome it dare not to buckle) commeth neere the flower it thus obserueth and keepeth, then it falleth to cryinge and makinge a dolefull noice without ceasinge vntill it hath diverted the birde, and ridd the flower out of danger. This flower openeth with the Sunne, and then flyes this birde vnto it, first openinge the [71v] small foldes of the leafes, and so with her beake most curiouslie dressinge, pickinge, and trymminge it, as if it were euery day a bride adorned by her handmaide. When shee hath thus opened and dressed it, shee spreadeth herselfe with winges displayed vpon the toppe, and gathereth vp the odour of the leafes with singuler delectation. Thus shee is vpon the flower as it were in a Paradyse wherein it batheth, stretcheth, turneth, and pleaseth itselfe aboue measure. At last it falleth to singe most sweetely, and so contynueth till toward midnight, at which tyme the flower shutteth, and then the birde departeth to take her repast and rest till the next day Noone when the flower openeth againe, and the birde returneth to her former delightfull pastime.

They haue a very greate birde in Affricke which they call *Nesir*,[113] yet his beake, necke, and leggs are shorter then a Cranes, his flight is as high as any Eagles for hee flies out of sight, yet is his sight so quicke and stronge, that hee espieth easilie any thinge vpon the earth: for he will fall sodeinlie downe vpon a dead karkeis which is his foode whereupon hee lyveth. They lyve in Companye together, and lyve very longe vntill the[y] loose their feathers especially from his head: at which tyme they keepe their neasts and cannot flie abroade, but then their younge doe nourishe them. The Italians call them *Buetts* when they are olde bycause of their baldnes.

They haue in India certeine Night-birdes without name, which neuer come abroade till the Sunne be sett. They are enemyes to the Owles, and fight with them vnto death: yet they are litle bigger then a swallowe, hauinge wings ashecolour and blacke beinge crossed ouer with a white lyste.* They flie also as swifte as any swallowe; all the night longe they flie, but in the morninge they appeare not. Neither is it founde, saieth Ramusius, where and in what place they hide themselues.

In the Island Hispaniola, there is a birde called *Cocuie,* hee is not bigger then ones thumbe, hauinge foure wings, two [72r] harde ones aboue, and two softe and tender ones vnderneath.[114] His eyes are as bright as a candle, and shine in the night as a candle, for where hee flies there is the aer lightened; as it were with a Candle: wherefore the Indians carry them in darke evenings insteede of Candles. By the light thereof, they reade, write, and doe other busines in their chamber. They ioyne three or foure of them together, and they serue insteede of torches. Therefore they vse them principallie for their warres and marches in the night: beinge thereby freed from extinguishinge through winde, rayne, and tempests, as are torches vpon such occasions. They take these

* *lyste* list, border

birdes and nourishe them for these and such purposes: but if they keepe them longe their eyes growe dymme and nothinge worthe: then they kill them not but let them goe away at libertie, whereby they recouer and becomme as cleare, as they were before. It is also reported of this birde, that it hath eyes vnder the wings which neuer are seene but when the bird flieth, so as in Captiuitie there is no vse of these, neither will they suffer them to be discouered: by which it is apparaunt that their light is much greater that they giue in their libertie then in their captiuitie. These birdes the Indians will fasten to the Collars of their neckes, whereby they shewe themselues to their friends a league of in the night. When they kill one of these birde[s] they drawe an annoyntment out of them, which they mingle with a kinde of paste, and put it vpon their faces and naked breasts which maketh them seeme like a flaminge fire, or as they saie like an Angel of heauen. Ramus. Volume.3. fol. 140.

There is also in the foresaide Island Hispaniola, a strainge birde as bigge as a greate Sea Cobbe, whose feathers are white mixed with gray, and he is called *Amphibion,*[115] that lyveth both on the land and vpon the water. His right foote is like the talant of an Eagle and his lefte foote like a gooses, vpon this hee standeth when hee is beneath vpon the land; and seinge a fishe hee flieth vpon the water stayinge himselfe from sinkinge by his broade foote, but with his other crooked clawes taketh the fishe and eateth it vpon some rocke, or neere adiacent tree: and these strainge birdes I haue caused to attend this birde of Paradise as well for their rarenes and difference from other, as also to giue [72v] learned Trauaylers an occasion to searche abroade for a more copious description of such admirable Creatures.

[73r–v—blank]

[74r]

[XVII]

[Canary Birds]

These birds haue bene denominated of certaine Islandes lyinge in the Atlantique sea on the left side of ffez or Barbary. These Islands were first caled *Insulæ fortunatæ,* the fortunate Islands, because of the moderate temper & clemencye of the aer. Afterward they were caled *Canariæ,* because (sayeth Iuba) of the greate doggs bredd in them.[116] They haue also little singinge birds not exceedinge sparrowes which the Latines call *Canoræ,* singers, & *passeres Canarienses Canarii & aues sacchari,* sugar birdes because the best Barbary sugar is brought from those Islands.

The first kinde of Canary birds

This bird is thus described by Gesner. The quantitye like a Titmouse, a small white beake & sharpe, the winges & tayle of a greene collour. They are neuer or seldome fatt but often full of fleash, the feete & leggs ashe colour & the other feathers also. The male differeth from the fæmale in the brest, belly & vpper part of the head next the beake which are deeper earth colour; they are neuer or seldome fatt as I haue sayde-before. They singe very sweetely & shrill hauinge a longe breath which they intende and remitte at their owne pleasure, now at the highest & then at the lowest, with [74v] an harmonious voyce like a musitian. The shrillnes of their sound by strecthing their small chappes maketh a reflexion vppon the eares of the hearers so as to some it is pleasinge & to other an obtusion. By reason that they are brought from farr & are desired for theyr voyces they are sould somewhat deere in all theis parts & therefore few except noble & rich persons doe make much of them & nourish them: of their musicke I haue read this Epigram:

Quid miror digitis quando rudis organa pulso.
Suaue tot è cannis ire, redire melos?
Plures vna sonos auis haec nil passere maior
Gramineis herbis aequa colore dedit.

an harmonious voyce like a musitian. The shrillnes of their sound by stretching their small chappes maketh a reflexion uppon the eares of the hearers so as to some it is pleasinge & to other an obtusion. By reason that they are brought from farr & are desired for theyr voyces they are sould somewhat deere in all theis parts & therefore few except noble & rich persons doe make much of them & nourish them: of their musicke I haue read this Epigram.

Quid miror digitis quando rudis organa pulso.
Suaue tot é cannis ire redire melos?
Plures vna sonos auis hæc nil passere maior
Gramineis herbis æqua colore dedit
Illa tonos apte medios, quos maxima moles
Nec calami poterunt mille sonare canit.
Ergo chelys cytharæq fides vos dicite nostram
Vel mutam si fas est, vel αμουσον auem.

Whie doe I muse at musicks melodye:
From stop or stroke of pipe that comes & goes
This herbe-greene birde of sparrowes quantitie
More pleasinge tunes from little throte out throwes
No Eagle greate nor thouzand penns can frame
Or singe such notes so sweetly modified
Therefore my harpe & lute say you the same
Or wishe hir dumbe thy muse that vilified.

For the better chusing of theis Canary birds, my authors teach theis two obseruations, first those wch are least in bulke of bodye, & secondly those that haue the longest tayles for then you shalbe hardly deceaued, especially in the first, for such is the gift of God unto birdes, that the least are the best singers: the greater are unquiet in their cages & leape up & downe very seldome settinge themselues to singinge. Such are the birds broght from the green & palme Islandes wch are deceiptfully obtruded uppon the ignorant for Canary birds & therfore iustly

Illa tonos apte medios, quos maxima moles,
Nec calami poterunt mille sonare, canit.
Ergo chelys, cytharæque fides vos dicite nostram
Vel mutam, si fas est, vel ἄμουσον auem.[117]

Whie doe I muse at musicks melodye:
ffrom stop or stroke of pipe that comes & goes?
This herbe-greene birde of sparrowes quantitie
More pleasinge tunes from little throte out throwes
No Eagle greate nor thouzand pens can frame
Or singe such notes so sweetly modified.
Therefore, my harpe & lute, say you the same
Or wishe hir dumbe thy muse that vilified.

ffor the better chusing of theis Canary birdes, my authors teach theis two obseruations, first those which are least in bulke of bodye, & secondly those that haue the longest tayles for then you shalbe hardly deceaued, especially in the first, for such is the gift of God vnto birdes, that the least are the best singers: the greater are vnquiet in their cages & leape vp & downe, very sieldome settinge themselues to singinge. Such are the birds broght from the green & palme Islandes which are deceiptfully obtruded vppon the ignorant for Canary birds & therfore iustly [75r] caled *passeres stultos*, foolish sparrowes. When these birdes were first brought into these parts they brought with them a small seede for their foode which they call *semen phalaridis,* grasse-corne seede, for it seemed that they delight much herein at home in the Canaryes & this seede is more plentifully nourished in our Europa because of this bird. They also eate lyne seede, poppye, & millet, but sugar is exceedinge welcome vnto them, for they delight in the sugar canes of theyr owne countrie: as soone as they haue eaten sugar or mouse-eare or hennbitte, they will presently singe if they be right Canaries.

The Seconde kinde called by Dr Turner a Greene-fynche

[illustration on p. 122]

This litle bird [is] called *Chloris* of the greeke word *Chloros* signifyenge greene & by Aristotle *Ochros* because of the earth colour of the

OPPOSITE, *the third hand*

belly, therefore in Italy it is called *Verdon, verderro,* & *verdmontan, zaranto, Taranto,* & *Caranto.* Aboute Trent *Frinson,* in Sauoye, *verdeyre,* in ffraunce, *verdier,* in Germany *Gruenfinck, Gruenling, Kuttuogel, Tutter,* & *Rappfincke,* in Illiria *zeglolka,* and at this day in Greece *Assarandos.* This Canary-bird or Greene-finche is of the bignes of a larke. The brest of a bright earth colour, the belly & the rumpe [75v] yealowish, the other parts greene except the beake which one, the vpper part, is of a horne colour, & the vnder part of a fleashe colour, the necke & backe of a greenish ashe colour, the tayle of a greenish colour & forked consistinge of fower feathers, the hinder part of the belly next the tayle white, the leggs & feete of a fleashe colour & substaunce, the feete or clawes three & the midle longest. The femall is more pale then the male, & hath lesse earth colour.

They liue sometymes vppon earth wormes, & also they liue & abide in bushes, hedges, & amonge small trees. They eate the seede of herbes as thistles, wilde vines, & rapeseeds, for this last cause they are called in Germany *Rapfincke*: the seedes also of grasse-corne they delight in aboue all other. They growe tame sooner then other birds of this kinde, for if a man holde them with one hand, they will eate meate out of the other. Their beake & necke is very stronge, & like Linetts will drawe therewith vessells aboute their cages, & if they be vsed to the fiste, they will fly to the finger wherevppon they are accustomed to sitte. They make their nests of Comfrie & in the bottome, for the ease of theyr eggs they lay wooll & haire. They lay not aboue five eggs & many tymes the Cuckowe layeth in their nests. They are troubled with risings like pimples or bunches in the head whereof many tymes they dye, if they be not well attended. The remedy is to anoynte them gently with fresh butter, or cocks grease vntill they be ripe, then must the purulente matter be pressed out gently, so after their anoyntment once or twice more they are cured. Yf they be troubled with lyce let them be washed in wyne, for so will the lyce bee killed & theye inabled to ouercome that maladye.

The Third ffigure

[76r]

This little bird is an Indian Canary as I may so call & terme it, for, sayth Aldrouand, it was brought aliue out of Iapan by the princes that came to see the Pope. Yt was lesse then the former, but more greene, yet the beake & feete not so thicke, the forepart, both brest & belly, are

very white, the beake a brownish or pale greene, but the head, backe, & rumpe altogither greene, the longe feathers of the winges & the tayle blew, the thighe white & the feete blacke. Yt did singe also very sweetely & was tame, therefore they gaue it to the Pope for a rare liuinge iewell out of their countrey. And thus much for theise Canary birdes.

[XVIII]

A Cenchram

[illustration, lower group on p. 123]

[76v] This litle bird is an Italian bird by them called *Miliaria* which was the old latine word in Varro: of Aristotle & the Grecians *Cynchramos, Cenchramos,* & *Cenchramas,* of *Cenchris* which signifieth millet seede. The Latines call it *Hortulanus,* whereof I haue here expressed fower kinds, litle differing from one another except in colour.

Yt is hardly so greate as is a larke, the beake, leggs, & clawes of the feete are red, the head, necke, & brest in the male yealowe with some saffron coloured spotts. And in the female these parts are distinguished into yeallowe & greene. The male is distinguished into yeallowe & greene at the side of the tayle feathers; he haith a spott vnder the sides of his eyes, which is round & of an earth colour; yn the female there is none such, the short winge feathers next the ribbs are equally blacke & yealowe but ye longe feathers & the tayle blacke.

The other kinde was yealowe as an oringe exceptinge the ribbs of the feathers, & typps of the longe winge feathers which weare white, but the beake & leggs were redd as in the former.

There is an other as white & whiter then the swanne yf it be possible, exceptinge the beake & the leggs which are red as aforesayed.

There is yet a fowerth whose head was couered with pale ashe coloured feathers tendinge to yealowe. The necke likewise coloured & noted with blacke spotts, the belly, leggs, & feete of a saffron colour, the winges white, blacke, & ashe colour, the tayle is browne beinge somewhat redder on the sides.

There are others such as in ffraunce are called *preyer,* because it liueth in the meddowes, the beake whereof is as harde as any bone, the vpper

& neather part beinge so conioyned that [77r] there is a kinde of dicthe betwixt them. Yt is also crooked & bunched. The whole body is thus described by Bellonius. Yt is bigger then a crested larke, the belly pale with blacke spotts, the thighes, leggs, & feete, betwixt a chessnutt & a redd; the longe clawe is behinde & therefore it is coniectured that it liueth altogether vppon the earth & not vppon any trees. All theise propertyes & colours apertaine vnto this kinde. They are all of them wonderfully delighted with barley & millet seede & there with all they growe exceedinge fatt, of whome Varro giueth this testimony, *Miliariæ a cibo dicuntur, quod milio fiunt pingues. In ornithone præter alias aues has alunt, quæ pingues væneunt care.*[118] The Cenchrams take their name of millet seede wherevppon they feede & men nourishe them in their fowleryes or birde-howses, which beinge fatt they sell very deare. There was a lawe that none but senators & princes might eate hereof. ffor they were desired aboue pertriges, & better esteemed amonge nobles yelding a better rellishe, a sweeter & easier concoction and especially in the winter; for which cause they did then sett them vpp a fattinge, for they are a most delicate & wholsome foode. They take them in Heluetia & in all the continent where Quayles come. In Italy, they abounde most about Bononia, where they take them in greate plenty, & pullinge of their feathers send them in brann or meale flower vnto the Cardinalls & Lordes of Rome.

They build vppon the ground as ducks & Larks, especially in the feilds where are sowed barley, oates, or millett. Their voyce is like this Barbarous worde *Tirtertirteriiz* & therefore in ffraunce they also call it a *Teriz*; they flye with greate motion of their wings & their legs hanging downe not gathered vp together.

They are the companions of Quayles: *Coturnices ducibus Oto, & linguacula, & Ortigometra proficiscuntur, atque etiam Cenchramo, a quo etiam reuocantur noctu, cuius vocem quum senserint aucupes intelligunt parari discessum.*[119] The quayles goe & come vnder the guydaunce of the horne owle, the Crane & their inseperable captaine, the Schreecke, & also the Cenchram by whome they are called home at night. By the voyce whereof the fowlers knowe the quayles are departinge & [77v] going to rest. And the whole prayse of this bird I will conclusiuely expresse in the wordes of Pliny. *Coturnices comitatur, ac se perseuerantiorem præbet quam Glottis (quæ nunquam plus vno die cum iis pergit & in proximo hospitio eas deserit,) sed hæc festinare cum eis ad expetitas terras itaque eam noctu excitare & itineris admonere solet.* He alwayes accompanieth the Quayles & is their more assured & vndiuided companion then the Crane who comonly forsaketh them at the first hostage. But this birde goeth alonge with them to theyr desired landes: & in the night tyme by a strayned voyce doth excite & stirr them vpp remembringe them of their iorney which they are to accomplishe.

Thus he is a preacher vnto other birds as preachers are vnto other men by voyce & example to prepare them for their last iourney to their lande of happinesse.

[XIX]

The Cercyon.

This is an Indian bird & propper onely to that countrey of whome only Ælianus[120] maketh mention out of whose wordes I must make my description. This bird (he sayeth) is of the bignes of a stare but paynted or adorned with delectable variety of colours. Yt is more docible then a Parrott, imitatinge the voyce of man with greater playnesse & shewe of discretion. Yet it [78r] cannot indure to be fedd in a Cage. When *Alexander* had conquered India, he built diuers cityes as *Beucephala* & *Cyropolis* which he gaue to his countreymen the *Macedonians* to inhabite, with all the territory aboute them. When these *Macedonians* had well considered this fowle they found that the tonge & tayle did neuer stand still, especially the last, & therevppon they called it *Cercyon* because of the perpetuall motion of his tayle.

[XX]

The Chaffynch.

These little birds are many tymes called *Vincones,* ffynches, such are the linnetts, & the bullfinches, greenefynches, goldfynches & other, so as the most prime & vulgar place from whome they are all deriued, or vnto whose kind they must bee all ascribed ys the *Chaffynch.*

The Grecians in *Aristotles* tyme caled it *Spiza* & now they call yt *ffringillaria,* like the latine worde *ffringilla,* so the Italians *franguello* from the same stampe, the *ffrench pinson,* the *Sauoyens Quinson,* the germans *ffyncke,* the *Heluetians Buchfyncke,* the *Belgians Vinck,* the *Illirians Pinkawa,* & the *Polonians Slowick.* The description might be omitted but for order sake yt is a birde so well knowne in all nations, yet I will not forbeare to delineate hir amongst others, that in so little a birde you may behowld the works of so greate a God.

The quantity of the body is æquall to a Sparrowes, the beake [78v] thicke & stronge, at the end blackishe & of a fleashe colour vppwards, the vpper part of the head, necke, & backe to the rumpe is of a blewish colour; next to the rumpe a Chessnutt, & the rumpe is greenishe, the brest & belly somewhat tawnie. In both the winges are twoo white spotts cutt like ragges, & at the sides & ends of those spotts the feathers seeme blacke. The fellowe or female differed only in the paleness & reddness of the brest & bellye. Their colour is not constant, for they are founde all white & yeallowishe white: & of this last I finde this description.

The whole body & especially the backe was yealowishe white, the vnder parts as the necke & brest more Iron coloured & the belly ashe couler within towards the sides, yet all the quills or roots of their feathers weare like leade, the leggs & beake of a Rose colour & the tayle partly murry* & partly white & thus far their descriptions wherein their colour euer varieth.

Theise birdes are Caged & kept for their voyce, especially in the winter, for then they singe & it is thought that they are for that cause called *ffrigillæ* or *ffringillæ* for their singinge in the Winter, for they are most properly Winter byrds, almighty God hauinge appoynted fower kinds of birds to be the messengers & proclamers of the fower quarters & seasons of the yeare, accordinge to these verses of Alciatus.

Aduenisse hyemem Fringilla renuntiat ales.
Ad nos vere nouo garrula hirundo redit.
Indicat æstatem sese expectare Cuculus.
Autumno est tantum cernere ficedulas.[121]

That winters come the Chaffynch synges apace
The bablinge Swallow telleth it is the Springe
The Sommer crieth all the Cuckowes race
The Eate-figge Autumes presence forth doth ringe.

Their voyces differ, first, the male from the female, for his voyce is cleere, stronge, & lowde, hir body is weake & faynte: & againe some of them are shorter & more concise in theyr tunes, other longer, & some are both at their owne pleasures. Yt is thought the worde of *Plautus ffringutire* is the verbe to expresse this ffynches voyce: for when *Cleostrata* ouer earnestly reasoned with hir husband aboute Cassinaes mariage, he replyed to hir in anger, *Tu quid fringutis?*[122] Other thinke that as the bird so the voyce is denominated from chillnesse or cold, & therefore *fringilla frigore* [79r] *cantat,* the ffynch singeth for cold weather. Their song beinge a kinde of complaynt as *Martiall* caleth them *fringillarum quærelas* they are like to prophaine men that neuer speake to God but in theyr aduersitie as these ffynches their dolefull complaynts in the winter. Their longe strayned voyces are very gratefull & with locusts & wormes when they are kept in Cages they are prouoked to singe. They

* *murry* purple red, the color of the mulberry

are more quiet in Cages then other singinge birds, & therfore they are more nourished of birders, in windie & tempestious weather they singe not at all: & in that morning when they singe vppon the howse toppe it presageth a rayneye & tempestuous day. They singe in the Autumne & Sommer if they be kept in darke places & brought to the light but now & than. They loue thornes & bushye places & eate the thornes seede. They are subtile & crafty birds & cannot be taken without very secret traps & fayre baytes. They are stronge in the beake & head & will drawe out the boxes of their meate & vessells of water. They are not easely tamed, but a longe tyme out of the impatience of their Captiuety beate the sides of their Cages to gett forth, & so hurte themselues & some of them will neuer be tamed. At the first they bewayle their captiuitie for a moneth & if they see any body come vnto them they sigh & complayne for sorrow, feare, & indignation; they are much more subtill then linnetts or Sukyus for if they espye a fowler lyminge the twiggs of trees, they for euer abandon those trees, & will not be called or deceiued by any tune or voyce like other birdes, wherefore the fowlers must vse moe singinge birds in the springe & Autume, which haue bin longe tyme kept close from light, otherwise they will neuer singe in the Autumne or winter, which is the only cause for which they are preserued. They take them in *ffraunce* (say *Bellonius* & *Stephanus*) by picthinge vp* three yonge trees in a plaine triangularly, whereof the topps are made bare & so lymed, & the vnder boughes are couered with leafes. Aboute these trees they place other singinge fynches like flatterers to allure them, at whose voyces the Chafynches that fly ouer those plaines are intysed to rest & alight in those false trees & so are insnared. Sometymes they also take them in netts, & if the wynde be Westerlye or very lowe without blusteringe & tempestious rage then they are taken more abundantly because they flye more frequently. They obserue a middle place for makinge their nests so as when [79v] they build in high trees they make them in the lowest boughes, but when they build in lowe trees they frame them in the highest branches. The outside is of mosse for the most parte & the inside of Cob-webbs or a softe woolley substaunce gathered from trees & thistels. They lay not aboue fiue or six eggs & abide not longe in one place or countrey, after they are able to flye: & Gesner is of opinion that in the winter tyme they separat & liue aparte, the male & female, because in *Heluetia* in the winter tyme they finde noe femalles.[123] And *Aristotle* sayeth that they differ in one poynte of their

* *picthinge vp* placing upright; "*erigi*" (A.)

habitacion from all other fowles, for other birds in the winter forsake cold countreys & seeke for warmer & in the sommer flye from the extremitye of heate vnto regions more temperate; but these birdes flye onely from heate & liue most pleasingly in the Winter in cold countries, & in the Somer in the whottest. Yet immoderate cold taketh from them the vse of flyinge, so as when yce & snowe abound, they are so enfeebled in the woods for lacke of meate, that they may be taken with the hand. They are subiect to all the diseases which wee haue described in other Canary-birds & more especially to blindnes, which if it be not cured (as in other) it is in vayne to nourish them any longer. And so much for this little birde.

[XXI]

A chalander or Galander

This little bird is also of the race of Larks for besides *Calandra* & *Chalandros* yt is also called *Korydalos* & they [8or] call it *Chalandra of Kalos adein,* the sweete voyce, for there is no other bird of this kinde which singeth more sweetely. The latines also call it *Chalandra.* The *Italians Calandra.* The *Germans Kalander* & *Galander.* The *ffrench Calandre* & the Spaniards *Chalandria.*

The fashion of this bird resembleth a Buntinge, but the quantitye or greatenesse thereof equalleth a stare wherefore yt is called a greate Larke, the colour of the feathers, head, feete, & tayle, & other manners are like a larke. The beake is thicke & strong, & the necke longe & thinne, compassed about with a mane of feathers, descendinge from the head to the sholders, when they are wilde they eate graine & being tame they eate the Crumms of whitebread safely without danger. Yt is a bird desired for the fleash being of very good taste & nourishment but more desired for the voyce exceedinge all other both in sweetnes & immitacon of tunes & voyces of other birds whereof the *Italians* when they commend a good voyce they say prouerbially he singeth like a *Chalander.* ffor this cause they are sold very deare in *ffraunce* & *Italy,* yet they are taken in *ffraunce* & not in *Italy*; they quicklye forgett their captiuitie, & will singe within twoo or three dayes after their first takinge, They take them as they drinke by spreadinge netts on the brincke of the Water whereinto when the fowle descendeth to drinke yt is taken by the fowlers speedye drawinge of the nett together by a longe Corde which he himselfe holdeth so farr of as the birde canot suspect the snare wherin it is taken.

[XXII]

A Chough or Cornishe Chough.

[Space for illustration blank]

[80v] Theise fowles are of the race of *Crowes* or *Rauens* wherfore the *Hæbrewes* expresse them by no other names then *Anapha & Oreb,* the *Greekes* call it *Koloios & Celtos,* the latines *Gracculus & Ciagula* so the *Italians Ciagula, Taccola, Tattula, Cutta & Pola, &* this last *a pullo colore,* of the blacke ashe colour. The *Spaniards Graia & Graio.* The *ffrench Chucas, Choca, Chouette, & Gay* but this last worde is more propper to a kinde of pye called *Pica Glandaria.* The *Sauoyens Chue.* In *Germany* it is called by diuers names as most commonly *Tul*

Dole, in *Saxony Aelke, Kaycke,* in *Holland zealand & ffrizland Ka, Cau, Chau, & wachtell Tahe, Talhe, Dale Doel.* In *fflanders Gaey Hannckyn* the *Illirians Kawka,* the *Turkes Tschauka,* the *Polonians zegzolka.* The antient Latines named it *Gracculus,* which haith a treble deriuation accordinge to the fancie of seuerall authors. ffestus sayeth, *Gracchus à gerendo,* from caryinge, *quoniam iacta semina gerant,* because they will gather vp the new sowne seede & cary it away, or because when they flye from oliue trees to goe to their rest, they carry with them three oliue sprigs, in each foote one, & one in their mouth.[124] Varro deriueth *Gracchulus a grege* because they flye in flocks & companyes, but *Quintilian* reproueth this opinion as improbable. The last & best *Etimologye* is taken from their voyce, for they crie *Gra gra* or *Cras Cras* or from their little leane bodyes, *Gracculus* of *Gracilis,* for when the feathers are pulled of they are so leane that they appere very little.

The first kind

There are seuerall kinds especially five, the first is called *Coracias,* the second is *Lupus* or the *Iack-daw* commonly called a *Cad-dawe,* the third *Scurrae* for the illfauored voyce, and the last *Palmipes,* a broad-foote, which is only proper to *Lydia & Phrigia.* And vnto these Gesner addeth the fift called *Torquatam* because of the ringe about his necke, but I will first beginne with our *Cornish C[h]ough.*
[81r]

Cornishe chough.

[illustration on p. 131]

This without all doubt is the same which the antients called *pyrrhocorax quasi igneus gracculus,* a redd or fiery Chough called by the *Germanes Bergdoel, Alprapp Alpkachel, wilde Tul Bergtul & Steinhetz* & by the *Rhætians Tahen*: They are lesser then ordinary Crowes, & exceede the Iacke-daw but very little, wherefore in ffraunce they are called *Chouca Rouge,* the red choughe. It haith a russet or clay colour head, & backe, a redd fiery beake, & leggs of the same colour, but the beake small, in other parts very blacke like crowes. Yet Pliny & after him *Dr Turner*[125] say that the beake & leggs are of a clay colour, which may be true in some particular wherein nature varyeth. They liue nowhere in England but in Cornwall or thereabouts, because of the warmth of the Clymate. They are also found in *Aruergne,* about the mount *Iura* & in *Rhætia* in the winter only, in *Creete* & in the Ilands *Cy*[*c*]*lades.* They eate graine & fruits in the feilds, & will be easily tamed, learning to imitate the voyce of men. Yet the flesh of the old choughes is not good for meate, the yonge ones are somtymes taken out of the nests & eaten by the poorer sort of people: they are very harmeffull when they are tamed, & will breake windowes, carry away linnin, or money & doe such anoy-aunces as hardly the pleasure taken in them [81v] doth not counteruaile the losses & detrments [*sic*] sustayned by them. Their voyce is more shrill then the Iackedawes & nerer to the voyce of a pipe. They sitt vppon trees or howsetops & when they flye high or alofte the people obserue that it presageth extremitye of cold, but flyinge lowe & nerer the earth signifieth warmer & more temperate weather.

The Barbarian Chough

[Space for illustration blank]

This is another kind of *Choughes* called *gracculus Barbaricus* whose rare colours different from ours in Europe I cannot chuse but expresse especially seeinge it was comuncated [*sic*] to me by my good friend Dr Bonham. Yt is in bignes equall to one of our cornish Choughes, & in nature like vnto them, but the head, necke, brest, & forepart of the wings & tayle are blewe, the backe & midle perte of the winges a Chess-nutt colour. The ends of the winge feathers as blacke as any iette, ther-fore I lett the reader vnderstand the same that in the abundance & variety of diuine workes, he may more abundantly prayse theyr maker the diuine maiestye.

The mountaine Chough

[82r] [illustration on p. 134]

This is called by the *Greekes* & *Latines Coracias* in *Italy Speluier, Tac-cola, Tatula, Pason, & Zorl*: about *Valois* in *ffraunce Choquar* &

Chouette, in Germany *Steintahen* & *Steintulen.* They are in quantitye as bigg as any Crowe, the beake very bigg & crooked like a halfe bowe, of a red colour like a pomegarnett, & so are theyr leggs & feete: & the residue of the body as blacke as any Rauen. While they are wilde they liue in mountaynes, rocks, & steepe places, feedinge vppon such wilde graynes & fruits as they can there meete withall, but being tamed they eate meale mixed with milke, bread, wheate branne or any other thinge which is giuen to tame pullen; they are also of a theeuishe nature, like other Choughes, & therefore I will amplifie both this & our former Cornish Chough with the description & generall history of the common Chough.

They are gregall or sociable fowles liuinge together in flockes & companeys, wherevppon came the vulgar prouerbe, *Gracculus assidet Gracculo,* one Chough sitteth by an other: for they are not solitarye like Eagles & hawekes, but sociable like menn & bees, exceptinge only their singularitye in foode & particular nests so as the Græciens call them *Agelaia,* that is, gregall, but most, *Polytica,* ciuill & politicall, & therevppon saint Austen calleth them *aues congregales,* congregall birdes. This [82v] their fellowshipp or societye ariseth out of their nature & naturall loue not for any proposed pleasure which therby they take but for similitude of kinde & naturall actions. Their manners or naturall inclination are thus coniectured by a laudible poet:[126]

Dignoscitur de tergoris coloribus,
Quodcumque viuit mite, seu ferum pecus.

Candore Cygnus, atritate Gracculus,
Leo fluentem Barbarus crispat iubam.

Weeke birdes & beasts from sauadge kinds
By colours of their parts are scannd
White swanns, blacke Choughs we gentle find
But Lions feirce are curld & maand.

Aristotle & Athenæus commend theise Choughs for their mutuall loue which the males & fæmales beare one to another, for they will dye raither then chaunge & giue ouer & if it happen that one of them by chaunce or naturall infirmitye bee killed, the surviuour remaineth in perpetuall widdowhood. They are *loquacissimum genus, & vocibus importunum,* a pratlinge & clamorous kind of fowles, neuer silent but voycinge to one another, for their voyce haith not in it any varietye, but like a *Cuckoes,* repeateth often the same notes without pleasure or delectation. Yf they be tamed, they make most noyse after that they haue drunke wyne; & beinge wilde, at the tyme of their coniunction & copulation: for then they are lasciuious aboue measure, & afterward all the tyme that they nourishe their yonge. When they are held fast in a mans hand they flye often at the eyes of him that holdeth him, whereof *Leonicus* giueth these reasons: because the eyes often moue & are very cleare therfore they pecke at them to drawe them vnto them selfes, for such things they loue, & for this cause they bite at a finger or a sticke moued about their mouth or head. Or else they espye in the apple of the eye their owne picture *ideo ad cognita desideria tendere cupiunt* & so they make at it as to the Image of their wished desire.

They are docible & are taught to speake if they be taken & trayned therevnto whilst they be yonge, & of this they make a common practice in ffraunce; they teach them in the morninge before the sunne risinge after day lyght, because at [83r] that tyme they are found to haue better memoryes & more aptnes to learne. The broadenes of their tongue & subtilitye of their witt maketh them more capable. Otherwise their voyce is neuer pleasinge, for *Gracculus ad fides, Sus Mineruam Asinus ad lyram*[127] are three vulgar prouerbs of our signification, A pipe & a Chough, Pallas & a sowe, an asse & a harpe are neuer good musicke.

They learne not of themselues but must be taught with great diligence otherwise *Gracculus inter musas,* an vnlearned Chough amongst the *Muses,* signified an vnlearned man in the schooles. Yet she will vtter hir owne barbarous voyce like as fooles will be more talkeatiue then wiser men. *Argutos inter anser strepit Olores*, the goose will be keck-linge amonge the prudent Swanns. The importunitye of their voyce made this comparison betwixt a prater & a Chough, *Gracculo magis obstreperus,* but there is an other, *Tunc canunt Cigni, quando tacuerunt Gracculi,* the Swanns singe when the Choughes hold their peace to signifye that when fooles are silent, then wise men may teach profitable things.

These Choughes will eate all manner of grayne, & besides, locusts, for which cause the people of *Lemnos* & *Thessaly* & *Illyrium* had them in greate reuerence, for they wold meete the Locusts in the aier & destroy them before they fell vpon the greene fruits of the earth: therefore they feede them & preserue them free from slaughter. They abstaine from carrion; yet Tragus reporteth that they will eate fleash & walnutts. Yn the springe tyme they ingender treadinge & not conceiuinge at their mouth as *Enceleius*[128] fondly imagined. They loue seacobs & neuer fight with them, but they are in warre with eagles although to their owne damage; the like contention they make with dawes, pyes, crowes & Hawkes, for which cause Homer doth thus describe the warrs betwixt the Troians & the Graecians:

> *Τῶν δ' ὥς τε ψαρῶν νέφος ἔρχεται ἠὲ κολοιῶν,*
> *οὖλον κεκλήγοντες, ὅτε προΐδωσιν ἰόντα*
> *κίρκον, ὅ τε σμικρῇσι φόνον φέρει ὀρνίθεσσιν,*[129]

> Much like to stares* or crowes or Choughes they flye
> Cryinge alowde for helpe against their foe
> [83v] when as the hawke aprochinge somewhat nye
> that maketh spoyle of smaler birdes also.

Their flickeringe or staying ouer the heads of men was wont to be accompted ominous wherevppon one cryeth out in *Aristophanes, Hei mihi infoelix* [*&*] *Gracculus mihi it præ timore*:[130] woe is me, the vnhappy Chough comes vnto me for feare. About the yeare 1484 *Cornelius Gemma* writeth that there was a miraculous fight betwixt Choughs & pyes in Germany, & presently followed a greate warre. When they rest in troopes together, or flye at eueninge from the South or crie more eagerly then their custome with some chaunge of voyce or gett into couert, beatinge their wings as they sitt & not flyinge, it betokeneth rayne & stormes. Yf they mounte alofte & then fall downe againe to a lowely flyght it foretelleth cold & rayne: and if they forsake the woods

* *stares* starlings

or the vsuall places of their abode, it presigniefyeth a famine or ensuinge sterilitie. Their most vsuall & accustomable flyght is lowely & vppon the ground they eate their meate which caused *Pindarus* to compare himselfe to the falcon soaringe high, but the poet *Bacchilides,* his riuall in fame, to ducks, geese, or Choughs eatinge their meate vpon the lowly earth.

Sic scit humi tantum serpere Bacchilides[131]

By reason that they are so subtill & suspitious they are taken with greater difficultye. Yet Oppianus sheweth this maner of their huntinge: they set springes for them with a bayte in the midle of a circle vppon the earth, wherevnto the fowle putteth his necke & head to feede; but so soone as he lifteth it vpp the rod flyeth vp & taketh fast hold by the necke. Also if there be sett in an open feild which they haunte a vessell of oyle, they will come vnto yt & behowldinge their owne shape or figure in the bright oyle they thrust in their heads to salute & smell vnto yt, as yf it weare an other Chough: when they drawe out their heads againe they are so besmeared & wett with oyle that their feathers cannot take wynde or their winges cary away their heauie bodyes & a little boy may come & take them vpp. This their loue to their owne [84r] kinde is a meanes of their destruction for yf a dead Chough bee cunningly flayed & the skinne be stuffed & sett vp in a lymed bough, other will flye vnto yt & fall into the lyme, whereby they are surprised at the foulers pleasure. And for the driuinge them away from the new sowne corne let but one of them be hanged vp by the legg dead & then will all the residue be terified for feare of snares. Their fleash is not vnsauorye yf they be flead before they be eaten wherefore *Germains, ffrench,* & *Italians* make some vse of them. There is a pleasinge apologue of this fowle which because it is well aplyed by Theophylactus Simocatus I will relate in this place:

Vppon a tyme Iupiter fayned that he would create a kinge of birds & therfore summoned all of them to apeere before him that he might take his choyce amongst them all. Then began the water fowles to dresse & washe themselfes, that they might appeere more beautifull, & the landfowles did picke their feathers adorninge them for the same purpose. Amonge whome the Chough, beinge guyltye of his proper deformitye yet ambitious of that honour, gathered vp the cast feathers of other birds & so pricked them artificially vppon hir owne, that with varietye of stolen colours shee seemed the fayrest & goodlyest of the companye: at whome they all maruayled not knowinge from whence that beautiful fowle came. The night owle wonderinge more then the residue came neere & espyed one of hir owne feathers which she knewe & tooke away imediatlye: at which sight all the residue of the fowles did the like & so left him in his owne naked & naturall deformitye which my forenamed authour applyeth in this manner: *similiter nos homines etc,* Yn like manner men possesse nothinge of their owne in this lyfe, but iette vp & downe for a little space in a borrowed braueryе, vntill they dye, at which tyme they are stripped of those things wherof they boasted & remaine as naked & poore as they came into this world; *Fac igitur, o Chrisippe, vt pecuniam et corpus negligas et animam immortalem excolas. Hæc enim æterna et immortalis est, & cætera mortalia & ad breue tem-* [84v] *pus nostra.*[132] Looke vnto, O Chrysippus, that thou make more accompt of thy soule then of thy body or money, for this is imortall & capable of æternitye, but all other things are transitorye & ours but for a small tyme. Lucian also made vse hereof against those that carped at his inuentions, & not out of their owne learning. And another.

Rogas quis is sit in meis scriptis canis,
Is Struma quidem est, Gracculusque Æsopicus
Qui meum panem vorauit, et latrat farinam.

Doest thow but aske what dog is hee I name
In open verse: tis struma, that Æsopian Chough,
Who greedely doth eate the bread I frame
Yet at my meale doth euer barke & puffe.

Let no man rayse himselfe with other mens vertues, for they are feathers which will fall of & not helpe a soule to flye vp to heauen, & euery owle shall be able in due tyme to descrye an hypocrite, who haith no care of vertue but for externall shew (by example of Babilon in the sacred treat[is]e) shalbe stripped out of their nominall honours & titles, & turned into their reall shame & deserued ignominye. I will conclude this fowles historye with a narration of antient Idolatrye out of Athenæus,[133] & how diuels transforminge themselues into Choughs were honoured by men to the end they should not harme them.

The old inhabitants of venice were much anoyed by these fowles, which wold come & deuoure all their Corne feilds. Wherfore they made a league with them, & gaue them meate mixed with oyle. And when they came in troopes or flocks they sent out vnto them two or three citizens, who gaue them certayne grayne & other meats together with red thongs of leather: wherevnto the fowles (alias the diuells) would descend & eate & then depart away with out doinge any spoyle: but if they liked not the præsent they would not touch it, nor once alyght vppon it & then they flewe vppon their corne, digginge vp that which was newe sowen, & deuouringe all they found aboue ground. [85r] Thus raigned the diuell ouer infidells & vnbeleuers in the shape of fowles & beasts because they had turned the æternall glory of this worlds maker into the similitude of beastly creatures.

Wherfore happy our eyes & eares which heare & see the Stratagems of Sathan & haue learned to auoyde them as much & more carefully in the shape of a litle bird that eateth vp our heauenly seede, as in a roaringe lion that maketh spoyle of our mortall lyfes: but wee feare him in neither of both* because his power is suppressed by our sauiour, & his subtiltye discouered by heauenly scriptures.

[XXIII]

Chuquareo

[illustration]

This is a Virginia bird resemblinge our owsell or blacke bird in quantitye & qualitye: for the beake is of a clay colour & the whole body blacke except the forepart of the wings which are a deepe scarlett colour as by the picture you may perceiue.

Chuwheeo

[85v] [illustration]

This is also a virginia bird whose picture I receiued from that worthye industrious, & learned Compiler of nauigations, whose prayses will remaine to the worlds end in the monument of his owne labours, I meane M[aste]r *Hackluyt*. But before I sawe this picture, I receiued this breife description from *Dr Bonham*. Yt is the greatest Virginia pye, hauinge an ashe coloured beake, but all the body, head, & necke blacke, except

* *in neither of both* that is, in neither shape

the belly & leggs, which are a compound of white & chessnut. The tayle is very longe, like our english common pyes, & haith vnderneath two white feathers, which because it is proper to that countrye, I haue expressed by that proper name whereby the people there call it.

Chungent.

[86r] A Virginea bird without description

Chawankus

[illustration]

Chungent

[illustration]

This is also a *Virginia* water bird hauinge the beake head necke & all the vnder parts of a heron colour, the backe & wings of a Chessnut. When it swimmeth it resemleth [*sic*] a swanne for the maiestie & stately carriage of the whole bodye. Yt is wilde & our countrymen make good vse thereof both of the fleash & feathers, for it most frequenteth the fresh waters. Amonge fowles it deserueth the same place which is giuen to greyhounds among doggs for the comelynes & agilitye of the bodye.

[XXIV]

The Colmouse or Gnattsnapper

[86v] This bird is called of the greekes *Darda, Merops, & Melissophagos* because it eateth & destroyeth bees. In *Arabia* (sayeth *Rhasis*) *Alkemum & Alkeuium.* The Latines name it *marochus, merops, parra,*[134] *& Gangrena* & *Apiaster.* The *Italians Dardano gaulo Ieuolo.* The *Neapolitans Lupo dell' api, The Sicilians Lupo dell' api picciaferro, The ffrench Guespier* & the Spaniards *Iuruco. Merops* was one of those *Gyaunts* which builded Babell in whose tyme the diuision of languages hapened & therfore *Probus* deriueth *Merops* of *Merismo-opos* because the word admitteth a manyfold partition of voyces, & from hence it

arose that the greate *Thessalian* mountayne (whereon by reason of the many different & vnæquall passages & risings are sounded many Ecchoes) was called *Meropa.*

The first kinde.

[illustration]

I find that there are two kinds of these fowles. The first or greatest kinde haith a longe, blacke, & croked beake being very sharpe at the end. The head, necke, & almost all the belly yeallowe, from the roote of the beake backward doth arise a greate longe blacke spott. The backe is of a Chessnutt colour, & toward the rumpe the feathers blewe & greene. The winge feathers haue many colours: the first are blew, the second blewe & yealowe, the third yeallowe, the fourth or longe feathers blacke & redd at the ends. [87r] The tayle very greene aboue & yeallowe vnderneath & the feete of a clay colour with blacke clawes, & so much for the description of the first kinde.

The second kinde

This bird is in quantitye like a stare or blackebird, the beake is longe, crooked like a sickle, & very hard, the chinne & forehead are of a clay colour hauinge a greate visible blacke lyne, & vppon both sides two blewe spotts one ridinge vppon an other; the eyes are very small, the iris or humor of the apple beinge the most perfect red in the world, & the eyes & eyelyds blacke, the passages of the eares are couered with blacke feathers. The Crowne of the head & the vpper part of the necke & backe betwixt a yeallowe & a Chessnutt, the brest greene & blewe at the sides, the belly greene to the ribbs. The winges partly greene & partlye yeallowe, Chessnutt, & blewe at the ends, the tayle blewe mixed with some greene, the leggs short [87v] & blacke like a swallowes. They haue fower feete & clawes, one behind & three before. The fæmale is not of so deepe a colour, the backe is greenish & the vpper part of their tayle totally greene, the longe winge feathers blewe & greene & the other like the male. Their inward parts are also notable, the tounge very long & thinne, the mouth opened is very wide & moyste, & when they gape they receiue a greate number of flyes, which followe their moysture: but when they feele a sufficient mouth full they suddenly close their mouth & eate them. The bones or scull of their head is most hard. Their gall is large & filled with a liquor coloured like an Emeraude, the mawe is double yet small & straight: & thus much for their description.

They are most plentifull in *Greece* especially in *Creete*, some-tymes they come into *Italy*, or *ffraunce,* but sieldome into *Germany,* or our artherne parts. They are very beautifull & their voyce sonorous, being destinctly heard a greate distaunce: for they sound *grul gruru ururul* articulatly like a man, which sound was first obserued by Albertus,[135] yet another calleth it *zinzilulare,* a mornfull whistlinge.

Regulus atque Merops & rubro pectore prognis
Consimili modulo zinzilulare sciunt.

The Colmouse wren & swallow brested red
Like dolefull notes doe sound from little head.

They flye in flocks & companies togither keepinge aboute the mountaines & all sweete flowery places where they meete with bees which is obseruable because they followe sweete flowers not for sweetnes but for the prey & bootye they find vppon them, like flatterers which loue no mans person but his substaunce. Their flight is different from all other birds, for it is not onely slowe but contrarye to kinde, for they moue backwards & not forwards so as [88r] their tayle & not their head leadeth the way, which is their naturall policie because so they catch the more flyes which followe after motion, & like sluggards & euill seruants they care more for their meate then for their journey & busines. They refuse no flyinge insecte but especially they delight in flyes & bees, which caused *Virgil* to aduise the husbandman, that he should not sett his bee-hiue neere their nests, for they are ill neighbours to that creature.

> *Absint & picti squalentia terga lacerti*
> *Pinguibus a stabulis, Merops, aliæque volucres.*[136]

> Keepe from thy fatt hiues the longe back Lyzard greene,
> The Colmouse or what other bee-deuouringe beene.

They refuse not rape-seeds, grasshoppers, or wormes. They build in holes of rocks or trees not aboue eight foote high because they flye not easilye, & they digg those holes three or fower Cubits deepe for the more safetye of their eggs & younge ones. They lay six or seuen eggs & hacth so many after the custome of other birds: they also make their nests soft in the bottome, when they are flidge they passe from one countrye to another. And they are very subtill especially hauinge younge, for they will flye to sundrie places (yf they be wacthed) before they betake themselues to their right nests to auoide discouerye & somtyme they remoue their younge from place to place. *Aristotle* reporteth of the younge towards their parents this memorable acte of pietye, *Sunt qui confirmant genitorum senectutem inuicem educare vicemque etc.*[137] There are that affirme the younge ones do nourishe their parents in age, as they were nourished by them, & suffer them not to moue out of their nests for meate except for pleasure & delight but bringe [88v] them home their foode for nourishement. Therfore Ælianus præfereth them before the Storke as more pious, for the Storke doeth not helpe his parents till they be old & past strenght; but this bird returneth gratitude so soone as he is able to flye & forrage abroade not tarryinge to the infirme & old age of his parents. They are taken with snares & lyme & when they fynde themselfes insnared they drawe other birds into daunger with them.

> *Ne præs esto, Thales dixit, sic illita visco*
> *In laqueos sociam parra meropsque trahit.*[138]

> Beware of surtyshipp,* quoth Thales wise & old,
> The Colmouse snard, in snares would others fold.

Wherefore they are examples both of pyetie to our parents as haith bin sayed & of impietye towards their fellowes, betrayinge when they are betrayed & vndooinge when they perceiue themselfes vndone as *Eue*

* *surtyshipp* an obligation undertaken in another's behalf

destroyed Adam or malitious banquerupts their freindly secure neighbours. The boyes of *Creta* take them with a hooke in a liue grashopper where vnto they fasten a stringe or small thred, for when the grashopper feeleth the hooke it mounteth high at the sight whereof the bird falleth downe & swalloweth both hooke & bayte to hir owne destruction.

The fleshe of this fowle is not good for meate yet in case of inflammation it haith bin prescribed by phisitians: the gall mixed with galls* & the oyle of vnripe oliues haith a double virtue for by anoyntinge therewithall the head and beard it maketh the haire perfectly blacke; & if it be rubbed vppon the hands & face it keepeth the partye from stinginge of bees. Also, sayth *Kiranides,* if the bird & hir heart be eaten it is profitable against the paines of the heart, stomacke, & the bloodie flixe. [89r]

[XXV]

The Corlieu

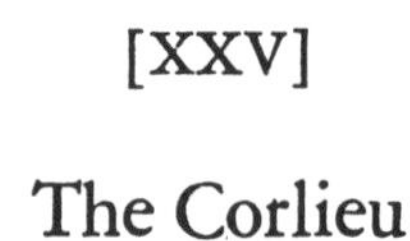

This is a water fowle called *Numenius* & *Arquata* bycause the fashion of the beake resemblinge the new moone or a halfe bowe. In *Italy* it is

* *the gall . . . galls* that is, bird-gall with oak-galls (*"fel eius si cum gallis . . . misceatur"* A.)

called *Arcase piuier Tarlinum* & *terlinum* & at *Venice Arcuatum,* at Millan *Caroli* & besides *Charlot, Torquatum, Spinzago d'aqua.* Yn Germany yt is called also by diuers names, as *Brachvogel,* a bird of Iune, because it cometh aboute that tyme, *Regenvogel,* a bird of rayne, *windvogel,* a bird of windes, & *Wettervogel,* a fowle of fowle weather, for they prognosticate tempests & stormy seasons. The ffrench *Corlis* & *Corlieu.* The *ffrisians* & *Hollanders Hanikens,* en *Gruey,* en *Schrye, Schryck* & the *Grecians* at this day for the lenght & fashion of the beake doe call it *Macrimito.*

There are two kindes which differ in nothinge but their quantitye & therfore one description may serue for both. The greater is in lenght about three foote, & in weight about two pound, the leggs are longe, of a brownishe ashe colour, their feete blacke at the end & are partlye Clouen & part- [89v] lye broade footed with very thinne skinne which they let vp & downe at their pleasures makinge it broader or narrower. Their Clawes bee very blacke, the beake beinge blacke, of eight or nine ynches longe wherof fiue are crooked or bended. Their colour is brownishe & full of spotts ashe coloured, especially betwixt the wings & backe; they stand like vnshorne silke, blacke in the middle & reddishe round about. The necke is six inches longe, the feathers whereof are very soft & of an ashe colour. The tayle feathers are aboute fiue ynches longe being noted or distinguished with blacke & white rowes of feathers, the typps of their winges are blacke & the other are partye coloured, blacke & white & browne: vppon the brest round about the blacke spotts there are some reddishe feathers, vnder the belly it is white adorned with blacke spotts. The thyeghes aboue the ioynt are halfe bare of feathers. The forefeete are longe & thicke, but the spurr or hynder foote is short & weake. The tayle is not very longe but adorned with feathers blacke & white. The tounge is most admirable both for the smallnes in so greate a beake & also for the fashion, it beinge framed like the head of a dart; & thus much for the description, wherein there is no remarkable difference betwixt the male & the fæmale, except in the quantitye which is lesser: & the backe & winges which are not so blacke as the males but the spotts are more notablye browne.

They will eate wormes & therefore doe seeke them most exquisitely amonge plants & herbes, & sometyme digg them out of the earth with their crooked beake; they flye by troopes & companeys. In Aprill they lay eggs in quantitye as greate as a henns egg, fower in number & they are very pale to looke vppon. They are excellent meate & heere in *England* & ffraunce preferred before hens, especi- [90r] ally yf they be eaten younge: otherwise when they are old they tast no better then the fleashe of a hare. They loue the meddowes & the sea sydes.

[XXVI]

The Cormorant.

[space for illustration blank]

The *Hæbrews* call this fowle *kaath* & *Schalac Deut*: 14, the *Greeks Æthia* & *Corone thalassios,* a sea Crowe. & the *Greeke Poets dyptes, poynges, Bunge,* & *plongeo,* & *Phalacrocorax.* The Latines *Mergus* & *Coruus marinus* & *Carbo marinus* The Italians *mergon* & *Smergo.* The ffrench *plonget* & *plongeon,* from the greeke word *plongeon* & *plunai.* The *Spaniards Cuoruo marino* or *Cueruo.* The *Germans Daucher Tucher Teucher* & *Duchent.* The *Belgians Dueckeckin, Duycker, Schlouer,* & *Schlouaer.*

The antients made but one kinde of these birds bycause they confounded them with ducks, but *Albertus,* our *Dr Wooton,* & the late writers write otherwise, *Mergus non tam species auis, genus multas sub se continens.*[139] The *Cormorant* contayneth many kindes of birds, for sea *Cobs, ducks,* & *Barnacles* [90v] are called also by that name. *Sulpitius* sayeth that there is one kinde called *species cornuta,* a horned *Cormorant,* because it haith redd feathers on the fore head standinge out like hornes. So the *Duckers* [are] called *Colymbi* & *Colymbides vrinatores* & the fowles *Thraces, Dytini, vria,* & *Phalarides.* There are amonge vs two kindes, one blacker which haunt the sea, the other more browne or ashe coloured which frequent land, riuers, & ponds. And these are those which I purpose to prosecute in this chapter & present historye. But first I will breifely declare some other æquiuocally called *Cormorants.*

The Cormorant of Rhyne

[illustration on p. 148]

The description of this waterfowle is thus gathered out of Gesner.

Amonge those fowles of *Rhyne* which are called *Rhynenten yszenten* & *Duchenten* amonge the *Germans* or people of *Rhyne,* this whose figure is here expressed is the greatest & most knowen which some haue called a ducke of *Rhyne* bycause it resembleth both a ducke & a Cor- [91r] morant. Yt is also called *Merch* by corruption of the *latine word, Mergus* & *Nunnen,* a *Nonne* bycause of the varietye of colours.

This *Cormorant* is *antiformis,* of the quantitye & fashion of a ducke. The bodye of this fowle is white distinguished or besett with blacke spotts, the beake & forepart of the head aboute the eyes is blacke; & in the hinder part of the head blacke spotts, & the residue is partlye blacke, browne & ashe coloured: the foreparte of the necke or throate togither with the brest & belly are white, sprinkled with ashe colour spotts, which toward the bottome & sydes are like waues engrauen, ranked one in another very delectably. The leggs hang forth of the lowest or hynder parte of the bellye, the feete with their Clawes & membrane browne outwardly, but inwardly blacke. The tayle blacke, the wings & backe blacke, & white, by an euen course or seperation of spaces, & this bird is by some termed the *White Nonne.* Yt is whole footed like a ducke & liueth vppon the waters or banks wherein sometymes they are found ensnared, by the weeds & small plants groweinge there vppon. They abound not only about the riuer of *Rhyne,* but in ffraunce aboute the riuer of Soame & are there called *pyette.*

An other Cormorant

[91v] [illustration]

This kinde is lesser then the former beinge called in Germany *wisse Tuchent,* a white Cormorant, in *Italy Morgon* & *Gyuen polono* & *Garganello.*

Yt is somethinge lesse then a wilde ducke. The lenght exceedeth not twentye ynches beake & tayle included, the head is white with blacke spotts about the eyes, & so rose vp to the head, beinge parted in the Crowne with a white lyne, the brest, necke, & belly altogither white. Vppon the toppe of the backe there stood vp very beutifull feathers, ranked artificially layed in order & true distaunce, with blacke & white colours & so fall downe to the sydes like laces or filletts party-coloured.

The beake like a ducks but narrower & toothed, coloured browne, blewe, & crooked downward, the legs & feete like the former. The wings blacke destinguished with white spaces or feathers & two white lines vndermost. The backe white, the tayle browne & a hand bredth longe, the white [92r] belly feathers were browne within: they liue vppon freshe water fishe & with their beake turne vp stones to take gudgeons & broade-heads & this is that kind which is called by *Albertus Mergus variius.*

The Cormorant called Daucher

[illustration]

This is also a diuers coloured bird called in Latine *Albellus* & so about *Mantua Albello* & yt is greater then a teale & lesser then a ducke. Their beake is a watchett blewe crooked & sharpe at the end, the head all white except three blacke spotts, two aboute the eyes, & one behind vppon the head, the necke & brest white, but the necke under the beake & middle of the brest were somewhat ashe coloured, & so was the belly white ashe colour, the backe & wings blacke full of white spotts, the tayle blacke, & leggs of a lead colour mixed with some greene, the feete & clawes were like the legs.

Another of this kind is thus described by *Aldrouand:* yt was about a foote in lenght, the beake a little blackishe [92v] toothed like a sawe & crooked at the end: the head white with two blacke spotts compassinge the eyes; there is vppon the head a tufte of feathers consistinge of

[*The Ise Cormorant.*]

[*The Weasel Cormorant.*]

blacke, white, & greenishe blacke excellently beautifull. The necke, brest, & belly white but vppon the brest descend two blacke lines, one from the backe, the other from the winge which is broader & more windinge but not so longe as the former which falleth to the midle of the brest. The backe blacke except next to the rumpe where it is browne. The wings blacke with two white spotts & the longe feathers are first blacke then browne & withinside whitishe, the tayle short consistinge of sixteene browne feathers. The legs & feete of a leaden & blewe colour but the skinne or membrane of their flatt* is browne. This bird beinge anatomized by the same Doctour is also worth the knowledge, & consideration amonge other the woorks of the greate Creatour, for the *aspera arteria* or throat-bole, neere the toppe is very narrowe, but toward the bottome it waxeth broader & thicker, where it is as thicke as the litle finger, beinge tyed with bones on both sydes & a greate muscle & from thence passe two other muscles to the fore ribbs. Before their diuarication or partinge to the lungs, there is a vessell shaped like a colts hoofe† swellinge in substaunce on the lefte side toward the heart in which there are two passages like windowes broade & marked with this letter. A. couered with a thinne & transparent skinne. And from the inferiour or lower partes of this boanye vessell beginne the seperation of [93r] the arterye, which from the poynt of the tounge to the lungs was aboute ten ynches long. They feede vppon little fishes, & withall deuoure litle small stones.

The Ise Cormorant.

[illustration on p. 149]

This kind is peculiarly termed by the Germanes *Yszentle* & by *Albertus* with other good authours, *Mergus varius,* a partye coloured *Cormorant,* but most commonly *Mergus glacialis,* a *Cormorant* of the Ise. The head & vpper parte of the necke is a light redd & vnderneath a browne & sometymes ashe colour. The feathers of the head doe somwhat stand vp but more eminently in the male in whome also the vpper parte of the beake is red, but in the fæmale it is white, the backe is all blacke. The wings blacke besett with ashe colour-spotts, first in an ample broade,‡ then with two lynes as in the former, in the extremityes or typps of the feathers, the belly, & vndermost parte of the necke white. The leggs short, browne [93v] & blacke feete. The vnder parte of the beake blackishe blewe. They are lesser then ducks in all parts except their necks which are well nigh eyght ynches longe, the body seuen ynches

* *flatt* flat surface, that is, feet
† *colts hoofe* a weed so called from the triangular shape of the leaf
‡ *an ample broade* breadth

& the tayle fower. They allso liue vppon fishes & small stones, & haunt riuers & lakes of waters & are taken in the winter. They are as good meate as wild ducks.

The Weasel Cormorant

[illustration on p. 149]

The name of *Mustillaris Mergus* or *weasell Cormorant* is giuen to this fowle, because the head hereof is a weasell colour, that is, a darke red hauinge feathers in the hinder parte of the head standinge vpp like a tufte: it is in quantitye like a Teale, hauinge a narrowe beake yet sharpe & crooked at the end, of a blacke & blewe colour, they haue teeth on both sydes of their mouth & the vnder parte of the beake is hollowe like a Chanell. The necke is of colour like the head except that it is compassed aboute with a white ringe, through which passeth a reddishe line to the backe, the vnder parte of the necke or throate [94r] is blacke & so is the backe except the hinder feathers thereof which are ashe colour & browne wrought together & fashioned like the scales of a fishe; the brest towards the sydes is of a leade colour, otherwise the belly & it are ashe colour. The ribbs or feathers vnder the wings are marked with the like scales as is the backe, the longe feathers & tayle are blacke but on their ypper parte there is a conspicuous white spott & the neather parte is diuided by a white lyne, the leggs & feete are blacke & lead colour, but the skinne of their flatt feete is blacke & so much for this kind called in *Germany Wiselgen*.

There are also red & blacke Cormorants of the quantitye of a greate ducke, the first is called by the Germanes *Roter Teucher*: bycause the hinder part of the head & vpper part of the necke are red, the throate is blacke & yeallowe, & the whole body with the wings are of diuers mixt & compounded colours, exceptinge the head; it is greater in all things then a greate ducke.

The blacke Cormorant is called *Schwartzer Teucher,* beinge not greater in any parte then is the ducke, the beake hereof is blacke, the necke of a reddishe colour, the wings blacke with a white lyne runninge thorough them, the belly blacke & yeallowe, the feete & skinne thereof are also blacke. But I shall not neede to expresse any figures of these kinds, they are so common & well knowne beinge in no essentiall parte different from the former. The like I may say of the *Nonne Cormorant,* which Gesner affirmeth to liue about Arguentorate in Germany which there they call *Grawe merch.* The beake is redd yet the crooke there- [94v] of is white at the end, the head & necke red with a small tufte of feathers turninge backwards, the legs yellowishe, the backe blacke but the brest & belly white, the tayle & longe feathers of the winge are coloured like the backe. The vpper parte of the wings is dunne or ashe colour & the midle parte white. The *Cormorant* called in *Holland Pylstert,* is very like to this fowle differinge only in the greene & blewe spotts of the necke & the red legs.

The long billd Cormorant

This is of the greatest syze being therfore called *Gan* & *Ganner,* because they are greate as Geese & they are found about *Constance* & *Verbanum* in Italy. The beake is narrowe & lesser then a ducks, being Crooked at the end and as longe as a mans little finger, from whence it is called *Longirostra,* a long bild *Cormorant.* The skinne at the sides of the vpper part of the beake is red & in the middle blacke, the teeth firme & turned backward, the head red like a potsheard or as the reddest loame, the tuft also bendinge backward. The necke next the head is of the same colour but after- [95r] ward the same with the backe & wings are of ashe colour. But the longe winge feathers are dunne or browne hauinge one white spotte at their lower end.[140] The legs & feete are red but the skinns of their feete are browne & red, the necke aboute seuen ynches longe, the backe eyght ynches & the tayle fiue; the belly feathers are white & redd. They keepe in the waters bycause they cannot goe or walke vppon the earth with any facillitye; wherefore they are allwaye swimminge or flyinge. They build their nests amonge reeds when they hold vp their heads very high, as if they would flye vpward & they abide longe vnder water swimminge fourtye or fifty feete with out takinge any breath.

The Beuer or litle goose Cormorant.

The Beuer & Otter among all beasts are the greatest deuourers of fishes, & because this kind of Cormorant a greeeth with them in this greedie & insatiable appetite it is therfore called by the ffrench *Bieure,* the beuer: which is thus described by that industrious & learned [95v] *Bellonius.* This beuer *Cormorant* (sayth he) is a water fowle beinge as bigg & as good to eate as a wild goose of meane quantitye & it is called a *beuer* for the similitude it hath with the *Castor* or fower footed beuer, for as he dyuinge into the water bringeth greate dammage to the fishes, so this fowle hauinge a singular gifte of nature to dyue vnder water, which way soeuer it findeth game, quickly emptyeth lakes & fisheponds of all the fishes they find therein. The beake of this fowle is longe, small, &

toothed, crooked at the end like a sea pyes: the criste or tufte of feathers groweth not out of the Crowne like Larks, lapwings, & peacocks, but out of the hinder perte of the head like the Alcatraz & other Cormorants. The head is greater then the proportion of the bodye, for it far surpasseth a gooses head, & on the vpper perte to the midle of the necke it is yellowe, as yf it had bine stayned with oker, the eyes are not greate, the backe & wings of ashe & leaden colour, & the wings seeme as much to small for the bodye, as the head was to greate, beinge marked athwart with a white lyne. The belly a pale white, the beake three ynches longe beinge toothed & blacke in the vpper parte but red beneath & in the vpper parte ar[e] twoo holes or passages for the nostrills. The leggs & feete are red & the tayle round like other water fowles. They nestle in rocks & steepe craggye places, they are not good for meate at least wise in the opinion of the common people, for in *ffraunce* they haue a sayinge to signifye their distast hereof: Yf you will bid the *Diuell* to a feast giue him a beuer for his dinner. The throate bole of this bird is very miraculous for it is not round but inæ- [96r] quall & flatt, hauinge two roundells* in the midle, & from them greater toward the ventrickle & lungs, so of purpose framed by almightye God that it might contayne much aër while the fowle diueth vnderwater: & this is also common to other Cormorants & diuers other water fowles: howbeit to none in such a straunge fashion, for the lower end is a skinne distended vppon bones, & this is called by *Gesner, merganser minor,* the little goose *Cormorant,* bycause herafter followeth a greater. There is one like to this in the lake of *Acronium* hauinge a long necke, blacke feete, & greater then any ducke, they are called also *Aeschenten,* that is, the eaters of flowers & fishes of a sweete smell.

The greate goose Cormorant

[illustration on p. 156]

Some call this fowle *Mergum cirrhatum,* a Combed or tufted Cormorant. The head with the greatest parte of the necke is greene vppon blacke, but the lower parte of the necke with the backe is blacke, the tayle is of an [96v] ashe colour, the wings are mixt of many colours: first toward the backe they are blacke, next a pale white, then a pale blacke, then a

* *roundells* round holes or hollows

pure white & blacke at the ends & vnderneath the parte next the bodye is white, & the residue mixt of blacke & white. The feathers of the belly & the vppermost tayle feathers, are a colour compounded of white & yeallowe, the leggs & feete red & they are flatte & Clouen like a gooses. The feathers on the thighes checquered of pale white & blacke colours. The beake is like the other Combed Cormorant, vp to the eyes crooked at the end & æqualleth the midle finger in lenght being of blacke colour in the vpper parte, but reddishe on the sides. They haue twoo rowes of teeth; the outmost are greatest, strongest, & sharpest, beinge a little crooked backward when the feathers are plucked off. The skynne & fleashe are of a pale earth or clay colour, the mawe is as hard as horne and the whole body somtyme weigheth twelue poundes. Yt is also called an *Italian* bird & *Seefluder* bycause of his deuouringe of fishes & it may be a kind of our englishe Gulls which the ffrench call *morillan* & the latines *Gulones.* Of this *Seefluder Bellonius* & after him Gesner maketh this followinge description.

There is a fowle in the riuer of Liere or Ligier which they call *Herle* or *Harle,* somewhat lesse then a goose hauinge the vndernecke & belly feathers of an aurange colour, the head & vpper parte of the necke blacke, the wings white except the short feathers, the beake is three ynches longe beinge smooth & crooked at the end, which togither with the legs & feete are a pale red colour.

[97r] There is another called in ffraunce, *vn Tiers,*[141] a fowle bigger then a ducke of an ordinary colour much like the former but seemeth to be composed of a Cormorant & a ducke, for the beake is the beake of a Cormorant but the body like a duckes. They cannot walke or goe vppon the land & therfore I also take them for a kinde of Gull. They are greate deuourers of fishes liuinge & flyinge togither in flocks beinge of a whitishe yellowe colour & are not set by for their fleshe.

The Cormorant Shildrake

[illustration]

This is a fowle that followeth fishes with other of his kinde & driueth them into corners as into netts or as shepheards their sheepe into folds, & when they haue thus enthraled them, they diue after them & eate them abundantly. They are lesse then geese & bigger then ducks hauinge a

broade beake & sharpe at the end beinge full of sharpe teeth withinside, their brest & feete white, their other partes brownishe yellowe or various.

[97v]

The Cormorant morfex

Yt is doubted whether this fowle be not the same which the ffrench call *Cormarin* & the Germans *Aelguess, Schaluchorn* or *Scholucheren.* Yt is a very greate fowle & feedeth vppon *Eeles.* Like the hawke *Aelguess* yt is blacke & therefore is supposed to be the true *Coruus marinus,* yet the belly & brest are of an ashe colour. They are slowe of flight & therfor when they haue filled themselfes with fishes, they must first drye their

feathers before they can flye & then also yf they be ouerfull they are not able to soare to their nests vntill they haue vomited some of their eeles vp againe. They build in trees & their dunge or excrements kill the boughes of the trees wherein they make their nests like as herons & other water fowles.
[98r]

The greate goose Cormorant

The blacker are the greater which *Albertus* calleth *Carbones nigri,*[142] blackcolls. *Ouid* describeth them in this manner.

> *ffecit Amor maciem: longa internodia crurum*
> *Longa manet ceruix. Caput est a corpore longe,*
> *substricta crura, spatiosum in guttura etc.*

They are leane through Copulation their legs & necke longe & the head standeth farre from their backs, the ioynts or shins short, hauinge a very wide throate apte to swallowe downe greate fishes. *Mergi contra omne genus auium pedes habent in cauda, ita vt in terra stantes instar hominum pectus erectum proferant.* Cormorants haue legs growinge backwards vnder their tayles contrarye to all other fowles, so as when they stand vppon the earth they shewe them selfes like men bearinge vp before them their brests. Their heads, backs, & tayles are blacke, their beaks [98v] broade but not as ducks & haue vppon the brimms of their beake inward little teeth, their legs beinge placed so farre backward doeth hinder their walkinge vppon the earth.

The lesser & smaller kinde of Cormorants are most plentyfull in Creete & exceede not a teale in quantitye hauinge a white bellye, but a head, wings, tayle, & backe of a blacke colour wantinge the spurre or hinder foote. The feathers are short, small, & thicke like mosse, stickinge deepe in the skinne. The beake hollowe & sharpe at the brimmes but half couered with short, blacke, mossye feathers, beinge blacke vppon the vpper parte & white beneath. In other things yt differeth not from our Cormorants of *England*.

They liue bothe on the sea & land, & diue vnderwater wherein they remayne vnseen a greate tyme, especially in windy & stormy weather, wherfore *Ouid* sayeth:

Æquor amat, nomenque manet, quia mergitur illi.[143]

They loue the sea & therof take their name
Bycause they diue & ducke deepe in the same.

They are fearfull & when they are persecuted they goe vnder water at which tyme they doe not only auoid daunger but also hunt & take fishes for their foode; when they are full & the sunne shineth they come to land & delight themselfes in the beames thereof which caused *Virgill* to versifye in this manner.

Est procul in pelago saxum spumantia contra
Littora, quod tumidis submersum tunditur olim
ffluctibus, hyberni condunt vbi sydera Cori,
Tranquillo silet immotaque attollitur vnda
Campus & apriciis statio gratissima mergis.[144]

ffarr in that sea there is a stone aduanced
[99r] Which was once hyd within the swellinge waues
When winter bird in silent Calme is [haunsed?]*
And feilds drye land aboue the waters haue
There when the sunne doth shine most bright
The Cormorants doe take their safe delight.

ffor by reason they liue in the waters drye land & fayer weather doeth drye them & therfore after their water toyle they make to the banks & fields adioyninge for rest & solace. They are most cunninge in swimminge & therfore doeth Homer compare Ino to one of these helpinge Vlysses:

ἥ ῥ᾽ Ὀδυσῆ᾽ ἐλέησεν ἀλώμενον, ἄλγε᾽ ἔχοντα·
αἰθυίῃ δ᾽ εἰκυῖα ποτῇ[145]

Who pittyed much Vlisses in his dolefull case
And Cormorant like to sea did speede apace.

* [*haunsed*] lifted, raised (see note)

When they swyme in Calme weather they will diue & hold vp one wynge aboue water for a sayle & bycause of their insatiable desire to fishes they keepe vnder water longer then other fowles. They swallowe downe liuinge fishes as Eales, Congers & such like which they can take into their mouths, & like dolphins & dog fishes, persecute the sea & water creaters for their foode: & yf other waterfowles doe disgorge their stomacks of any fishe these come & eate yt vp, for they haue no mawes but their throates runne directly into their bellyes. They build nests both in trees & steepe rocks in the beginninge of the springe at the very end of winter & lay not aboue three or fower eggs, which they hatch like other fowles, & when they bringe their younge to the waters, they are so naturally enclyned to fishinge that they attempt it the first day like [99v] young Crocodills so as yf by any mischaunce they loose their damme yet they perishe not in the waters or for want of foode. Their voyces they vary accordinge to the seuerall occasions which they vndergoe. They are enimies to Storks and Moorehens bycause they liue vppon fishe. Yt is fayned that *Æsacus,* the sonne of *Priamus,* fallinge in loue with the nymphe *Hesperia* was by *Thetis* turned into a *Cormorant* after [s]he was bitten by a snake. Therfore they loue the waters & cannot liue yf they visitt them not very often, wher vppon a Cormorant forsakinge the waters is an adage for an incredible thinge.

Nam prius incipient turres vitare Columbæ
Antra feræ, pecudes gramina, Mergus aquas
Quam male se præstet veteri Græcinus amico.[146]

When doues refuse the towers hye
Wild beasts their denns & cattell grasse
And Cormorants the waters flye
Then for an old freind I will not passe.

Their fleashe is not good for meate yet they are taken for other purposes and especially to take fishes which is thus described by Odericus, *de foro Iulii*:

In ciuitate quadam ad magnum fluuium sita in Oriente, hospitem piscaturum comitamur, vidi in nauiculis mergos super perticas alligatos quibus ille guttur filo ligauit, nepisces captos deuorare possent. Ponunt autem ad singulas naues tres magnas cistas, vnam in medio et ab vtroque extremo singulas. Tum Mergos solutos dimisit, et ipsimet in cistas illas imposuere etc.[147] Being in a certayne cittye of the East, wee followed our hoast a fishinge, who brought vs to his boates wherein wee sawe Cormorants tyed fast to perches, and hauinge their throate bound round with a thred that they might not swallowe downe the fishes they take. Yn euery boate they haue placed three greate [100r] chests, one in the midle & two at the ends. So they lett loose the Cormorants & turned them into the riuer who of their owne accord doe take the fishe & bringe it into those Chests till they were all fylled: Afterward the threds wherewithall their necks weare tyed were loosed, & so they were suffered to fill themselfes of the fishe they had taken, & then they returned againe to their pearches. The like thinge is reported by Scaliger and wee in England fynd it also experienced, that with profitt to their keepers and delight to the behowlders, Cormorants take fishes and are made to cast them vpp agayne.

The ancients were wont to obserue the beatings of their wings, for yf they spread & flapped them vppon the ground it præsaged wynde; yf they diue vnderneath a ship as yt sayleth it sheweth a storme (sayd Kiranides), but yf it flye ouer a ship or sitt in sight vppon a Rocke yt foresignifyeth a happye voyage. Our *Dr Wooton* giueth this reason of their dyuing before tempests & stormes: *Tranquillo mari progredi non audet Æthia, marinarum belluarum metu: at quum tempestatem præsenserit, audacter progreditur, quod tunc temporis marinæ illæ belluæ in altum abierunt.*[148] When the sea is calme the Cormorants dare not descend into the waters to fishe for feare of sea monsters, which in fayre weather haunt the vpper face of the waters: but when tempests & stormes are comminge, then these monsters descend into the bottome of the sea, & the Cormorants dare to dyue and fishe vnder water more bouldly; when they come from the seas or greate waters to the earth yt signifyeth wynds also, sayth [100v] *Virgill*:

> *Tum sibi tum curuis male temperat vnda carinis*
> *Quum medio celeres reuolant ex æquore Mergi*
> *Clamoremque ferunt ad littora.*[149]
>
> Then to yt selfe & crooked shipps that sayle
> The water is destempred in the mayne
> When Cormorants on midst of seas doe quaile
> And speede to shore with cryings & complayne.

This foreknowledge (sayth Isidore) they receiue by dyuinge in the waters, *aurarum signa sub fluctibus colligunt,* for euer vnder the floods they gather sure tokens of the chaunge of the weather aboue their heads. Peradventure they learne yt by the departure of the fishe who better knowe the fallinge of stormes then these or any other fowles, & therfore doe forsake the toppe & descend downe into the bottome of the waters into couerts, which the Cormorants missinge retyre speedely to the land, least the stormes make short their iourney, for they are stronger vppon the sea then on the land. Their fleshe, as wee haue sayd, is not good for meate in the nature therof bycause the same is blacke & hard to bee disgested wherfore Horace blamed the Roman youths for praysing the same:

Si qui tunc Mergos suaues edixerit assos
Parebit praui docilis Romana iuuentus.[150]

If Cormorants doe please mens luscious mouth
It liketh well our ill taught Roman youth.

But yet they are best in wynter because then in their quiet they are fatter. They are best for hawkes, sayeth [101r] one Demetrius, for they will neuer surfett of them, bycause vnto them they are so easye of disgestion. Their medicinall virtues are more acceptable for the vse of men & therfor I will breifly relate them.

The whole bodye boyled & eaten cureth the Leprosye & the spleene, as *Kiranides* writeth, & their blood is good against all venemous wild beasts. The hart taken out of their belly vntouched with any iron, dryed to a powder & drunke in warme water was the medicine commended by the old magitians against a quartan* feuer. The ventricle is commended against the weaknes of the stomake, yet Gallen doth vtterly disallowe the same. The liuer dryed & drunke in two spoonefulls of water & wyne expelleth the *Secondines* & sodd in oyle (sayth Ætius) doth wonderfully helpe such as are bitten with madde doggs yf salt be added there vnto. Yf the sicke patient doe after the receiuinge hereof growe thirstye yt is an assured signe that he shall recouer: the gall mixed with rosyn dissolued or turned into liquor keepeth hayre from groweinge vppon the eyes browes by anoyntment after they haue bin once pulled of. Their eggs (sayth Kiranides) cure the bloodye flixe and runninge of the raynes.

The Gentlemen of *England* who haue adopted the Cormorants into their armes are breifely these that folowe:

Childerlighe. Arg: a Cheueron azure between 3 Cormorants heads erased sable.

[101v] Norton . a cheueron gules betweene 3 Cormorants heads erased sable

* *quartan* recurring every third or fourth day

Walton of wiltshire Argent a cheueron betweene 3 Cormorants heads erased sable.

The Earle of Lagmere gules a Cormorant Arg:
[102r]

[XXVII]

The Corrier or Carrier

[space for illustration blank]

This is a water birde as swifte of foote as of flight. The Græcians call it *Trochilos* and *Koruthos,* and *Steganpodem.* The Italians *Corrira,* for the swifte pace. The Latynes *Trochilus, Tabellaria,*[151] and *Celeus.* And this last name is thus poetically fayned by Ouid and Antonius Liberalis:[152]

In Crete was a Caue consecrate to the sacred Bees, who did helpe Rhea, Iupiters mother in her trauaile of Childbirth. Out of this Caue euery yere there flamed fire, which they say ariseth out of Iupiters bloud. This Caue is giuen to the sacred Bees which were Iupiters Nurses, and no man may dare to enter into the same. Yet Laius, Celeus, Ægolius, and Cerberus desirous of the honye which was therein treasured by the sacred Bees adventured to enter, hauinge first couered their bodies all ouer with brasse: wherein they did not onely satisfie themselues with honye, but also sawe Iupiters Cradle. Then Iupiter wroth herewithall with thunder and lighteninge brake the brasse of from their bodies, and wolde haue killed them, had not the three fatall Sisters resisted him affirminge that no man must die in [102v] that holy Denne. Whereupon they were turned by Iupiter into Laii, Cerberi, Ægolii and Celei, foure kindes of birdes, and so flewe away alive.

It is a birde of many colours like a Pye, hauinge a straight beake of a Clay colour, blacke at the ende, and gapinge wide, the eyes blacke enringed with a while Circle, and vnder that, another of redd. All the vpper part of the belly is white, the taile is couered with two white feathers which are also blacke at the ends. The head, necke, backe, and outside of the wings are a rustie colour. The leggs very longe, the thighes short, and the feete like a gooses. They runne alonge by the Seashore with wonderfull celeritie, feedinge vpon the fishe which the Sea casteth vp. They also loue all greate waters especially the Riuer

Nilus, or where the Crocodils breede. ffor as the Swallowes and other small birds doe picke out the fleshe and bones which remayne in and betwixt the Crocodills teeth, when hee sleepeth gapinge vpon the earth, so doeth this Carrier, and is therefore loued of the cruell Creature. ffor besides when the Ichneumon which lyeth in wayte to destroy the Crocodile discouereth it selfe to surprise his Aduersarye, this fowle keepinge a faithfull watche about him, by his strayned voice giueth warninge to his friende the Crocodile either awakinge it or stirringe him vp to avoide the perill of killinge.

I will conclude the History of this Fowle with this narration of Oppianus.[153] The Males and Females lyve asunder vntill the Springe of the yere, and then the females by their voices invite and entise the Males to copulation, who are not easilie drawen to forsake their first fellowshippe and followe the females; but overcome by nature, they treade the hennes, and so both sexes part asunder againe, like as before or as some Amazonian race, lyvinge in peculiar feedings,* wherein the Males come not at the females nor [103r] the feamales at the Males. So the Males giue ouer most vnnaturallye to looke vnto or nourishe their younge leavinge all that labour to their females to be diuided amonge them, who make their oune neasts and while they sett vpon their egges, they chainge neasts and sitt by courses, some forraginge abroade for meate for them that keepe home, and those that keepe home visitinge in the meane space the neasts of the purueyours which are abroade, and warminge their eggs till they returne. And so by courses like reasonable Creatures they chainge, and succeede one another in their naturall amitie and neighbourly societie vntill the younge be hatched. At which tyme they leade them to the shores and Riuers where the Males make their abode and feede: and there they make a partition of their broode, leavinge the younge Males to their Fathers, and the females they retayne to themselues, euen as shepheards doe devide their flocks, or separate the Rammes from the Ewes. And so much for the History of this water fowle.

. . . .

* *feedings* feeding grounds

[119r]

[XXVIII]

(8) Another Indian Cocke.

[119v] This birde was giuen to Aldrouandus by the greate Duke of Florence, which he describeth in this manner. The body was all over blacke without a Combe on his head, in place whereof he had a tufte of feathers as you may see standinge vp like longe curled haire. He also wanted a Tayle and Spurres, his beake was of two colours; yellowe in the vpper part next the head and blacke towards the ende hauinge it also crooked downeward, and insteede of nostrills (as in other Cockes) hee had a round knob as big as a cherry, some of his feathers of his rumpe were white, and so were the leggs, shankes, and feete.

(9) The Indian Hen

There are three sorts of Indian Hens to be seuerallie expressed whereof this last figure [is?] the least. The shape and colour differeth

much from the last menconed Cocke, for the feathers of the body were of a sandy or red russet colour; her head tufted with feathers like the Cocke but shorter. The beake more thicke then the same Cocke, and full of litle bunches in the middest of the vpper part, of a whitish colour besett with litle blacke spotts. The eyes blacke, [120r] and their iris or hollowe beyond the apple of a yellowe saffron colour. Her wings or sides of a verie sadde rustie colour. The leggs and feete of blewishe clay Colour. It hath no tayle, as in the former Cocke, wherefore by the resemblance of the head I thinke it one of the same kinde with the former. The Nape or small of the necke is naked like an Apes, and not couered with feathers as the Cocke, other differences or resemblances worthie of notinge I finde none at all.

(10) Two other kindes of Indian Hens.

[two illustrations on p. 165]

Although some call these Numidian or Barbary Hens, yet other vpon greater reason doe name them Indians. ffor the Numidian Race are the same which are before called the African. It appeareth by their figures that one of them is tayled, the other without a tayle, and therefore it is a reasonable coniecture, that one of them is the Male, the other a female. And yet seinge they are expressed by the name of Hens in Aldrovandus, I will not vary from their first receaued title nor from his description which is as followeth. The one of them (supposed to be the Male) from the beake to the typpe of the tayle was of a blackishe or verie browne colour havinge the tufte white at the typpe, and the same [120v] adorned with some blacke spotts. The beake verie stronge, red, and crooked, the rumpe and vndermast part of the tayle somewhat white, the leggs of colour like the bodie, except more pale, and in the hinder part more blewe. The clawes blacke, vpon the forehead from the roote of the beake vpwarde groweth a greate bunche of colour and quantitie like a blewe figge. A longe taile not turned vpwards as in comon Hens but stretched out in leingth as in Pheasants or Pyes.

The other or lesse Hen was of a russet colour, the wings and necke enclyninge to an Ashecolour. The Bunche in the forehead altogether like the former. So was the beake but nothinge crooked. In conclusion it wanted a longe tayle.

. . . .

[122r]

[XXIX]

(12) The Hethcock

[illustration on p. 168]

Hector Boetius and Dr Turner doe both make mention of this kinde, which in England wee call a Heathcocke and in Scotland a Blacke Cocke. These (I meane the Male and female) doe so differ in colour, that you wolde not take them to be both of one kinde. The Male is in quantitie lesse than a House Cocke and the colour betwixt a browne and a verie sad greene: hauinge a little white to couer his excrementarye. The colour of his feathers are not vnfitlie resembled to the blacke ringe about the necke of a wood pigeon, vpon his head he hath a red tufte fleshy and two lapps of fleshe and fleshe colour. The Scottish Cocke hath his necke, breast, wings, and sides full of red spotts, and the female (which is more graye, they call a Grey-hen) is full of white spotts, and in both sexes the eylids and beard feathers are adorned with a thinne and visible red skynne. The female of this kinde in England is spotted like a Partridge, and coulde hardlie be discerned from a Partridge but that it is more ruffe,* blacker, and greater. They lyve in forrests and heathie places, such as are most desert and [122v] lesse frequent. They feede vpon any kinde of grayne, and the seeds and topps of heath. There voice is not much vnlike a younge Cockes savinge it is not so loude nor so longe, and it semeth they lyve together Male and female, and when the female is absent from the Male, he calleth her by his Crowinge. They breede in the earth and verie sieldome are their younge ones seene. Sixe or seauen is their nomber, they are verie good meate in the winter. And so much for these kindes.

* *ruffe* that is, with a bristly plumage

[XXX]

(13) The Moorehen and Myrcocke or Dab-chicke.

In the next place you may here beholde another kinde of fowle which besides the name I cannot tell what agreament they haue with Cockes and hens. They lyve in freshe waters eatinge no kinde of grayne but three leaued grasse. They will dyve vnder water, and there remayne a greate while, when they are hunted and sometimes rise out of the water and flie away. Their backes are blacke, and some white or red vnder their wings. The yonge ones are many and will dyve vnder water with their dammes: They haue many spotts vpon them, if they fall out to be of other colour then blacke. Their voice is not vnlike the call of a Partridge. [123r] Their fleshe is verie good for meate.

. . . .

[200v]

Coates and Crests of Heath Cockes
and Moore cockes

Baome. Ermyn on a Cheife dancett sab. 2. Moorecockes Arg.

Bashe of Hartfordshire party per Cheueron Arg. & Gules in Chiefe 2 Moorecockes proper and in base a Salture coupe Or.

Corben of Staffordshire Arg. on a Chiefe or. 3. Moorecockes proper.

Delamoore of Deuon. 3. Moorecockes proper.

Drewe of Bristoll Or a Cheueron Sab. betwene 2 Cottises Gules and 3 Moorecockes Azure.

Heth of Shelswell Ermyn a Cheueron Sab. betwene 3 Heathcockes proper.

Heath of Norff party per Cheueron Or and Sab. 2 mulletts in Cheife and one Heathcocke in base Counterchainged.

Kockerell Or a plaine Crosse betwene 4 Moorecockes Gules.

Mynde of Salop a Heathcocke proper sett on a wreath Arg. and Gules. Creast.

[201r] Mannyngten. Arg. a Cheueron Sab. betwene 3 Moorecockes Azure.

Middlemore party per Cheueron Arg. and Sab. in Chiefe a Moorehene proper. And againe a Moorecocke proper pearchinge on a hill vert sett within a wreath Arg. and Sab. a Crest.

Sir Thomas Moore Arg. a Cheueron Sab. betwene 3 Moorecockes proper.

Moore Eborum Argent. a Cheueron Sab. betwene 3 Moorecockes proper memberd Gules.

Moore Dorsett Arg. on a Fesse Sab. 3 Mulletts Or betwene 3. Moorecockes proper.

Moore Darb. Sab. on a Cheueron engrayled Or 3. Leopards heads Gules betwene as many Mulletts of the second vpon a Cheife Arg and the same number of Moorecockes proper.

Moore London. Ermyn a Fesse Gules betwene 6. Moorecockes proper membred of the same.

Morrice Barkshire. Or on a Fesse Coupe Gules a garbe of the first betwene 3 Moorecockes proper.

Mowre towne. Arg. 3. Moorecockes proper.

Ringwood Arg. a Cheueron Counter compony. Or and Sab. betwene 3 Moorecockes Azure.

Thwaytes Eborum a Heathcocke risinge proper on a wreath Or and Azure a Creast.

Warder a Moorecocke proper creasted Gules. ielloped Or on a wreath Or and Azure.

Zelkheth Gules a Cheueron betwene 3 Moorecockes risinge Argent a border engrayled of the same.

These are all that I can obtayne to expresse in this place. Wherein if I have failed to remember other, beinge as worthie as these I must craue pardon for I have not expressed any for affection nor suppressed for hatred to any mans person. Therefore when I shall gaine more particulars I professe all readines to adde them in due ranke and plase vnto the former. ffor *non Ouum ouo similius.* One egge is to me as good as as another, and all Gentlemen alike except for vertue which I esteeme aboue honor as the good mother aboue the faire daughter. [201v]

[XXXI]

The wilde Cocke or Cocke of the wood.

[illustration on p. 172]

When I had finished this History of the Cocke and hen I mett with a Gentleman of Irelande of whome (after many conferences) I enquired for the fowles of that Countrey, from whome I learned that they had a greate wilde Cocke which they called a Cocke of the wood, which after diligent searche I founde to be the same which the Iewes at this day call *Dukiphat,* the Græcians *Tetrix* and *Ourax* from which last worde the Germanes call it *Vrhaen* and *Orhaen.* The same doubtlesse which the Latynes call *Vrogallus* and *Tetrao* of the blacke colour, wherefore also Hermolaus calleth it *Retrago* and *Tetrago* and sometymes *Trao* and

Erythrotao, the Italians *Cedron,* and the Frenche *Coc de Bois,* a Cocke of the wood. The Rhætians *Stolzo, Stolcho,* and *Stolgo* of the greatenes thereof, so the Latines *Vrogallus* as *Vrus* a *Vrcoxe,* a greate Oxe. The Germanes doe also call it *Auerhaen, Birkhuener,* and *Pirkhuener.* The Illyrians *Tetrez* and *Tetrzeuu.* And so much for the seuerall appellations.

This bird is of the race of Cockes beinge therefore comonly called *Gallus Syluestris* and *Syluaticus,* a wilde Cocke, and a Cocke of the wood. The seuerall kindes whereof shalbe nowe described in order, and I will first beginne with the greater.

[202r] By reason of the large bulke of his body Gesner thought him to be a kind of Bustard for he is very neare of an equall stature, insomuch they say there is not any fowle of the earth greater except the Estrich. Stretched out in leingth they are from the head to the sole of their feete, two foote of Assise* and in weight twelve or thirteene Germane pounds which conteyne sixteene or seauenteene ounces to the pound, the necke halfe a foote longe, beinge couered with blacke feathers somewhat pale. The longe feathers of their wings of a browne colour and stretched out did reach five palmes, the residue of the wing-feathers of a chestnutt colour marked with blacke spotts. The head blacke and blackest vnderneath the beake. The beake like a Cockes short, bunched, broade, and stronge. The eyelids redd, the forepart of the necke adorned with Ashecolour spotts vnder which lye greenishe feathers, the breast and belly blacke. In the middest of the breast against the hole or mouth of the stomacke, are a small lyne of white feathers mingled with the blacke, the small feathers vnderneath the wings white and blacke at the endes, and the residue white and browne. The Tayle fyve palmes longe, the feathers thereof blacke, adorned with white spotts, and the extremities of the smaller feathers full of diuers coloured spotts. The blacke feathers coloured and spotted like the longe winge feathers, and next the backe more beautifull spotts of Ashe colour. The hippes and thighes white, and from thence the leggs couered with browne to the very feete which are foure, three before and one behinde, and there are certeine combed feathers hanginge downe about the feete or clawes which are very short. The female hath no manifest difference externall from the Male, except in the feathers about the head which stand not vp so highe. And so much for the description of this first, and greatest kinde of wilde Cockes.

* *Assise* size, measurement

[*The wilde Cocke*]

[202v] [XXXII]

The Smaller wilde Cocke.

This smaller kinde exceedeth the common and vulgar Cockes and in quantitie commeth nearest to the former of all the wilde fowles. It is called *Tetrao* or *Vrogallus minor*. In Germany *Kleiner Orhan* and *Laubhan*, because it eateth the leaues and fruites of trees. In Italy they name it *Fasan negro* and *Fasiano Alpestre*, a Pheasant of the Alpes. ffor Stumpfius writeth, *Sunt Phasiani montani nigri & fusci veris phasianis maiores* &. That there be Mountayne Pheasants greater then the Comon pheasants, which liue in the topps of Mountaynes and in the middest of woodes. And they are thus described by Gesner. The eyelids are greater then in the former, hauinge a redd pellicle which they couer, the feathers on the Crowne of the head are blacke, the beake blacke, also short, and of the leingth of an inche. The necke fiue or sixe inches longe, couered with blacke blewishe feathers, and from the necke alonge the backe and wings more blacke, but the middle part of the winges are white and so are the insides: the belly blacke, from the middest of the backe to the tayle of a more blewishe colour as in the necke; yet the outsides and typpes of the feathers are coloured somewhat like a Peacockes. The Tayle is short in the middle standinge [203r] vpon three feathers in the leingth fashioned like a flower de lyce. ffrom the hippes down to the thighes, leggs, and feete, are very roughe and thicke feathers purposelie made by Almighty God to shielde and cover the poore fowle from extremitie of colde. The clawes of their feete scaly like the tayle of a Sea Crabbe. The feathers of the legges growe vpon the shinnes and forepart, beinge bare behinde, beinge blacke with white spotts in them. The female is more browne and lesse blacke then the Male. They are sieldome taken alyve but they are found in snares hanged by the necke. Olaus Magnus[154] writeth that they lyve in Goateland and other the colde northren parts, in the winter tyme three monthes vnder snowe without meate and so are often taken by the fowlers. The writer of Aristotles wonders relateth a more strainge propertie of such like birdes in Pontus whose tale I will for his credit relate in his oune wordes: *In Ponto, aiunt, in hyeme aues quasdam reperiri, quæ neque excernant, neque quum pennæ eis auelluntur, sentiant, neque cum veru transfiguntur sed tum demum cum ab igne incaluerunt.*[155] They finde certeine birds in Pontus (men say) which are blinde, see not, neither haue any sence when their feathers are pulled from their bodies or when they are broached or pierced with a spitt, vntill they feele the heate of the fire, and then they mooue and shewe their life. Indeede Cicero saieth that Dormyce when their members are frosen, are senceles, and yet aliue, for beinge pricked they stirre and shewe their vitall spirits. I will sooner belieue Olaus then the

writers of such wonders. And so much for the description of this bird.
[203v]

A Thirde kynde

This thirde kinde is called by the Latynes *Grigallus minor* and by the Germanes *Spilhan,* and *Sphillhan,* and some take it to be the same which about Colen they call *Birkhun, ab arbore Betula,* from the Birch-tree. And I finde it thus described by Longolius.[156] It is like a Partridge, but in the quantitie it is greater. They loue the thicke woods for their safetie, especially the Birch-tree and yet so as for their foode they forsake it and runne abroade into pastures and adiacent Cornefieldes. The colour is browne like a Birch-trees-barke when the outmost of vpper skynne is flayed of. ffor it is redder then a Partridges and hath spotts on the backe also. The females are more beautifull then the Males as it happeneth in Hawkes and Falcons where they exceede the Males in quantitie and comelynes of body. And thus much for this *Spilhan* or *Grigallus minor.*
[204r]

The fourthe kynde.

This fowle is thus described by the Poet Nemesianus:

Et Tetracem Romæ, quem nunc vocitare Taracem
Coeperunt, Auium est multo stultissima namque
Cum pedicas necti sibi contemplauerit adstans,
Immemor ipse sui, tamen [*in*] *dispendia currit:*
Tu vero adductos laquei cum senseris orbes
Appropera, & prædam pennis crepitantibus aufer
Nam celer oppressi fallacia vincula colli
Excutit, & rauca subsannat voce magistri
Consilium & læta fruitur iam pace solutus.[157]

In englishe thus.

The Tetrax olde
which nowe at Rome they *Tarax* call
A foolishe byrd that sees the Fowler fold
The snare for her: yet doth in danger fall
Then hast when nett thee helpes thou doest perceaue
And take thy prey with cracklinge feathers sett.
ffor some thy bands from necke she reaues,
And scornes in peace this thy deceauinge nett.

So the Poet proceedeth to the place of their abode and saieth they builde in Peltinnum, a wood at the foote of the Appennines, beinge like a partridge on the backe, and as big as a goose, *Tarpeiæ custos arcis.* The whole bird is a very beautifull Creature, hauinge the beake a little crooked, bunched and blacke as in the first and greate Cocke. The head smooth, and from the beake vnto the eares of an Ashecolour: aspersed with blacke spotts except in the lower part of the necke where are no spotts at all. The backe and wings [204v] of an Ashecolour with spotts of the same: but the longe feathers are white at the typpes and the winge feathers blacke and Ashecolour at the ends. The Tayle so redd as it inclineth to a Chestnutt adorned with large blacke spotts and the shinnes or legges with Ashecolour feathers vpon blacke quills. The feete foure beinge naked and of an Ashecolour also and the eyes compassed about with redd. And this is no other but *Grygallus maior* whereof Gesner saieth they haue plenty about Clarona in Heluetia. Thus hauinge described their seuerall kindes I will proceede to the other obseruations vpon this fowle.

These fowles liue in the highest hills, or in the thickest and most vnpasseable woods, wherefore Germany, Icelande, and other colde Countreys are full of them: It is a marveilous and almost incredible thinge which Encelius[158] reporteth of the copulation of these Cockes with their hens which I will not conceale from my Reader, leavinge him to his election and free will to belieue or refuse this narration of my Author.

In Marche (saieth hee) the Cockes call their hens euen as a common dunghill Cocke by Clockinge, and when they are come together they make cleane a place of the earth whereon they stand. Then the Cocke excreateth out of his mouth his genitall seede vpon that faire place so cleansed by them, which the hens doe greedily gather vp into their mouth and eate it downe. Afterward the Cocke leapeth vpon euery one of the hens as it were in sport, and so they conceaue. ffor if the Cocke doe not treade and presse them before they depart, they lay no other then vnprofitable wind eggs. But if any sodeine terror come vpon the hens and drive them away from the place before they haue swallowed vp the remaynder of the Cockes seede: by the benefitt of the Sunne and of the dewe, that remayninge [205r] vncollected seede engendreth wormes and serpents called by the [Germans] *vrhanschlangen* and *Birg-schlangen,* that is, serpents of the Mountaynes or of the Cockes of the wood. And if it happen that neither rayne nor dewe doe fall vpon this remayninge seede, then it is congealed by the Sunne into a bladder or pretious stone very white and transparent, whereof the Shepheards of those places (especiallie in Marchland about the ryver Tangera[)] gather some plenty, sellinge them for greate somes of money because they are esteemed very helpfull to women labouringe in childbirth, and for filthie minded persons giuen to the beastlie delight of Venus. Thus farre Encelius.

Crowes and Doues are also saied to conceiue at their mouth although Aristotle denyeth the latter. Howsoeuer this be true or false, many in Germany and about Marchland aforesaide doe belieue the same. At the tyme of this copulation they are both blinde and deafe; for it hath ben tryed that the noice of a fowlinge piece hath not made them stirre from the action, although the fowler haue ben in their sight. The fleshe of these fowles is very delicate meate such as hath found acceptance at the table of Princes. And Suetonius writeth that Caligula amonge other such pretious fowles caused these Cockes to be sacrificed vnto himselfe. Other vses I finde not of this fowle. And therefore at the table I will conclude his History.

[205v—blank]

[206r] [XXXIII]

The Crane.

The Crane is a noble and princely creature, wherefore when fables ruled the worlde, and they had no other Teachers then Poets, nor better divine knowledge, then the Metamorphosis of men into beasts, or transmigration of one soule into another; then it was belieued that one Oenoe or Gerania, a proude and prophane Queene of Pigmeæs, was by Iuno and Diana turned into a Crane bycause shee taught all her people to neglect other Gods and worshippe herself: and besides she sowed an vnreconciliable warre betwixt Cranes and Pigmeæs to this day. Wherefore they euer fight one with another. But wee must followe a better rule then fables in declaringe this fowle; and without poeticall fiction beholde him as a noble and wonderfull workemanshippe of the most blessed Trinity created for the benefitt of all that knowe them: which God assistinge wee will declare in our first described Methode.

The Hæbrewes call a Crane by diuers names as *Sus, Sas, Senuit* and *Agur.* The Chaldees *Senukita,* the Arabians *Cataph,* the Greekes *Geranos* or *Gereunos,* because it seeketh seede in the earth: and it is called for the same occasion *Spermologos,* for it diggeth not vp any fruite, but eateth such as it findeth vncouered vpon the face of the earth. The Male is called some tyme *Syristes,* and the Female *Geres,* and both of them *Lybiæ aues,* birds of Lybia, because in the approach of winter they come out of Scythia, into Lybia and Egipt. The Latynes call them *Grues* of their gruntinge voice, and therefore of that worde for both sexes. They also call it *Palamedis auem,* the bird of Palamedes, bycause Palamedes about the tyme of the Trojan warre did by imitation of the Crane invent foure Greeke letters not knowen before, $\theta.\xi.\chi.\phi$. Also the vse of waights and ballannces, the order of a battell and watch in warres, and the game of Chesse-play were taken vp by the imitation of Cranes. They are also called *Grex strymonius,* of the Ryver Strymon in Macedonia, where they liue in greate flockes, and *Naupliades volucres* by a patronimycall worde because *Nauplius* was the father of Palamedes. *Bistonias aues,* of Bistonia in Thrace. The Italyans *Grua* and *Gru,* the Spanyards *Grulla* and *Gruz,* the Portugalls *Ema,* the Frenche *Grue,* the Germanes *Kran* and *Krane, Kranich,* or *Kranch* as wee in England a *Crane,* no doubt all of them derived of the Greeke *Geranos.* The Heluetyans *Kreye,* the Belgians *Kranæ,* the Illyrians [206v] *Gerzab,* the Polonians *Zoraw.* The small or yonge Cranes *Vipiones* in Latyne, in Greeke *Gerania,* in Frenche *petites*

Grues, in Italy *piccole grue,* in Spayne *Caydas* o[r] *Crukias, pequennas Gruzes,* in Germany *kleine krenchlin,* in Belgia *kleine Kraentiens,* in Hungary *Dariu Fru,* in Polonia *Ml'odzi zorawie.* And so much for their names.

The kindes and diversities of Cranes are very many. ffor Paulus Venetus[159] describeth fyve kindes in Tartaria: some, he saieth, haue blacke winges, like Crowes and Rauens, and some white as Swannes, with some feathers coloured in circles like the feathers of Peacockes. Some litle ones, but with very longe feathers beautifullie mixed with blacke and redd colours. Some verie greate with blacke and redd eyes, and their feathers of gryseld ashecolour, and lastlie some like those which are seene in Europe. Peter Martyr writinge of America and the newe found worlde affirmeth that the Spanyards founde Cranes in Cuba twise so bigge as our vulgar Cranes and Columbus also that he sawe Cranes in Lordeste of redd and scarlett colours in greate aboundance.

Tarawkow Konekautes

The Crane of Virginia

19

[illustration]

[207r]

The Balearian Crane.

[illustration on p. 179]

Plyny and the Auncients make mention of this fowle and distinguishe him for a speciall kinde, differinge not in the common nature, but in the externall forme and ornaments. ffirst hee hath a tufte on his head like the Coronett of a Peacocke, with many small thinne feathers of a goulden colour. The beake a darke Ashecolour, the toppe or Crowne of the head blacke, vpon eache side of the Temples is a longe white spott descendinge doune to the gills which are of a Rose colour. The necke, belly, and breast of a darke ashe colour. The backe betwixt blacke and greene wonderfull livelie. The wings of three diuers colours, the first and shortest feathers next the bodie of the colour of the necke and breaste, the next are white, and the last of a rustie yron colour. The taile as may be seene by this picture is very small or none at all. The female differinge nothinge from the male except in the thinnesse and leanesse of her bodie. The eyes haue a blacke apple compassed about

[*The Balearian Crane.*]

9

[*The Crane of Japan.*]

with a yellowishe substance like the gylles. Aldrouand out of the description of a friende of his at Rome by the daily viewe of a couple that were kept by Cardinall Sfortia addeth these properties folowinge. They are in quantitie æquall to common Cranes; when they runne, they lift vp their winges a litle, and so with wings and leggs pace very swiftlie like [an] Ostriche, but at other tymes they walke or (yf [207v] you will) stalke very slowlye. They never keepe within doores, except in the heat of the day: but in the night they flie vp to rooste vpon the toppe of some wall or other eminent place, euen like Peacockes: whome they alsoe resemble both in voice and disposition. They eate greene hearbes and alsoe branne, or other grayne with pullen.

The Crane of Iapan.

[illustration on p. 179]

Amonge the gifts and presents sent to the Pope by the Princes of Iapan, Aldrovand maketh mention of this Crane, communicated to him by the Marquis Fachinetto, which he also describeth in manner followinge: The body no bigger then a common Crane, beinge white all ouer except the beake, the vnder side of the necke, his feete, and the short feathers of his wings. The Crowne of the head was very redd sprinckled with some blacke spotts, and the middle of his necke beneath blacke: vnder his wings did hange downe very large quills blacke and marked with other appendances, and all the residue of his body or other parts beinge blacke. So much for this Crane. There are also other birds like to Cranes, such was that Gromphena[160] once seene at Sardis, and neuer but once, bycause Pliny writeth that in his tyme it was not so much as knowen [208r] either by name or description. And so I will proceede to the Comon Cranes.

[illustration on p. 182]

Gesner hauinge seene a Comon Crane doth describe her in this manner. Shee was sixe foote high from the feete to the beake stretched out. There were certeine feathers in her wings backwarde reachinge to the taile curled and very faire which men weare adorned with goulde in their hatts or Cappes. Otherwise the quills of their wings be blacke, exceptinge those feathers which were vppermost and neerest to her body, for they were of an Ashecolour. Her necke was sixteene inches longe, and her height from her feete to the toppe of her backe two and thirtie inches or there abouts. Her whole weight about twelue pound. Her taile short and therefore couered with the longnesse of her wings: her leggs were feathered vpon the thighes and vpper part, but beneath the knees they were couered with a hard skaley skynne like the barke of a tree. The clawes of her feete as longe as the nailes of a man. The outsides of her necke blacke, and the forepart white, the residue of an ashecolour besides the greate quills of her winges before rehearsed. The crowne of her head blacke with a redd spott, and that bigger in the Male then in the Female. So farre Gesner before whome neuer any man did so exactlie describe all the parts of a Crane. Onely some of them haue made mention of his longe throate, for which a [208v] certeine glutten in Gellius wished to exchainge his oune, that so he might devoure the more meate, whereas the foole that delighted so much in eatinge had more neede to haue desired the throate of a Camell or of an Elephant; such a one was Philoxenus Cithereus that longed for a throate of three Cubites.

Tricubitalem optauit habere gulam.[161]

Saieth the Poet. Some haue enquired the reason of the voice of the Crane, howe it cometh to passe it shoulde be hearde so farre of, whereunto there are many aunsweares, but the truest is drawen from the anatomie of the birde which Bellonius did finde out. ffor by dissection thereof he found the *asperam arteriam,* or throate bole, to differ from all other fowles. ffor by reason, saieth he, that it is fastened to the fleshe, as deepe as the ribbes without dependance on the intralls, as in all other creatures, he crieth out with a shriller and more continuall voice beinge neuer weary, though he flie out of sight. And this is the true cause why their voices be hearde, before their bodies be seene.

And seinge wee are fallen into the mentioninge of their voice, it shall not be amisse to discourse further hereupon both phisically and metaphisically. Therefore as the auncient Latynes call a Crane *gruem* so they call their voice, *gruere. Grues dicuntur gruere vt sues grunnire, vnde tractum est congruere, quid id genus volucrum minime solivagum est.*[162] As swine are saied to *gruntle* so Cranes are saide to *iangle,* from whence commeth the worde *congruere,* for agreament or gatheringe together: bycause that kind of fowle is neuer founde alone.

Caput ardua tollens
Clangit & ingenti mouet internodia passu.[163]

By Ianglinge lowde and liftinge head on hie,
he moueth changinge places speedilie.

Yet some there are which had rather call the voice of Cranes *clamorem,* then *clangorem,* so Virgill and Homer expresse the Cries of the Troianes against the Græcians.

Clamorem ad sydera tollunt,
Dardanidæ muris, quales sub nubibus atris,
Strimoniæ dant signa Grues, atque æthera tranant
Cum sonitu fugiuntque notos clamore secundo.[164]

ffrom earth to heauen the Troians lift their voice,
like as doe Cranes when from blacke cloudes they flie,
[209r] And cutt the aër with signes and soundinge voice,
To avoide the rayne that in the South doth lye.

The manner or sounde of their voice is very dolefull or lamentable, accordinge to these verses of Dantes, the Italian Poet:

E come i Gru van cantando lor lai,
Facendo in aer di sè lunga riga;
Così vid'io venir, trahendo guai,
Ombre portate dalla detta briga.[165]

As cranes in the aër make their long lines

And singinge their laies alonge as they goe
So ofte haue I seene in their ianglinge tymes
Their sorowfull voyces encreasinge mens woe.

Concerninge the age of Cranes there is some difference, amonge writers: all of them agreeinge in this, that they beginne to chainge at eight yere olde, yet so as they liue sometymes to fourtie which was experienced by one Leonicus Tomæus, who kept a Crane fortie yeres together: Aristotle is of opinion, that in their age their quills growe blacke, for by nature they are white and such as are white by nature are blacke in age, but such as are blacke by nature are white in age. Solinus speakinge of the beginninge of their chainge, saieth that they are yellowe in their age, whereby wee gather that they are not sodenlie chainged but euery yere by litle and litle, as men which chainge from blacke to graye, and from graye to white, so Cranes from blacke to yellowe, and from yellowe to white.

They are most delighted to liue in fenny places, lakes, and standinge pooles or ryvers, yet so as they will not be tied certeinelie to any place. ffor there is no Nation in the worlde that is fruitefull but they visite it at one tyme or other in the yere: yet they loue the warmest places best, and therefore when they remove from Countrey to Countrey it is obserued by the people from whome they flie, that their winter is cominge: and by the Nation to whome they flie that their sommer is comminge accordinge to these verses of Mantuan:

Iam satio vicina fabis Grus ordine longo,
Cum clamore volat, proiectaque semina campis,
Esurit,[166]

[209v] When Cranes come hither tis springe and sowinge tyme,
They feede on grayne vncouered which they finde.

ffor they love the ploughe, as the wolfe loueth the goate, and the goate the herbe Tryfolye.

Contemplare etiam quum Grus e nubibus altis,
Assiduos agitat clangores, inuocat imbrem
Ventorumque hyemem,[167]

Marke and beholde when Cranes from Cloudes æthereall,
doe iangle loude, then tempests showres doe call.

So a Greeke Poet hath left these three elegant verses to that purpose:

σπείρειν μέν, ὅταν γέρανος κρώζουσ' ἐς τὴν Λιβύην μεταχωρῇ·

καὶ πηδάλιον τότε ναυκλήρῳ φράζει κρεμάσαντι καθεύδειν,
εἶτα δ' Ορέστῃ χλαῖναν ὑφαίνειν, ἵνα μὴ ῥιγῶν ἀποδύῃ.[168]

Then sowe thy seede when Cranes in Lybia land,
Come croakinge: then the skilfull pilot takes
Vp mast and foreyard, takinge cloth in hand,
Orestes like to weave least cold him take.

In the Summer they are in Thrace but in the wynter they are in Libia or in warmer Countreis. They also abound in Thessaly, in Scithya about Strymon Gerania, Hebrus Hadrianopolis, Cayster, and, to conclude, in euery warme Contrey of the worlde: for as the weather chaingeth so doe they their habitation.

gruibus similes quos bruma coegit,
Quærere littoribus vicina tepentibus arua;[169]

Like Cranes whome pearcinge winter straynes
To seeke newe seates in warmer landes.

The sences of Cranes are verie sharpe both in smellinge, hearinge, and seinge. Therefore whatsoeuer they smell or perceaue, presentlie they bewray with clamour, and flie away from danger. In their flight there are many notable and obseruable discourses. Of their comminge, goinge, abode, order, height, in what windes, with what Captayne, watche, and other accidences, wherein the Reader may vnderstand many pleasinge and delectable varieties. St Ambrose saieth that Cranes are like the Kings of Persia which haue both their winter and Summer dwellinges, Susis, Ecbatane, Ninyuee, and Babilon; therefore although some of them stragle into all nations, yet for the most part they obserue a certeine lymitted, and determinated tyme wherein they chainge their habitations. [210r] Albertus dwellinge seauen and fortie degrees from the Æquinoctiall, affirmeth that Cranes abode in their Germany all the yere longe. Nature or rather the Creatour of nature hath taught all imperfect and weake Creatures to chainge their habitations, and for their better preseruation to foresee colde and heate: and also many other accidences of their oune mortalitie: as Quailes remove their habitations in August, which the Greekes call *Boedromion* and the Cranes in September, called by them *Mæmacterion.* Therefore Pliny praisinge the constant order of Cranes and Quayles writeth that euery yere the Quayles come one moneth before Cranes, and in like sort goe away againe. And Gesner obserued that they went away about the Æquinoctiall in September.

When they are to leaue Thrace where are the greatest flockes of

Cranes in all the worlde they assemble themselues about the Riuer Hebrus not disorderlie pel mel but in rankes and formall troupes marshalled like Souldiers. And when the day of their departure is come, the eldest amonge them all fleeth three tymes about the whole house wherewith beinge wearied he falleth downe and dieth, whome all the residue bury in such a solemnitie as is naturall vnto them. After which Ceremony they rise and take their flight toward Egipt and the mouthes or heads of Nilus wherein they prouide for their winter sustenance.

Et velut Æthiopum veniunt, Nilique fluenta,
Turmatim Palamedis aues, celseque per altum
Aera clamantes.[170]

Oppianus.

As Cranes by troupes to Nilus flowinge streames,
ffly high, crye lowde in Æthiopian Realmes.

ffor even those that are fedd in Thrace impacient of the sharpe winter there, thoughe neuer so short, doe also chainge their natiue soile in the middest of Autumne, and seeke other dwellinges vntill the Springe, at which tyme they returne backe againe, and spende their Summer in their oune Countreys. Wherefore they are called in Euripides, Λίβυας / οἰωνοὶ στολάδες / ὄμβρον λιποῦσαι χειμέριον.[171] The propheticall Lybian birdes flyinge from wynter. It is agreed that they flie with greate speede, although they seeme to moue but slowlie, which caused Cyrus to order and dispose his postes and Carriers in so wise and prouident [210v] Courses, that they might by chainges and newe supplies, outgoe the Cranes, whose flight, first described by Ariosto, is thus englished by his Translatour. *Come sol far la peregrina Grue Che correr &c.*[172]

li. 2. st. 49.

And as wee see strainge Cranes are wont to doe
ffirst stalke a while ere they their wings can finde,
Then soare from ground not past a yard or two,
Till in their wings they gathered haue the winde;
At last they mount the very cloudes vnto,
Trianglewise according to their kind.

These two thinges are obserued in their flight. They flie high and triangular. The causes of their highe flight are diuerslie discoursed by the Authors. ffor some ascribe it to their desire to descrye the land betymes and a farre of vnto which they flie. Other adde vnto this another, which in myne opinion ought to be none at all: ffor they say that by flyinge so highe, they discerne the beginninge of raynes and tempests, and so avoide them more easilie by lightinge on the grounde: but if they haue no other remedie then flyinge to the earth it were better they shoulde flye lower, bycause they are neerer to their Sanctuary and defence against stormes: for by the helpe of woodes and mountaynes: the windes shoulde the lesse trouble them. Lastlie, when they are dispersed and some of them growe weary and behinde, they which are highest can best discerne them and helpe them, for they flie night and day[173] which no other fowle doth beside themselues.

The other thinge obserued in their flight is the forme and fashion wherein they ranke themselues, for while the aer is calme and not troubled with boistrous windes they flie triangularlie like the Greeke Λ Lambda pointed before and forked behinde, that so before them, the aer may be cutt and pearced more easilie, but behinde them, the open passage both foremost and hindmost may be benifited by the blast thereof. Yet at their first risinge, they make many fashions, vntill they haue ordered their oune places abo[u]e in the aër. But if it happen that the winde be high, and blowe vncerteinely then they flie in compasse like a halfe Moone vntill it cease or chainge; and so they fall [211r] againe into their triangle. When they are sett vpon by the Eagles they cast themselues into a ring or fashion of a heart forked before, that they may with greater courage, streingth, and nomber resist and saue themselues. They chainge places in their course, as Harts in their swymminge. And for the same cause, as is thus expressed by Cicero: *In tergo preteruolantium colla & capita reponunt, quod quia ipse Dux facere non potest, quia non habet vbi nitatur reuolat vt ipse quoque quiescat. In eius locum succedit proxima iis quæ acquieuere eaque vicissitudo in omni cursu seruatur.*[174] That is to saie: euery one layeth or resteth his necke vpon the backe of him that flieth next before him. And bycause the Captayne or foremost cannot doe so, hauinge none vpon whome to rest, he turneth aside and commeth behinde, and so layeth his head and necke vpon that Crane that carried nothinge: and so doth the same that had the next foreplace, euery one in his order, after a certeine distance of tyme and place. By this chainginge they imitate the letters of the Alphabet in writinge, wherein they are chainged one after another accordinge as the spellinge of the worde requireth. *Grues vnam sequi ordine literato.* The Cranes followe one another in an Alphabeticall or Writers methode: (saieth Ierome) which caused also Claudianus thus to describe their flyinge:

Ingenti clamore grues æstiua relinquunt
Thracia, cum tepido permutant Strymona Nylo:
Ordinibus variis, per nubila texitur alis
Litera pennarumque notis inscribitur aër.[175]

When Cranes doe leaue their Summer dwellinge, Thrace,

And chainge Strymona with warmer ryver Nyle:
With wings they write playne letters varyinge place,
Scriblinge in aër with quills vncutt and wilde.

And Martiall thus:

Turbabis versus & litera tota volabit:
Vnam perdideris si Palamedis auem.

Take but the letter which the Crane did make:
ffrom verse, then sence from it, her flight doth take.

The letter (I meane in the Greeke for Græcians first of all made this obseruation) is Υ. or as some Α. or Λ. Yet it is most certeine that Cadmus brought out of Phœnitia into Græcia sixteene letters wherein were V. Α. and Λ. and Palamedes duringe the [211v] Troiane Warre added Ξ.Θ.Φ.Χ. whose place and vse hee affirmed that he learned from the orders and rankes of Cranes. Which if it be true, then can neither Α. Λ. nor V. be ascribed to Palamedes. Aristotle saieth that of olde there were eighteene Greeke letters, and that Epicharmus added vnto them, Θ. and Φ, and so is Palamedes quite shaken out of the Alphabet. And Virgill speakinge of this V. ascribeth it to Pithagoras of Samos, *Litera pythagoræ discrimine secta bicorni.*[176] Pithagoras of Samos invented the vse and fashion of this two horned letter: So it is both vncertaine why a Crane should be called *Auis Palamedis,* and also who first invented any of these letters. Yet by Martiall (as wee haue before expressed) and also by Cassiodorus it is affirmed that the whole Greeke Alphabet was collected out of the flight of Cranes, by the God Mercury (peradventure deified for this invention) as may appeare by this testimonie of Cassiodorus. *Vt aliquid exquisitum & studiosum dicere videamur, has literas primum, vt frequentior tradit opinio. Mercurius repertor artium multarum, volatu Strymoniarum auium collegisse memoratur. Nam hodie Grues qui classem consociant, Alphabeti formas natura imbuente describunt: quem in ordinem decorum redigens, vocalibus consonantibusque conuenienter admissis, viam sensualem repperit, per quam alte petens ad penetralia prudentiæ mens possit alta peruenire.*[177] To saie some thinge worth the knowinge, the most common opinion is that Mercury, the inventer of many artes, by the flight of these Strymonian fowles, first found out the letters of the Alphabet. ffor if at this day, you marke those Cranes which followe or accompany Navyes of Shippes, by the rules of nature, they describe the very forme of the Alphabet which Mercury brought to a certeine order and vniformitie, makinge some vowells and some Consonants, and so found out a sensible and playne way by which an industrious minde may in tyme attaine the very secreats of wisedome. And thus much for the letters ascribed to the imitation of Cranes.

There be other obseruations of their flight very memorable and worthie to be related: for when they flie they all looke vpon their Captayne or foremost, and so carry themselues in their rankes and courses in such a geometricall proportion, that the foremost doe not hinder the last from the sight of him that leadeth the way. At their first risinge, the eldest leade the way, and so chainge from one to another, till all of them be setled and rancked, and then as it falleth to their lott, both olde and yonge are leaders in their seuerall Courses and chainges; they ever flie cryinge and ianglinge that so none of them be lost or seperated in the night from the [212r] Company. If any chaunce to be weary before the restinge tyme: then two other take him vpon their wings or backes, if neede be, and so carry him till he be refreshed; orells vpon their feete stretched out behind in quiet and calme weather, for they sieldome flie against the winde except when they are pursued: therefore also they avoide a backe wynde that bloweth vp their feathers and maketh their bodies bare, for so they are enfeobled and discouraged: and of the twayne it is better for them to flie against the winde, for so they are warme in their oune feathers and want onelie the benefitt of their tailes; ffor as fishes swymme against the streame, so may Cranes flie against the winde. And vnto this opinion agreeth Plutarche.

It is questioned amonge Authors whether when Cranes are to take this longe flight, they swallowe a heauy stone, which serueth in their bodies as ballis in a shippe, to prize them against the streingth of the windes, or whether they carry it in any other fashion or manner: Ælianus did confidentlie belieue it and affirme it, that they doe carrie such a stone vnto their iourneyes end, and then they disgorge themselues and cast it vp againe. Aristophanes Bizantinus is for the carriage of the stone but he assigneth another cause which is this. When (saieth hee) they are well wearied with flyinge beinge highe, and may not looke either downeward or backward, but straight forwarde to finishe their course, and compasse their iourney they let fall a stone, and by the noice of the fall they can tell whether they be ouer the sea or ouer the land that so they may either light or goe forwarde till they haue passed the Seas. Vnto the carriage of the stone also agreeth Maximus Tyrius, but hee saieth that the Cranes knowinge well ynoughe their oune levitie by takinge this stone in their mouthes doe establishe and streingthen themselues against the sodeine gusts of wynde, which many tymes wolde overthrowe them. And this opinion is in all things like to the first. Other say, that the Cranes of Sicilia beinge to flie ouer the Mountayne Taurus, which is full of Eagles to keepe themselues from makinge a noice in the night tyme, and so passe vndiscried, they take in their mouthes euery one a stone, whereby they stoppe their voices, and so escape all dangers. Assoone [212v] as they are ouer the Mountayne, they cast them out of their mouthes, and carry them no longer: which thinge is also reported of Wildegeese and therefore may be as true in the one as in the other, And thus much for their opinions which are affirmatiue.

On the contrary diuers learned men haue denied the same, in the first ranke of whome Aristotle is to be placed. ffor he writeth thus: *Grues vt dictum est, ex vltimis in vltima abeunt. Volant flatu secundo: quod de lapide narrant, falsum est. Lapidem enim eas tenere fulcimento, quem vbi ceciderit, accipi vtilem ad auri probationem aiunt.*[178] Cranes, as hath ben saied, flie from one extreame to another, they take the winde with them but that which is reported of a stone they beare is false: for they say that they beare a stone to stay themselues withall, which when they let fall is turned into a touchstone to trie golde. So farre Aristotle.

Albertus also is of the same mynde, that the stone falleth casuallie from their feete, and not out of their mouth.[179] ffor by reason their feete be crooked, they fill the hollowe thereof with a stone, and so risinge sodeinely to flie, they careleslie carrie it within their clawes vntill it fall out of his oune accorde. So that one opinion and other beinge compared together, they maie both be true, that is to saie, when Cranes take a longe iourney they carry a stone in their mouthe especiallie those which are lightest and swiftest of flight, least they shoulde overgoe their fellowes and lose their Company. And againe, when they make but a short flight, whereunto they are often driuen through feare, then they carry a stone in their feete, and yet no choise stone but such a one as they vsed to walke vpon, for it were too laborious for them to flie farre with a heauy stone in their clawes. It appeareth by Pliny that before they flie, they fill their gorge with sande and alsoe beare a stone, which stone Albertus saieth hath many tymes fallen from them into shippes as they flewe over the sea: *Certum est* (saieth Pliny) *pontum transuolaturas primum omnium angustias petere inter duo promontoria Criumetopon, & Carambin, saburra stabiliri, quum medium transierint abiici lapillos è pedibus; quum attigerint continentem et è gutture arenam.*[180] It is certeine when they flie over the Sea Pontus, they make to the Straits betwixt the two Promontories Criumetopos and Carambis, wherein they stay themselues as it were with ballis by [213r] the stones in their feete, which they let fall when they haue passed halfe way, but when they come to the Continent and touche the earth, then they also cast vp their sande. It is but a fabulous thinge reported by Isidore that the Cranes come from the East Countrey after winter, wherein are Mountaynes of golden sande whereof they swallowe so much as maketh the stone Aurichalchus, which at their iourneyes ende they vomite furth beinge digested in their mawes to a perfect stone, which afterwards skilfull workemen through the helpe of the fire doe convert into goulde. And thus much may suffice to haue written about this question.

When they are to take their flight into Ægipt they choose a Captayne, bycause they knowe they shall meete with enemies there: but when they come backe againe into Europe they vse no Captaynes nor yet obserue watch as they doe at other tymes. *Ducem etiam habent* (saieth Aristotle) *& eos qui clament, dispositos in extremo agmine, vt vox percipi possit.*[181] They haue a Captayne who together with them that make a noyce keepeth Company behinde, that his voyce may more easilie be discerned accordinge to this Greeke sayinge, ἔχουσι δὲ καὶ φυλακὰς καὶ οὐραγὸς πρὸ ὁδου [from Aldrovandi], they haue their watches and Captaynes of the last troope which prepare and make way for them, that is to say, as Pliny doth interpret it, that their watchmen and Officers which keepe all in order, are in the reare and behinde other, aswell by voice to signifie to the foremost that all followe, as by force to constrayne the Loiterers to passe and flie forward. When they choose a guide they take one of the strongest and oldest, who hath alreadie gone those wayes, and therefore can best direct the iourney in a right and straight course, and also with the streingth of his wings be able to breake the violence of the windes and counterblasts: in the middest they put the youngest and weakest, that both by example of the foremost and power of the hindmost they may be encouraged to holde out and not to faint before the iourneyes ende. When the Captayne is weary they chainge him, and substitute another in his place; namelie one of them that flie next vnto him, and so doe they with him that ruleth the reere, when his voice groweth hoarse.

And bycause the name of a Ruler or Captayne is very noble, ambiciouslie sought after by aspiringe mindes, the Crane doth exemplifie the office and charge thereof in three greate and [213v] waightie duties. ffor first he flieth before all, bearinge both heate and colde from all the company. Then he must direct and skilfully guide the right way beinge alway in action of flyinge and cryinge till nature faileth: neither doe they offer to forsake their guide and ringleader till hee of his owne free will surrendreth and giueth place to another. Lastlie as they neuer light on the ground but for foode, restinge onely when they are hungrie, so while the flocke is at meate the Kinge and Ringleader is the Watche, to the ende that his troupe may feede more securelie and also sleepe, which they take by puttinge their heads vnder one winge and standinge vpon one legge. Ælianus and Albertus doe write that in the night they appoinct many watches and sometymes euery nynth or tenth birde watcheth.[182] But the Captayne walketh about to espie all occurrences of daunger, and at the appearance of man or beast, gyueth warninge by his loude ianglinge whereunto the other ioyne and make vp the Alarum. So the Company awaked they either remoue or sit still accordinge to the present necessitie. Their watch (as Plutarch saieth) stand like Hercules, leaninge head and hand vpon his clubbe, so those watchinge Cranes stande vpon one legge, holdinge vp the other with a stone in the foote aswell by the waight thereof to keepe himselfe wakinge (though neuer so weary) as also if sleepe doe overtake him, the fall of the stone, awaketh him and all the company, whereby his negligence is made knowen and rebuked as it were by the common crye of all. Greate Alexander followed this example, settinge beside his bedde a brazen vessell and holdinge in his hand stretched out over the vessell (when hee was not willinge to sleepe) a siluer or golden ball by the fall whereof into the vessell, when hee fell asleepe, he was throughlie awaked by reason of the sonorous and tincklinge noice which was made thereby.

The pace and walkinge of Cranes is full of maiestie and gravitie, for Ennius thus describeth it,

Perque fabam repunt, & mollia crura reponunt.[183]

Which Virgill interpreteth, *Altius ingreditur,* &c. speakinge of a horse.

As Cranes growe highe so doe they lift and chainge,
Their leggs before, behinde in statelie raunge.

[214r] But I will ende the description of their pace, and the Contents of this Chapter with these verses of Mantuan.

It grauis & raro incessu vestigia profert
Strymoniæ de more Gruis, quæ semina campis
Iacta legens æque tepido sub sidere libræ,
Si vicina ferat gressus per rura viator
Tela ferens, arcumque manu caput ardua tollens
Clangit & ingenti mouet internodia passu,
Paulatimque viam suspenso gutture carpit.[184]

But I will ende the description of their parte, and the Contents of this Chapter, with these verses of Mantuan.

It grauis & raro incessu vestigia profert
Strymoniæ de more grues, quæ semina campis
Iacta legens, æque tepido sub sidere libræ.
Si vicina ferat gressus per rura viator
Tela ferens arcumque manu caput ardua tollens
Clangit & ingenti mouet internodia passu
Paulatimque viam suspenso gutture carpit.

Hee goeth like stalkinge Crane when in the fieldes hee fyndes
On pickinge graynes wch lye upon the lande
With pace vaine enquiringe after seedes,
In warmthe of Libra sowen by an husbandman.
But if he espie the Archer and his arrowe
Up liftinge head he mounteth hastilie,
Janglinge lowde from necke so longe and narrowe
So getteth grounde, ere he his bowe can drawe.

Chap. 2. The Generation Education and other naturall properties of Cranes.

When Cranes growe to theire yeres olde, then as they leave the colde Countryes, especiallie Thracia, (and such Cranes I meane as are wilde and at libertie) and flie into Egipt and warmer places, there they are inflamed with lust and mingle in generation: So the Cockes leape theire hennes, (for they are Couples) and the hennes receave and beare the Cockes not like Dunghill-hennes or pea-hennes stoopinge to the earthe, but standinge uprighte, as if theire generation required no helpe or assistance from the earthe, beinge herein somewhat like to the Manucodiats or birds of paradise that engender in the aire. They lay but two egges, and when they sitt upon them, they lay a stone in theire nestes, as Albertus reporteth upon his owne knowledge of Cranes in Collen. For thus he writeth. Grues domesticas vidimus quotannis lapidem inter oua sua collocare, sed hunc sine discrimine.

Hee goeth like stalkinge Crane when in the fieldes hee feedes,
On forlorne graynes, which lye vpon the lande,
With paces rare enquiringe after seedes,
In warmth of Libra sowen by an husbandman
But if he espie the Archer and his arrowe,
Vp liftinge head he moueth hastilie,
Ianglinge lowde from necke so longe and narrowe,
So getteth ground ere hee his bowe can weye.

Chap. 2. The Generation Education and other naturall properties of Cranes.

When Cranes growe to three yeres olde, then as they leaue the colde Countreyes especiallie Thracia, (and such Cranes I meane as are wilde and at libertie) and flie into Ægipt and whotter places, there they are inflamed with lust and mingle in generation. So the Cockes leape their hennes (for they are Couples) and the hennes receaue and beare the Cockes not like Dunghill-hennes, or pea-hennes shrinkinge to the earth but standinge vpright, as if their generation receaued no helpe or assistance from the earth, beinge herein somewhat like to the Manucodiata or birds of paradise that engender in the aër. They lay but two eggs, and when they sitt vpon them, they lay a stone in their neasts, as Albertus reporteth vpon his oune knowledge of Cranes in Collen. ffor thus hee writeth: *Grues domesticas vidimus quotannis lapidem inter oua sua collocare, sed hunc sine* [214v] *discrimine acceperint de lapidibus fortuito inuentis: Dubitari quidem potest, vtrum in libertate, lapidem peculiarem quæsituræ fuissent, an vtiliorem.*[185] Wee see that tame and domesticall Cranes doe euery yere lay a stone in their neast, amonge their eggs, makinge no choice or election thereof; but take any stone without difference. It may be doubted whether they wolde doe the like if they were at libertie. Soe farr Albertus.

By reason that they breede so farre from the sight and conuersation of men, none of the Auncients did euer make mention of their sittinge or hatchinge their younge. No, nor yet Albertus, although he visited tame Cranes euery day. Therefore it were rashnes to discourse of such thinges as no man ever defined. Bellonius and Petrarch haue taught vs howe to tame them, for if you cutt of their longe flyinge feathers

OPPOSITE, *the second hand, "my writer," as he is referred to by the author* they will forgett their wildenes, and growe very tractable and docible to learne, mimicke gestures, and other pastimes, as Albertus writeth, who sawe a Parrott and a Crane daunce and make many merry gestures with head, wings, and leggs after a Piper or Musitian of Sauoy. He also telleth this memorable story of a Crane in Collen. There were a couple of Cranes, a Male and a Female, kept in an Orchard, closed and walled in, where it fortuned that the female layed eggs and hatched two yonge ones. As shee lead her yonge ones vp and downe, they wolde sometymes forsake her and followe the Cocke, for which thinge she wolde call them from the Male, as it were checkinge them for their levitie in departinge from their damme. And one day as they were followinge the Cocke, she with her vsuall voice clocked them away vnto her oune sides, which the Cocke perceauinge came vpon the henne in wrath and furye, and overthrewe her gyvinge her with his beake twelue mortall wounds whereof shee died.

They may (as wee haue saied) be tamed, and not onely tamed, but fatted also, as they neuer or sieldome be when they are wilde. ffor this purpose they hoodwincke them, and shutt them vp in a darke place, and so by reason of their quietnes they growe fatt. They will eate all kinde of grayne like wilde geese, whereupon Petrarck saieth in one of his Dialogues, *Solito largius agrum seui,* I haue sowed, (saieth the ioyfull man) more land and Corne fieldes then I was wont: *Plures pasces Grues rure, plures domi mures. Volucrum hospes & vermium &c.*[186] Then saieth Petr., thou shalt feede the more Cranes in the Countrey and the more myce at home. [215r] Cornefieldes are the hosts of fowles and wormes. So Suidas, Γέρανοι γεώργου κατενέμοντο χώραν ἐσπαρμένκυ νεωσὶ πυρίνῳ σίτῷ [from Aldrovandi]. Cranes doe feede vpon wheate newe sowen in the fieldes. It is wittilie fayned that vpon a tyme the foxe invited the Crane to supper for whose entertaynement hee prepared nothinge but a dishe of broath, which liquid meate the Crane coulde not eate by reason his beake coulde not take it vp, so with thankes to the Foxe least hee shoulde bewray discontent he flewe away more hungrie then hee came. Afterwarde hee bad the Foxe to supper and put his meate in a deepe pott with a narrowe mouth, whereinto the Crane coulde thrust his necke and feete, but not the foxe: and so was constrayned to goe away as hungrie as hee had serued the Crane. Whereby, *dolus dolo repellitur,* selfe doe selfe haue. And so I proceede. They also feede vpon serpents. In Thessaly if it were not for storkes and Cranes which doe destroy them, the people wolde leaue the Countrey and goe away. Wherefore they are forbidden by the lawes to kill any of these fowles in testimony of the peoples gratitude, and this curtesie or immunitie they call in Greece *Antipelargia.* They feede also vpon grasse and flowers growinge in Marshes and on the brinkes of ryvers like Swannes and such other fowle which caused Claudian to write in this manner:

> *E Nylo Pygmæa Grues post bella remenso*
> *Ore legunt* [*rubri*] *germina cara maris.*[187]

> When backe to Nylus from Pygmaees warre they came,
> The water birdes are meate for euery Crane.

Havinge but mentioned this their Pygmæan warre, I cannot forbeare the full tractate and discourse hereof in this place, which is so much belieued and spoken of amonge Authours, insomuch as famous Homer calleth this by a proper name, *geranomachian,* the fight of Cranes. And so many haue written hereof that a man shoulde be hissed out of schoole that once dare to make a question of it amonge their disciples; wherefore it is a labour not to be despised to compare together the testimonies of both sorts aswell those that doe deny it, as those which haue with such greate constancie affirmed the same.

Hist. auiu. 8 Cap. 12.

I will first beginne with the testimony of Aristotle who is very plaine and confident in this matter: *A uerno autem ex tepida regione ad frigidam se conferunt æstus metu futuri. Et aliæ de locis vicinis discedunt, aliæ de vltimis nam* [215v] *Grues ex Scithicis campis ad paludes Ægipto superiores, vnde Nylus profluit, veniunt, quo loco pugnare cum Pigmæis dicuntur. Non enim id fabula est, sed certe genus tum hominum, tum etiam equorum pusillum (vt dicitur) est, deguntque in Cauernis, vnde nomen Trogloditæ à subeundis cauernis, accepere.*[188] That is to saie, In the Springe tyme, they flie from the heate into colder Countreis for feare of schorchinge; some of them depart out of neere places and some from farre. ffor Cranes come out of Scythia, into the Marshes lyinge aboue Ægipt where Nylus taketh his beginninge, in the which place they are saied to fight with Pigmæes, for this is no fable, for there is a certeine race of litle men, and another of horses which liue in the Caues of the earth, and from hence they were called *Troglodytæ.* Vnto this opinion subscribeth Philostratus, the life of Apollonius: *Pygmæos sub terra degentes supra Gangem posita loca incolere, & sicut fama de ipsis prædicat, viuere non vanum est.*[189] It is no vaine tale or idle which fame reporteth that the Pygmæes inhabite those places that lye aboue Ganges and liue vnder the earth. Bassiles in Athenæus saieth there be certeine Pigmæes or small men which ride vpon Partridges and warre with Cranes: But Menecles presentlie denyeth their ridinge, and affirmeth their fightinge with Cranes and Partridges. Hereunto agreeth Pliny, addinge also that these Pygmæes were driuen out of Geranea (which was their first Citie, wherein they were called *Catizi*) by Cranes. Eustathius[190] thus describeth the proportion of Pigmæes. They are not (saieth hee) aboue a cubite longe, and are called *Pygmæi* of *Pugon* in Greeke or *pugme*, a fist. They are also called *Spithamæi* of *Spithama,* a spanne, bycause they are but three spannes longe, or at the most two foote and a quarter. When they are to fight they vse Rammes hornes, or as some say ride vpon Rammes holdinge in their hands a kinde of Clappers, which make a noice. And thus they sett vpon the Cranes: who contemninge their statures, and makinge no account of such kinde of Creatures, are easilie driuen away by their despised enemyes. So ffarre hee. The latter writers haue wonderfullie magnified and encreased this fable of the Pigmæes, as if the bare name of antiquitie were sufficient without further searchinge to keepe men in euerlastinge blindnes: wherefore in steede of disputinge the truth, they adde one lye vnto another: ffor they saie that the Pygmæes lyve in the Mountayne Countreys of India in a pleasant [216r] soyle and wholesome ayer: all thinges beinge ever greene as in the Springe. Vnto these places the Cranes resort, with whome the Pigmæes lyve in strife. In the tyme of their breedinge, the Pigmæes arme themselues with iron weapons and darts, beinge mounted vpon Rammes and goates, descendinge in innumerable troopes vnto the water sides, where they finde the Cranes: sett vpon their younge ones and egges which they haue layed, destroyinge, spoilinge, and killinge both egge and birde. This exploit they performe in three monethes for otherwise the greate resort of other Cranes from all Countreys about September and October cominge thither wolde oppresse and ouerthrowe them by reason of their multitude. So Barth. Anglicus.[191]

Li. 16. De Ciui. Dei. Cap. 8.

St Augustine affirmeth the v[eri?]tie of the Pygmæan nation, confirminge the same by the same reason whereby Dwarfes and Monsters are begotten; so as wee see in the parts of mens bodies many tymes imperfect members, one much lesse then nature is wont to produce: so in the birthes of men and women, and from one man to a nation: for euen wee that are more particularlie preserued in a naturall proportion by Almighty God are not so greate at the perfection of our age and marriage bedd, as haue ben our forefathers in their cradles and swadlinge cloutes. And why might not Almighty God permitt a nation of men so farre to degenerate as they shoulde not seeme other then children compared to vs: as wee are not bigger then sucklings compared to our Forefathers. *Deus Creator omnium qui vbi & quando aliquid creari oporteat, vel oportuerit ipse nouit &c.* God the Creatour of all thinges best knoweth what and who ought to be created. So farre St Augustine with whome consenteth that notable instrument of learninge, Ludouicus Viues. And thus much for such as affirme the Nation and History.

Nowe for them that deny it, Strabo, a diligent observor of all the knowen parts of the worlde, cassiereth* the whole narration as a meere fable, fiction, and poeticall tale: & *traditos in fabulis pygmæos,* the Pygmæes spoken of in fables. And againe confutinge the diuision of the Æthiopians into Erembi, Cephronii, and Pigmæi: *alia innumerabilia, minus credulitate consequentur, cum præter hæc quæ haud fide digna sunt, historicæ & poeticæ confusionem demonstrant &c.*[192] (saieth Strabo). They broach innumerable fables not worthie to be belieued, shewinge nothinge els but a confused mingle mangle of poetrie and history together. And so in [216v] another place concludeth that *Æschili. &c.* as it is but one of Homers fables to affirme that there be men with dogs heads, or with eyes in their breasts, or with one eye in the middest of their foreheads: or that speake and write with their feete: no more are the fayned historyes of the Pygmæes, yet not taught through ignorance (for who wolde condemne Hesiod or Homer for ignorance) but taken vp by the way for delight and pleasures sake. ffor Homer tooke these fables out of the Historyes of India written by Megasthenes and Deimachus, and findinge them fitt Allegoryes to expresse the Troiane warres, by a poeticall sweetenes so tempered and applied the same: that almost all succeedinge Poets and Historiographers haue not onely followed his strayne, but also related a fable for a truthe. Such are Oppianus, Iuuenal, Mantuan, and the late Romane Conuert, Iustus Lipsius. Albertus also denyeth the Pygmæan men, but in steede of them, maketh a kinde of apes going vpright like men, that fight with the Cranes in manner before expressed. And thus haue I declared the opinions of learned men concerninge both the supposed nation of the Pigmæes, and the fayned warre betwixt them and the Cranes, wherein there is nothinge of moment, but the auctoritie of St Augustine, who may better be belieued in a poinct of Diuinity, then History, and yet is it most certeine, that he hath ben deceiued both in one and other.

Li. I. Geogr.

There is an open hostilitie betwixt Cranes, Eagles, and Hawkes as may appeare by a similitude of Calaber in these wordes followinge: *Circumquaque autem resonabant immenso ploratu omnes ædes ploratus vero foeminarum non dissimilis erat Gruum clangori, vbi cernunt Aquilam per aerem irruentem: Non enim est illis animus in pectore præsens, sed solum longo resonant stridore sacram fugientes alitem: Sic quoque Troianæ feminæ aliunde aliæ vlulatum edebant.*[193] Euery

* *cassiereth* cashiers, dismisses (OED)

where and in euery house, there was nothinge but cryinge and lamentation, and their women mourned like Cranes when they see the Eagles in the aër fallinge fiercelie vpon them: ffor then they loose their courage, and with greate stretchinge and ianglinge flye fast away from the sacred bird: So did the Troiane women make greate lamentation beinge transported out of their oune Countrey.

And of the Falcon or Hauke writeth Ariosto:

Più che sua vita l'ama egli et desira,
L'odia e fugge ella più che grù Falcone.[194]

[217r] But yet they are not alway so fearefull and white liuered that they cowardlie suffer themselues to be spoiled without all resistance: for as hath ben already declared in the description of their flight: when they are many and stronge enough to resist, they gather themselues into a Circle or Ringe against the onsetts of Eagles, and with their heads advaunced to the highest receaue and repell her assaults in such a warrlike and courageous manner as ofte tymes they force the Eagle to depart away with many blowes. And thus also they doe against the Hauke, and all other birds of prey. It is not discerned with what other kinde of birdes or Creatures they are in love and obserue any especiall sympathie in nature beside themselues: for they love one another exceedinglie both in safetie and daunger, to helpe and assist one another against Eagles and all other enemyes: therefore they are worthilie reconed by Aristotle amongest *gregales aues,* fowles sociable which liue together in Companyes without hurtinge or spoilinge any other lyvinge Creatures, like Doues or Pullen. Wherefore St Ambrose doth compare Loue to the innocent fowles, which liue together in troopes and Companyes one helpinge and mutuallie agreinge with another: but auarice and Couetousnes is like to the fowles of prey such as are Eagles, Haukes, and Kytes, who doe not loue one another to liue in flockes and Companyes, but single, or at the most by Couples: *quia auaritia refugit consortia plurimorum.*[195] Auarice wolde dwell alone, eate alone and gayne alone: avoidinge the common felowshippe of many. So Ambrose. Cranes beare also an incomparable loue to their younge ones, for ofte tymes the Male and female fall at strife and fight for their education, one of them contendinge to take them from the other, as wee haue alreadie shewed out of Albertus. And therefore they are iustlie noted for cholericke amongest themselues, and to maynetaine Antipathy one with another. ffor Aristotle writeth that: *Grues etiam pugnant inter se tam vehementer vt dimicantes capiantur. Hominem potius expectare, quam pugna desistere patiuntur.*[196] Cranes doe so fiercelie and ve-

hementlie fight together that many tymes they are taken by hande, sufferinge themselues to fall into the hands of men, then to forsake their particular revenge.

Many are the wayes to take Cranes aliue which men haue seriouslie invented for their priuate commoditie. And amonge others Aldrouandus beginneth with this. They tooke a bottell or a goarde and emptied it, then they annoynted it round with birdlyme and put into it a hummynge Bee. When the Crane heareth the noice of the Bee shee maketh to it, and thrusteth in her necke to catch and eate the same: and so the lyme glueth together her eyes, and maketh the gourde or bottell to cleaue [217v] fast to her feathers, so as of herselfe she cannot pull backe her head againe, standinge stonestill depriued of sight and courage, not movinge one foote till the fowler come and take him, by whome the grinne* was prepared. If a Bee were wantinge they tooke an onyon leafe or blade wherewithall they are delighted, and greedilie take it into their mouth with the perill of their oune lifes. Other take them with springes of reedes bayted with beanes; and many with ordinary snares and ginnes and netts whereof Virgil maketh this mention:

Tum Gruibus pedicas & retia ponere ceruis,
Strymoniamque Gruem funda deiecit.[197]

As Harts in netts are by the Hunters tane,
So snares and slinges are fourmed for the Crane.

Such a kinde of nett Budæus calleth *Pantheron,* bycause both beasts and fowles are taken therewithall. In Germany a Falcon or small Eagle and in Tartary a Girfalcon is taught to flie at Cranes and Swannes: and therefore the Germanes call such a Haw[k]e a *Crane Falcon* or *Girfalcon.* In like manner they trayne a Lannar to this game, and a small hawke, not much greater then a Ringe doue; whose qualitie is to trouble the Crane in her flight and make her to fall to the earth, where the Greyhounds watche her fall, and presentlie take her even as a Partridge by a lande spaniell. And so much in one worde brieflie for takinge of wilde Cranes.

There are many naturall questions or probleames concerninge Cranes which may be inserted into this History, aswell for the delight of a willinge Reader as for the vtilitie that may be reaped by their knowledge. I will beginne with the question of Ambrosius Nolanus, How it commeth to passe that Cranes seeme to flie very softlie without speedie motion and yet in short tyme dispatch very longe iourneyes. Hee aunsweared that their bulke of body seemeth heavy and therefore moueth

* *grinne* gin, snare

more slowlie: yet their leingth and compasse reacheth farre: and as a greate shippe scarce perceiued to moue, or stirre, outgoeth the most speedie small boate which is sensiblie discerned to moue with all celeritie; and an Oxe liftinge vp his legges heauily as it were with leaden paces, proceedinge in greate leasure, yet outgoeth the most swifte Emmet or spider, which seemeth to moue more nimbly: soe doe Cranes reache longe distances in short spaces by the quantitie of their bodies without swiftnes of flight. Other say that in deede they seeme to flie slowlie bycause they flie very highe: yet in very truth they make a marveilous quicke and speedie motion, even as the Sunne and starres, by reason they are so high aboue their heads doe not onely seeme much smaller then they be, but also in a manner to stand still without removinge, although they moue most speedilie. Even so Cranes seeme [218r] smaller as they flie, then when they are belowe vpon the earth. And for the same cause their speedie motion is not discerned although they flie wonderfull swiftlie.

It is also enquired why they both see and flie in the night like night Crowes and Owles, and in the day like Eagles and Ringdoues; and neuer cease day nor night vntill they be weary, which scarce any other fowles except these Cranes can attayne vnto. Vnto this question is it aunsweared that nature (I shoulde rather say the Almighty and most mercifull Creatour) hath bestowed his greate compassion vpon these fowles, who followinge the course of whott and warme Countreyes doe flie from all winters, and therefore are constreyned to take most longe iourneyes to be accomplished in a very short space, that they shoulde see both day and night, and be able also to flie and labour with a very litle or small refreshinge, vntill they attayne the harbour or Countrey which they desire, which other wise they coulde not performe at their wished tyme. But some doe vtterlie deny that they see in the night althoughe they flie, bycause they make a continuall noice: ffirst the Captayne that leadeth the way and then all the followers, one aunswearinge another as Souldiers by the drumme, when they cannot see one another raunge in an order, which they keepe more by the eare then by the eye: even as swallowes and quailes, which are with vs in our Summer, and afterwarde before winter flie into Affrick and crosse both seas and lands neuer restinge day or night till they arriue in the Countrey of their delight. And yet they see not in the night, but by a naturall discerninge of the aër and sides of heauen make their direct way both day and night without intermission. But it may be seinge that the night is nothinge els but the shadowe of the earth, and they flyinge so highe as the shadowe is diminished and darkenes lessened, which is greatest vpon the waters, and the earth and lesse vpward towarde heauen, that they alwayes see a kinde of drawinge and springinge light whereby they receiue sufficient helpe to goe on and accomplishe their iourney. ffor vpon Cassius in Seleucia, and Olympus in Greece, the bodie and light of the Sunne is seene many houres after it is hidden from other places of the earth. And therefore Cranes when they flie in the night rise vp and soare higher then they vse to doe in the day. Other thinke that there is a liquour in their eyes which is more susceptible of light in darkenes then in the Sunne, bycause it is extinguished by the greate light thereof. And also there is another substance, which seeth better in the light then in the darke, which is common to all Creatures (except Battes, Owles, and Moles) and therefore Cranes participate in both in a perfect degree: for in the day tyme they see nighe and farre of, *propter substantiam* [218v] *potentia lucidam,* and in the night tyme, *propter substantiam acta lucidam.* Soe doe catts, myce, dogs, horses, and all other beasts that labour day and night. And thus much for their flight and sight in darkenes.

Seinge it hath ben alreadie declared, that when they sleepe they stande vpon one legge, and lay their head and necke backwarde vpon their wings; it is enquired for what naturall cause these and other fowles sleepe and take their rest in this gesture, seinge that sleepe is nothinge els but the rest and refreshinge of weary members caused by certeine benigne and gentle vapours arisinge out of the stomacke vp to the brayne, by the helpe and mediation of naturall heate as fire in a distillatorye. Nowe except this naturall heate be preuented and kept about the hearte by a recoyle, the motion wolde not cease, and so want of sleepe through continuall motion wolde distroy life. And because the leingth of a Cranes necke and feete, wolde and doe disperse the naturall heat from the heart, when the one and other are stretched out, therefore the fowle by an instinct of nature plucketh vp one legge and layeth her necke vpon her winge, whereby the heart is warmed : and the coales of fire naturall raked vp together doe send up the sweeter vapours vnto the brayne which make the more easie and speedie sleepe. And this reason serueth for all other of the like condition, nature, and qualitie.

Cap. 3. Of Denomynations Historyes and Allegoryes of Cranes

I miht take occasion to praise this bird by the account which the

Auncients made hereof, as may appeare by their imitation in denomination of herbes, plants, regions, people, and men after their names, especially men: wee haue already spoken of Gerania, the proude Queene of Pigmæes, iustlie for her pride (supposed by the Poets) turned into a Crane. Also a Citie in Thrace and another Prouynce in Lacedemon were called *Gerania,* from the toppe whereof Kinge Ino threwe himselfe hedlonge when he fled away from Athamas. And some say that it is so called by Deucalion, or by a Megarian, who followed the noice of flyinge Cranes in the tyme of a greate floud vnto this Mountayne, wherein he and they saued themselues from drowninge, and in remembrance of that good towne called the same *Gerania* by and after the name of the Cranes. The people of Phocis were called *Geranidæ* in olde tyme. And St Iherome mentioneth an olde Monke called Pipizo, who for the hatred of fastinge and chastitie was called *Geranopypus,* the sonne of a Crane. And to conclude the worde *Congruitie* is taken from [219r] Cranes, bycause they liue, agree, and flye together.

Wee haue alreadie declared the presaginge of Cranes, but forasmuch as there are presages actiue and passiue, I will adde some more passiue vnto the former actiues. There was a famous Philosopher at Florence called Leonicus Tomæus, who beinge a disciple of Demetrius, the Græcian, did soe well profitt in that tongue, that afterwarde hee did reade Aristotle publiquely at Padua in Greeke which was a rare thinge and neuer heard of before in that Vniuersitie, of whome Iouius relateth this Historye.[198] Hee was vnmaried, and lyved till hee was seauentie three yere olde of an innocent and spotlesse life, lookinge to the cleanesse both of his vestures and his conscience, so as no man coulde be founde more happie for learninge and contentation: althoughe his estate enclined more to pouertie then riches. Hee had kept vp a Crane and fedd it at his oune hand and from his trencher about fortie yeres, wherewithall he was not smallie delighted. At last this beloued Crane died, for which hee did much lament; and so much the more bycause he conceaued that the death of his Crane was a presage of his oune; and the partinge of them twayne pretended the separation of his soule and bodie: wherein he was not deceiued, for within short space his oune destinye followed his Crane. But the Historye of Ibicus, the Lyrique Poet of Rheginio, is most strainge, who beinge fallen into the hands of Robbers did most humblie entreate them for his life; and not prevailinge, after he had receaued the deadly wounde, liftinge vp his eyes, sawe Cranes flie over his head and tolde the thieues and Murtherers that those Cranes shoulde revenge his bloude vpon them, and so hee died whiles they departed. After a good season had passed and no man coulde tell howe Ibicus came to his death, it fortuned that some of these Murtherers were in the Market place of Corinthe and at that instant came Cranes flyinge over their heads, whereupon one of them saied to another, *αἱ Ἰβύκου ἔκδικοι πάρεισιν*,[199] here are the Avengers of Ibycus; which beinge ouer hearde by some standers by the Murtherers were apprehended; and beinge demaunded the occasion of those wordes, through their oune slight aunsweare gaue the Magistrates occasion to examyne them by torture, wherein they confessed the whole matter, as it is related, and so receaued their deserts. Which history is related by Gregorius Nyssenius, St Basils brother, in his eight Booke of Diuine prouidence. And Sidonius made this followinge Epigram thereupon:

Quondam ad desertum venientes Ibice Littus
Vitam prædones eripuere tibi:
[219v] *Sæpe gruum nubem imploranti, quæ tibi testes*
Aduenere necis cum morerere tuæ.
Attamen haud frustra; siquidem clangore volucrum
Sysiphio cædem est Eumenis vlta solo.
Latronum genus heu cupidum lucri atque rapinæ;
Cur uos nequaquam terruit ira Deum?
Quando nec Ægisthus, vatem qui occidit olim,
Atrarum occursus fugerat Eumenidum.[200]

When Robbers once to deserts came,
O Ibycus thy bloud to spill:
Thou didst beseach a Cloude of Cranes
To witnesse their accursed will.
And not in vayne; The furyes brought
Reuenge on them in Corinth land.
O damned thieues, "loue gayne" youre taught:
Why dread yee not great Iouaes hand?
Thyestes sonne who had a Poet slaine
Blacke furyes drove to kill himselfe amayne.

And hereupon came the Greeke Adage, *αἱ Ἰβύκου Γερανοί*, the Cranes of Ibycus, to signifie a strainge and miraculous detection of any facinorous* secreat villany, as if the foules of heauen coulde not endure any such wickednes.

Many such Historyes are founde in bookes of learninge howe by extraordinary meanes the will of the Almighty Creator hath ben revealed in particular actions. All which I will overpasse, and proceede

* *facinorous* infamous

to such other obseruations of these fowles as are made by learned men.

And forasmuch as there is no vertue more to be commended then vigilancie, and watchefulnes, which is in Cranes after a miraculous manner, which the Auncients so highlie extolled, that they pictured a Crane to signifie a wise man that warily avoided the treacheries of his adversaries, bycause by a stone in their feete they keepe themselues wakinge in the night, and discouer in their flight whether they flie ouer land or Seas; whereof Reusner maketh this Epigram vnder the title *Cura sapientia crescit*:

Siue volat Palamedis auis, Grus, siue quiescit,
Arreptum lapidem gestat vbique pede.
Peruigilis signum curæ, mentisque sagacis
[220r] *Cessantem in vitium, ne malus error agat.*
Odi homines ignaua opera, vigilanteque lingua,
Stat vigili virtus firma labore diu.
Scilicet ars vsu, cura sapientia crescit,
Materiem vitiis dat diuturna quies.
Qui foelix, & qui prudens vult esse, laboret,
Commoda dii vendunt cuncta labore graui.
Sic et Aristoteles fertur plerunque lapillum
Peruigil in somnis sustinuisse manu.
Segnitiem fugiat, studii qui flagrat amore,
Ignauas odit sorsque deusque preces.[201]

Whether the Crane doe flye or sitt on ground,
Within his foote hee still doth beare a stone,
A watchfull signe of men wise and profound,
Least evill errour plunge in vice each one,
I hate the men whome slouth doth much possesse:
ffor vertue stands in paynes and watchfulnesse.

Arts in vse, in cares doth wisdome stande,
And daylie rest doth nourishe naught but ill:
Both blisse and skill come from the workinge hand,
With payne the Gods let men buy honours fill.
The Stagyrite with stone in hand did wake:
Colde love, slacke suites, God and good chaunce forsake.

And this industrious and constant vtilitie of the Cranes caused Ludouicus Dominicus to ioyne them, vnder Iupiters Gorgons flyinge or soaringe vp to heauen, holdinge a mace in her mouth: and lettinge a quyver fall out of her feete, the arrowes whereof did flye scattered through the aër; whereby was signified that a diligent man goinge to heauen, in peace leaveth the sharpe cares of this worlde behinde, as arrowes doe fall out of a quyver, sayinge in the voice of the princely prophet, O who will giue mee the winges of a Doue, that I may flye away and be at rest. The flight of a Crane did also signifie a wise man which studied Astrologie, or any loftie and sublime studie, the chainge of tymes beinge assimulated to the motion of their wings and altitude of their flight. Or a foole handlinge divine matters wickedly and without true wisedome is resembled to the flyinge Crane: so as Plotinus thought that such a man was afterwarde metamorphosed into a Crane. The noble and famous forme of Democraticall and popular gouernement was taken from the order that Cranes obserue; wherein the people gaue their voyces and consent in elections: whereupon came [220v] the worde, *Congruere,* to consent, even as Cranes that flie and crye one thinge and one way. When a man lyved in one constant good course from youth to age without alteration of manners they compared him to the feathers of a Crane. ffor whereas almost all other fowle doe chainge their colour in age from that which they had at the first the Cranes remayne the same for the most part at the last that they were in the beginning. They also obserue most excellent order in their flyinge; ffor which cause when Palamedes was taxed by Vlisses in Philostratus,[202] that not hee but the Cranes were the inventers of the letters first before rehearsed: hee made replye that the Cranes neuer inuented those letters but of good and constant order which Vlisses durst neuer obserue: ffor when he was encountred by Æneas, Hector, or Sarpedon he brake his ranke and flewe from them to combate with weaker and more feeble enemyes: which caused Aiax to scorne and disdayne him sayinge:

Tutius est tibi fictis contendere verbis,
Quam pugnare manu &c.[203]

Tis safe for thee to fight with wordes,
But not with Armes or warlike swordes.

To conclude, the nerves of the feete and winges of Cranes giue streingth to a wearried man; and therefore in olde tyme they signified tolleration of labour. When Oeneus, Kinge of Menis, had seene in apparition a two necked Crane hee was tolde by the Oracle that it signified plenty and that the yere followinge shoulde yelde double so much fruites as any former yere had brought furth. The Diuynes also and fathers in the Churche haue made singular vse of the actions of these fowles: amonge others I will most brieflie remember these followinge. St Ambrose writeth thus, *In gruibus politica quædam & naturalis* *militia in nobis coacta & seruilis* &c.[204] Cranes haue a naturall and politique warrefare, but men exercise that which is seruile and constrayned. ffor in the night they sett their oune watches, by a voluntary custome, obseruinge tymes, neuer all of them sleepe, nor all awake, but some stand still as it were sentinell and other walke the round to espie and preuent all secreate ambushes and perills, which they sustayne in an vnwearyed constancie for their oune safetie. Thus when the first parts haue discharged their appoincted tyme, then with their voices they awake those which haue rested, and are to succeede them, who most willinglie and readilie vndertake the charge not with delayes or murmures like men, but shakinge of sleepe and slouth goe [221r] speedilie to their charge. *Ideo nulla desertio, quia deuotio naturalis: tuta custodia, quia voluntas libera.* So there is not amonge them any withdrawinge backwardnes, bycause of their naturall devotion: so they remayne in all securitie bycause of their oune accorde. They attende a publique benefitt, which order of theirs caused a Kinge of Gothes to write thus in a publique proclamation: *Grues naturalem quandam nouerunt exercere concordiam, inter quas nulla priuata quæritur, quia iniquitatis ambitus non habetur; vigilant vicissim: communi cautela se custodiant* &c.[205] Cranes knowe howe to exercise amonge themselues naturall concorde, amonge whome nothinge is priuate bycause they want ambition. They watch by courses and secure themselues by a common guarde. They giue honour to no one, but preserue it in Common for all. And their Captaynes in flyinge take it by succession, so as the first is last, and the last commeth to be first, none vnwillinglie giuinge place to others; thus by a voluntary seruice they liue in freedome without Kinge or Tyrant in perpetuall amity one with another: gyvinge a good platforme to a Comon weale. ffor if Citizens wolde imbrace one another with the like ciuile affection, neither shoulde the fieldes be spoiled with tumultuous warres, nor Courtes of iudgements pestered with so many suites. So Athalaricus. Theodoric his Successor remitteth also such men to Cranes as by their immoderate priuate cares make themselues vncapeable to performe their publique offices, bycause Cranes beinge to flie overseas, neither loade themselues nor flie empty, but with a stone in their crooked foote gyve an equall peyze* to their light bodies against the winde, and yet hinder not their naturall celeritie. So Theodoricus. But to returne to the divine Allegoryes. Good Christians must imitate Cranes in watchefulnes, who are awakened by the stones that themselues holde vp in the hollowe of their oune feete. Euen so ought good Christians to carry and beare about them, one peble of the Chiefe Corner stone: by

* *peyze* ballast, poise

the retention whereof they may be kept from the fall of sinne. And if that deadly sleepe prevaile so farre vpon humane infirmitie, that they lett fall either the sounde of grace, the noyse of life, or the cracke of death, yet let them at the least be awakened by the voice thereof; that the burthen of their oune mortalitie may putt them in remembrance, that they must depart at the day springe as Cranes goe forward on their iourney. And therefore abstayninge from the vices of this worlde, let them watch in the stedfast contemplation of Gods omnipotent mercie, and mercifull omnipotencie. Diuynes doe also commaund vs to imitate the mercie of the Cranes, when they flie to strainge Countreyes, for the strongest leade [221v] the waye, and sustayne the greatest brunt of the windes, other flye about the troupe, to animate and encourage the yonge ones. And if wearynes oppresse the feeble, they are readie to support them vpon their backes and winges vntill they be refreshed, and able of themselues to performe the iourney. Even so must Christians helpe one another, that the greatest burden may lye vpon the strongest backe, and that such a mutuall care be had of the weaker, whereby no one may be scandalized, but encouraged and supported, till wee all come to the Countrey where wee haue our restinge place. They which are the guides flye highe to espie their desired land a farre of. And when one is weary another taketh his place. In like manner the vse and end of Gouernours is to goe before other and leade them to heauen, and so to direct the people that when they descrye it, by admonition, preachinge, and exhortation to signifie vnto other the sight and reuelation which they haue receaued of another worlde. ffor this cause let them not holde their prime places through pride, but for the good of others giue place vnto those that are behinde them, that so the last may be first, and the first last. And as the least cracke or annoyance by day or night maketh them all to crye out, mutuallie gyvinge and takinge warninge: so let vs when any perill, sinne, or enemye to bodie or soule approacheth both with worde and deede giue and receaue admonition.

The Eagle is the enemy to Cranes, so is the diuell to euery good Christian man or woman, whome they must resist aboue in the aër of their oune soules, and hee will flie from them: even as Eagles missinge their first encounter avoide an Army of Cranes. When they are readie to flie, they ballice themselues with sande, and a stone, least beinge too light to resist the winde and tempest, they shoulde bee carried hither and thither farre from their desired porte. So must the Lords members loade and ballace themselues with the graynes of repentance, and of the feare of God, and also with the heauy stone of their oune deathes remembrance, vntill they arriue in heauen, their desired hauen. Yt is better to beare salt, sand, and iron, then the seruice of implacable satan. In tyme of tempestuous weather they flie neere the earth: but in calme seasons they mount alofte to the cloudes. Euen so adversitie maketh the best to stoope yet not to giue ouer, but still proceede till affliction and sicknes be overblowen: and then when they haue obteyned a peaceable estate of conscience, health, and tyme, they must relinquishe their oune infirmitie, and flie higher in celestiall meditation and conversation. When a storme is comynge they call vpon their Guides to desiste, and all of them doe as it were advise not to be exposed to perill. [222r] So may wise people call vpon their Gouernors and Preachers to rest in tymes of danger, rather then to adventure their safeties of bodies and soules in a present or an eternall destruction. And, to conclude, yf the sand which they swallowe vp for ballace in the Mountaynes of the East, be so concocted, that in the end of their iourney it be turned either into golde or a precious stone, when they disgorge and disburden themselues thereof; & hereof came the prouerbe, *Grues lapillos deglutientes,* it yeldeth vnto vs a lyuely representacon not onely of advised actions, but of those graynes which wee gather out of the Mountayne of Holy Scripture, which by the operation of the blessed Spirit is turned into most pure and precious faith, neuer goinge from vs till wee haue ended our Pilgrimage and bee in heauen.

If Cranes fall out and fight, yet are they soone reconciled, and forsake not Company or leaue of their iourney. So if contention and iarres arise amonge brethren through heate and frailtie, let them be compounded with speede, that wee neuer forsake the fellowshippe of Gods people nor giue ouer our profession wherein wee are trauallinge to the kingdome of heauen.

Non aliter quam si Grus inter nubila clamans
Iuncta volet pennisque secet stridentibus auras &c.[206]

No otherwise then Cranes monge cloudes togither flye,
dividinge aer with wings, and ecchoinge crye for crye.

Chap. 4. The vses naturall, medicinall, Ciuill, & artificiall.

I cannot beginne this Chapter but with some auncient, ingenious, and merry Apologues gyvinge a savory introduction vnto the naturall vses of this fowle. It is fayned that Cranes and geese did light and feede together in one meadowe and piece of land, about which there attended

Fowlers ready to take and kill such a prey. As soone as the Cranes sawe them, they betooke themselues to their wings and flewe away; bycause they were leane and light of body: but the geese were taken by reason of their fatt and heauy bodies who coulde not arise speedilie for their oune safegarde. Whereby they vnderstoode that in tyme of warres and sackinge of Cities, the poore which haue nothinge escape [222v] very easilie, but the rich men while they cannot depart with their wealthe, are overtaken by the enemy and spoiled by the sworde.

The naturall vse which men make of Cranes is for the table, whereof Gellius in his Satyricall invectiue against Gluttons maketh plesant mention, *Pauus è Samo, Phrygia Attagena, Grues Melicæ, Hoedus ex Ambrachia, pelamis Chalcedonia.*[207] They doe not onelie make a Calendar of their meates, but builde houses and litle larders for the safe keepinge of their seuerall dishes. At one meale they serue at table the choisest meates of seuerall Countreys: a Peacocke of Samos, a Godwitt of Phrygia, Cranes of Melicia, Kids of Ambrachia, and Tunyes of Chalcedonia. So hereby it is most evident that Cranes were a delicate meate, for men most curious in diet. And Plutarch in his Booke of flesheeatinge[208] telleth that they were wont to sowe up the eyes of Cranes and Swannes, and so feede them in darkenes whereby they grewe very fatt in a short space: for men at the first invented diuers dishes not for any necessitie of life, but accordinge to their seuerall appetites, curiouslie followinge nowe one kinde then another. ffrom hence it came, that in the tyme of Cornelius Nepos, Cranes were lesse esteemed then storkes, and in the tyme of Pliny Cranes were desired, and no man cared for Storkes, or once asked after them. But Ouid speakinge of tymes more auncient, maketh the eatinge of Cranes a latter invention:

Piscis adhuc illis populis sine fraude natabat,
Ostreaque in conchis tuta fuere suis.
Nec Latium norat, quam præbet Ionia diues,
Nec quæ pygmeo sanguine gaudet, auem.
Et præter pennas nihil in pauone placabat,
Nec tellus captas miserat anteferas.[209]

The fishe yet swamme not dreadinge lyne or nett.
The Oisters safe did lyve and dye in shell:
Nor Rome did knowe what Græcia did begett
No, not the Crane that Pigmees bloud doth spill
No Peacocke pleasde, but for her beauteous quill
Nor earth bredd beasts the dayntie mouth to fill.

Therefore Statius saied thus.

[223r] *Ah miseri, quos nosse iuuat quid Phasidis ales,*
Distat ab hyberna Rhodopes Grue.[210]

Ah wretches that delight to knowe the difference,
Twixt Cranes and Pheasant fleshe the sense.

Domitian the Emperor accompted Cranes amonge his dishes of most price, especiallie roastinge them in the bellies of whole Muttons, goates, or swyne, which kinde of Cookery wantons vse at this day in Countrey Townes, at drunken feasts, and that which is more, whole Oxen, spittinge them on small trees, and keepinge them at fire two or three dayes burninge the outside before the inside be roasted; as if they were of Domitians family, or Pherillus were aliue againe to invent a brazen Bull to be sett on a fire for Phalaris to torment his people.

The Indian Kinges neuer refuse any lyvinge Creature which their Subiects offer vnto them, and therefore Ælianus saieth that they offer them Cranes, Geese, hennes, Duckes, Turtles, Godwitts, Partridges, Pindels, Bocales or Bareballs,[211] Gnattsnappers, Lynnets, and such like, which they bringe open and dressed to the intent hee may see their fatnes, and choose the best for his table. So the Inhabitants of the Baleares, did eate younge Cranes in the tyme of Pliny. But leavinge to proue that which is so well knowen, I will proceede to their dressinge and preparation, wherein wee shall trie the truth of that which Martiall hath so often verified, *Ingeniosa gula est.* The throate is [undecipherable] for meate. ffirst bycause their fleshe is harde and full of fibres, and therefore not good to be eaten before they be mollified, they lett them hange by the Heeles after they be killed three or foure dayes, with some waights vpon them: that beinge so stretched out at leingth they may growe more tender: some doe hange them vpon figge-trees by reason they affirme a secreate vertue in that tree to mollifie the hardnes of Cranes fleshe. There was neuer any man that doubted of their hard, fibrous, and churlishe fleshe, and therefore Mercurial affirmeth that no learned man liked thereof although they were brought to Rome from Melos, and other parts of the worlde. The younger are the moister, and therefore the better meate: for the olde Cranes begett blacke and [223v] melancholy bloud. Wherefore in Fraunce when they haue killed them, then they sticke them full of Cloues, and cover them with pepper: for so they endure many dayes sweete and growe more delicious, even as wee haue declared before in the Peacocke, for the fleshe is drye and colde, and they are best which are killed by Falcons, Eagles, or other such Haukes. And Platina relateth the forme of their dressinge in these wordes, *Gruem vel Anatem lauabis* [*vel alio quin ornabis*], *&*

ollæ includes &c.[212] You must washe your Crane cleane, or otherwise dresse him, and put him into a pott, and let him seeth till it bee hard, with salt water and Annyse; then take it out when it is halfe sodd, and washe it the second tyme, and putt him into a kettle of brasse with the liquour, oyle, a branch of Oregan, and Coriander. And when it is almost sodd ynoughe, adde vnto it some boyled newe wyne, and to colour it beate pepper together with Loueage, Cummyn, Coryander, rue, parsenep, and Carret, with hony infused thereupon. The broath is to be tempered with vinegar, and sett vpon a Chafingdishe serued in with saffron. The eggs also althoughe they be hard, pale, and vnsauery, are eaten amonge the poore Indians, as witnesseth Strabo and Bartholomæus Anglicus.

But let vs come to the medicinall vses of this fowle, which are more necessary then the former, bycause wee haue more meanes to feede our bodies, then to recouer them when they are ill disposed. And yet they are not many: but such as my authours the Phisitians haue obserued will I brieflie and faithfullie deliuer. In Arabia they nourishe Cranes against all Serpents and venemous Creatures, bycause their voyce or longe leggs and neckes make them afraied, and runne away from the places where these are fedd and nourished. Porta Baptist affirmeth that their fleshe is profitable against Cancers, Vlcers, Palsyes, and Wynde in the gutts. The broath wherein they are sodde cleareth the voice, and encreaseth the seede naturall. Arnoldus maketh a pouder by dryinge their head, eyes, belly, ribbes, and gutts for the cure of fistulaes, vlcers, and Cancers. The brayne hath ben vsed against sores in the seate. Pliny saieth that the nerves taken out of their leggs or wings doe helpe a wearyed man to recouer streingth, and beinge applied to Laborers keepe them from wearysomnes. The Lyuer helpeth the payne of the Reynes [224r] if it by dryed and drunke in a dram of Cyche-water.* The Marrowe of their bones is a good eyesalue. The white spotts of the eyes are taken away by applyinge the stones dried with Sea-froth, the dunge of a Lysarde, and fine sugar. And the same dissolued is good to washe those sore eyes which haue receaued any blowes. The Gall instilled into the Nostrills with the iuyce of Maioram helpeth the Crampe or palsie of the mouth, and the fatt which swymmeth when the Crane is in seethinge, if it bee taken of and instilled into the eares helpeth deafenes and hardnes of hearinge. And some mixe the Gall with the drugge Zambacele† to expell forgetfulnes and restore memory. If a mans melt be harde, lett

* *Cyche-water* a distillation made from cich, chick, or chick-pea, a vetch

† *Zambacele* A.: "cum Zambacelaes (quidam inepte oleum baccarum oliuae interpretantur)"

him mixe the before saide scum-fatt with vinegar, and drinke it in a bath to soften the hardnes thereof. And the fatt of Cranes (saieth Pliny) mollifieth hard swellings and tuberous bunches. And so much for the Medicines.

The vses artificiall and Ciuill are also to be dispatched with celeritie. They vsed amonge the olde Æthiopians to stuffe the skynnes of Cranes and so vse them in steede of bucklers: and the pipes which are nowe made of reedes were once made of Cranebones.

The Gentlemen of Englande make use of Cranes in their Escucheons beinge honoured no lesse for these Armes and badges of Nobility, then heretofore whole Nations, as wee haue shewed that tooke their names from them. Such as I coulde learne are these that followe.

Browne of London. Or. a Cheueron engrayled, barre of eight pieces, waue Arg. and Azure betwene three Cranes G.

His Creast a Crane Azure membred with an eare of wheate in his beake. Or sett on a wreathe Or and Azure.

Browne of Essex Sable a Cheueron battelle imbattelle betwene three Cranes Argent.

Clarawxe of the Northe, a Crane proper membred Or sett on a wreathe Or & Sable, a Crest.

Crane of Suffolke. A Crane proper membred Or sett on a wreathe Or and Gulles. a Crest.

[224v] Cranvile of Suffolke barre of sixe pieces. Arg and Azure, an Escucheon of the pretence Or charged with a Crane of the second.

Cranwell. Gulles. 3. Cranes Argent, membred of the same

Crawdenner a Crane pryinge into a whilke shell Arg. sett on a wreathe Arg. & Sab. a Creast

Cruce or Cruse of Deuon a Crane Azure membred or sett on a wreath.

Fenrother Gules on a Cheueron Arg. 3. Cranes Azure membred Or.

Scriuen. a Crane. Azure, with a Lobster in his beake, Sable sett on a wreathe.

Stattam Azure. a Cheueron betwene 3 Cranes. Argent.

And so much for men. There is a precious stone called *Geranitis,* bycause the forme thereof resembleth a Cranes necke. And as the Carcinias is named of the Sea-Crabb, Echites of the Viper, Scorpites of the Scorpion, Scarites of the Goldennye, Triglitis of the Mullett, Ægophthalmos of the Goates eye, so is Geranitis of the Cranes-necke, saieth Pliny. Lib 37. Cap. 11.[213]

[225r]

[XXXIV]

The Coote.

[illustration on p. 214]

It is in vayne to make disputations about this fowle, whereby tyme and learninge might be mispent. By the leaue of other late learned men, I will define it to be the same which the Auncient Latinists called *Fulica.* And so St Iherome or the Authour of the vulgar translation turneth *Schachaph,* Deut. 14. St Augustine and Arnobius turne *Chasida,* Psal. 104 into *Fulicam.*[214] The auncient Greekes had no name for this birde, but at this day they call it *Loupha* by transposition of the letters in *Fulica.* Cicero calleth it *Fulix a furuo colore,* from the blacknes of the colour. And therefore Albertus calleth it *Mergum nigrum,* the blacke Cormorant, and Kiranides *Albam frontem,* the white Forehead, bycause in the whole bodie there is no white except in the forehead. The Italians call it *Folega, Follata, Fulca,* and *Fulsa.* The Frenche *Foulque, Foulcre,* and *Pulle d'eau,* that is, a water Chicke. And so about Verbanum in Italy *Pullon* and *Polon.* At Neocomin it is called *Belleque,* in Heluetia *Boellhinen* and *Belchinen*, and about Acron, *ein Belch*, about Franckford *Florn*; and bycause of the white spott vpon the forehead resemblinge a Priests shauen Crowne they also call it *Pfaff*; in Sweueland it is called *Blesz* and *Bleszinge. Wasserhun, Rorhennle, Hagelgans, Schwartztaucher,* and *Zapp* are also Germane names for the same. [225v] In Holland *Meercoote,* In Illyria *Lyska,* and in Polonia *Kacza* and *Dzika.*

This is a water fowle and abideth in freshe and sweete waters, yet it is doubted whether it be clouen footed like a Bustard, or flatfooted like a goose and such other water fowles, for the skynne of the foote is so thinne and short, as it scarce appeareth when they are out of the water. Albertus maketh them a kinde of Cormorants, bycause they lyve alway in water and stray not farre from the place of their generation. Gesner affirmeth that they haue a water-fowle in Frizland which they call *Marcol*; the inhabitants of the Countrey hate them, like as Crowes. When they builde neasts they make them, amonge reedes, which when the people finde, they make a hole in the neast, and so the egges fall through and breake, but they always preserue one, to the intent that the fowle may not forsake this neast, and builde in some other vnknowen place, wherein her younge shoulde be hatched and growe to good: by

this meane, egge after egge is destroyed, and the younge sieldome or neuer hatched: but I take not our Coote to bee of this race: bycause these feede vpon carrion and dead corpsses. There are onely two kindes hereof that I can learne. The greater whereof is thus described: It is in quantitie as bigge as a pullett beinge all blacke over the bodie but speciallie the head and necke: yet the forepart of the head is balde in the fashion of an egge appearinge couered with a white skynne. The beake of a white and redd colour. The feathers of the belly are very softe and of an ashe-colour, the vpper part of the wings is white and transpierced with a narrowe lyne, the skynnes of their feete are not whole without fissure or partition, but parted vpon the clawes, yet are they broade and blacke, and are dilated and contracted at the pleasure of the fowle: yet sometyme they are contynued except in the middle clawe where they are parted: And the partitions of these skynnes doe resemble semicircles. The leggs and feete are blackishe, but about the knee where the feathers growe not, they are a kind of yellowishe greene: the necke very longe, and the taile very short. And Bellonius addeth that the fashion of the head is like a common hens, hauinge no white about it except in the foldes of the winges, which wings are very small, bycause it is ordeyned by our Graund Creatour to lyve in the waters and not to flie ouer land. The eyes of the Male black and of the female a red skarlet colour: and besides this note, there is none founde to distinguishe the Male from the female. [226r] Their leggs are longe to thende that they might the better walke in the moorishe and fenny places, they walke vpright and runne very fast, their tongue is very softe, and their clawes very greate: the mawe or ventricle is as greate as a Cockes vnto which the Melt is ioyned: beinge at thone side thinne and softe, but at the other side as thicke as a horse houfe, and fashioned like a halfe walnut shell. In the other inward parts they are as perfect as other fowles. And so much for this first and greater.

The Second kinde.

[illustration]

Some haue thought that wee haue no Cootes in England except one waterfowle, which is a litle lesser: beinge in all other things like the former except in a redd bunche growinge vpon the beake and redd leggs, and it wanteth the white spott vpon the Crowne of the head. They lyve in pooles and fenny waters, dyvinge deepe into them, and feede vpon gravell, mudde, and small Cockles they finde therein: abstayninge from all other fishe. It is reported that they cannot flie, except they fill the hollowe of their foote with water: and therefore they alway make their rises vpon the water.

Vnto this may be added the birde which the frenche men call *diable de mer,* the dyvell of the Sea, bycause of the blacke colour thereof. This birde doth euer lyve in sweete waters, yet it is so exquisitelie blacke, as no pencill can frame a better. It is bigger [226v] then the greate Coote, and hath a greater white callous spott vpon the head: when it swymmeth it draweth the leggs to the body, and in the feete it resembleth the first expressed Coote.

They lyve in fennes and moorishe places, which is the cause wherefore they are called *Æthia* and *palustres.* And therefore Mantuan doth thus expresse the Ægle snatchinge vp one of these Cootes:

> *Abstulit vt Fulicam pedibus Iouis armiger vncis*
> *Circum stagna volans patrii prope littora Minti.*[215]

> As in crooked clawe Ioues squire takes a Coote
> flyinge over the shores where Mintus sets foote.

Albertus writeth that they reiouce in tempests and fowle weather, for then they dyve into the bottome of the water and sport themselues amonge the billowes, and therefore in wynter they avoide those waters which congeale and freeze, covetinge the waters of the Southe. When they are hungrie and finde no present foode, they haue a whyninge and complayninge voice, which is thus described by Ælius Iulius:

> *Pascuntur volucres querulæ vndique, & vndique nigræ,*
> *Mersantur fulicæ, aut molli piscantur in vlua.*
> *It fluuio rostrata acies, alisque sub ipsis,*
> *Vnda latet, mussant rauco vada Coerula cantu.*[216]

> The whynninge birdes feede euery where, and Cole blacke
> Coote,

dyve deepe in flouds or in softe ponde doe fishe:
The beaked hoast in ryvers goe: to wings they sproote
With hoarse-voice-songe in blewishe foordes they hisse.

They will eate hearbes and any kindes of seede, yea, litle dead fishes in default of foode. They make their neasts on the ground like Duckes, and in sommer lay egges as bigge as henne-eggs. Alciatus seemeth to saie that they eate litle lyvinge fishes, as appeareth by this Epigram entituled, *obnoxia infirmitas*:

Pisciculos orata rapit medio æquore sardas
Ni fugiant pauidæ, summa marisque petant.
Ast ibi sunt Mergis, Fulicisque voracibus esca.
Eheu intuta manens vndique debilitas.[217]

[227r] The guiltheades eate poore spratts in midst of flood,
Vnlesse they flye vnto the shallowe water:
And there alasse for Cootes and Cormorants foode
They dye, so weakenes still is an oppressed matter.

Of this their weakenes Nicander giueth a fabulous reason,[218] which I will relate not for truth, but for noueltie that Christians may knowe what a miserable thinge it is to lyve without the knowledge of God, and his holy truthe, teachinge the originall and prime creation of all things. He saieth that one Mynichus, the sonne of Dryan, was Kinge of Molossa, who was a greate Prophet, and a iust man, and by his wife Lelanta hee had three sonnes, Alcandrus, Megalætor, and Philæus, and one daughter, Hyperippa, all very good and much loued of the Gods. It happened one night that theeves came and sodeinely sett vpon them, and beinge not able to withstand them, they fledd to their turretts and were pursued by those robbers, who sett the Castle on fire. Iupiter pittying their misery (wolde not quench the fire) but turned them into birdes, the daughter into a Coote, lovinge water, bycause shee fled from the fire, and the father, bretherne, and mother into other birdes, who at this day are saied to fight with Eagles; and Goshaukes: and to breake their eggs in their neasts bycause they hinder them on trees to hunt flyes and greene wormes. Thus Nicander: who shameth his heathen God, in the latter end of such propheticall iust men as hee maketh these persons to haue bene. But I will returne againe to our Coote, who is a weake creature, and neither in streingth or beautie comparable to many other fowles, especiallie in olde tyme, when they wolde expresse a greate dissimilitude, they wolde say as like as a Swanne and a Coote. So Ausonius.

Si confers Fulicas Cignis & Ædona Parræ,
Castaneis Corylos æquas, viburna cupressis.[219]

parra signifieth an vnluckie bird, which in the place I english an Owl

So Cootes with Swannes, and Nightingale to Owle,
With Chestnutt, hasell, with Cypresse, bendwith fowle.*
Are comparable. [etc.?]

They are Prognosticators of fowle weather, and windes. Against [227v] wynde they chainge place, and flye to a warmer harbour: but against stormes, they sport and play in the waters: for they feele the ascendinge vapours vp to the rayny cloudes. They are taken in springes and snares, sett in their walkes: and their fleshe if it be boyled in an open vessell or rosted drie before they be basted, is good and nourisheable meate: yet they are best in the Autumne, and fall of the leafe. Paulus Crassus, the noble Capadocian Phisitian, gaue the brayne of a vultur; the heart of a rawe Coote, and the fleshe of tame Catts against the fallinge sicknes. And Sextus prescribeth the reynes of a hare and of a Coote to be eaten rawe against the bytings and poysons of spiders.

The Coates and Crests are these followinge.

Caldecote. Argent a Fesse batelle imbatelle, gules betwene 3. Cootes proper.
Coote of Essex Arg. a Cheueron. Sab. betwene. 3. Cootes. proper. And againe. his Crest. a Cootes head erased proper sett on a wreath Arg. & Sab.
Coote of Suff. Argent. 3. Cootes proper. 2. & 1.
Southcoote of Deuon. Arg. a Cheueron gules. betwene 3. balde Cootes proper. And for his Crest a Coote proper sett on a wreath. Arg. & Sab.

[XXXV]

The Crex.

[illustration on p. 218]

[228r] This birde is vnknowen to the writers of this age beside the name, and it is thought to be the same which Athenæus calleth *Helorios,* takinge this name *Helorio* from the fennes and pooles where it lyveth,

* *bendwith fowle* "Bindweed, Withwinde, or Hedge Bels" and "of an euile smell" (Gerard), used to tie up faggots

and the worde *Crex* from the voice. The Greekes call it *Krekas* and *Krex;* Albertus *Crataz.* Bellonius lyvinge sometyme in Ægipt and about Nilus, maketh this description thereof. It hath very longe legs, a longe beake and a blacke beinge recurued and turned vp backewarde, a blacke head and leggs, but the necke, breast, and backe white, and the other vpper parts of the bodie, as the wings and taile of an Ashecolour. The wings are pieced or drawen through with a white lyne downe by the ribbes. It is thought by Varinus and Herodotus to be a blacke Ibis. When it flieth it maketh a greate noice and hunteth flyes in the aër, and fishes on the Sea shore in calme weather. By reason of the longe and sharpe beake, it is fayned by Aristophanes[220] to be one of the builders of the Citie of birdes in Libia; for the beake hath also sawed teeth wherewithall it grindeth meate; and is fitt to polishe stones and tymber. The Italians bycause of the fashion of his beake call it *Beccostorta* and *Beccoroella,* and about Verbanum *Spinzago d' acqua,* and the Turkes *Zeluk.* The quantitie of the bodie is like a wood Culuer. The hind clawe of the foote is very short. And it fighteth with black birds and other land fowle.
[228v]

[XXXVI]

The Crowe.

Bycause that Crowes are a kinde of Rauen the Hebrewes call it *Oreb* by the same name wherewithall they stile Rauens: and the beake of a Crowe *Algorab.* The Chaldees expresse it by diuers names as *Kurka,*

[*Rooke*]

[*Royston Crowe*]

[*Blewe Crowe*]

Kauth, and at this day the Iewes call it *Kik* and *Kra.* The Arabians *Gaudes, Kokis, Hacha, Barositis,* and *Xercula.* The Greekes *Korone, Kouronna,* and *Kouraca,* in Creete *Komba,* and at this day *Kerais.* The Latines *Cornix* and *Coruulus.* The Italians *Cornice, Cornacchia,* and *Cornacchio.* The Spanyards *Corneia* and *Gracchia.* The frenche *petit Corbin, Corneille, Graille,* and *Graillat,* and a younge Crowe in the nest *Corneilleau.* The Germanes *Kraee, Krahe, Hausskraee, Schwartzkraee*, and plurally *Krayen.*

I finde that there are generallie two kindes of Crowes, one a land Crowe, another a water Crowe. Of the land Crowes some are *Cornices frugiuoræ,* Rookes, and some are distinguished by varietie of colour, as those which wee call *Roiston Crowes,* or Ashecoloured Crowes. And another called by Gesner *Cornicem cerulæam,* a blewe Crowe. They are all of them bigger then Choughes or Dawes, and yet one of them exceedinge another. This first kinde is all blacke, shininge like Indico, but in the bright sunne-beames like a darke blewe. The roote of the beake next the head white, and the same as hard as horne, sharpe at the ende wherewithall he giueth a very smart stroke, breakinge all kinde of nutts: in other parts it resembleth a Rauen, except in the gristles or longe haires growinge about the eye-liddes, and a small blacke grayne vpon the neathermost. And bycause they are giuen to raveninge and devouringe, their throate is very wide, especially in that part which is neerest to their mawe. The Blacknes of this common kinde of Crowes is not so constant, but that it sometyme varyeth and declyneth vnto white: yet a white Crowe is a kinde of prodigy. Not longe before Rhodigium fell [229r—illustrations] [229v—blank] [230r] into Ciuill warres (sayeth Coelius) there appeared about their walles a white Crowe with a blacke head: Although the most comon colour of all nations* be blacke, yet nowe and then wee finde some of a pale white (saieth Perottus) yet such are compared to Eunuches which so differ from men as these Crowes from the Common kinde. And generallie all Crowes are like Eunuches bycause they participate not with Rauens nor Doues, as Eunuches are neither men nor women. These vulgar Crowes lyve not farre from houses, barnes, dunghills, and highwayes eatinge all things, beinge therefore called *Omniuoræ,* devourers of fruits, plants, wormes, garbage, carrion, younge Chickins, and small birds, olyves, nutts and other thinges. Wherefore the Poets saied they were hated of Pallas to whome Oliues were sacred; and Possidippus the Poet compareth one Phiromachus, a greate Trencherman, vnto these Crowes sayinge:

* *nations* species

Phiromachum veluti Cornicem multa vorantem,
Nocturnam tumuli fossa profunda tenet.[221]

This deepe digd graue doth hold Phiromachus
Who night-Crowe-like a glutton was and ravenous.

The Second kinde or Royston Crowe.

This is very well knowen in England, and it can be no other then *Cornix varia,* the partie coloured Crowe, called in the Lowe Countreys *Pundterkrae,* and in Germany *winter kraey,* bycause in the sommer tyme it keepeth in the fieldes and vpon the hills, and when winter approacheth it draweth neerer to the houses and villages. Whereupon in Westphalia they haue a Prouerbe, *Vna Cornix non facit hyemen,* One Crowe doth not make wynter, as wee say in England: One swallowe doth not make sommer. It differeth in nothinge from the Comon Vulgar Crowe, except in the vpper part of the necke, backsides of the wings, and buttocks which are an Ashecolour, but the head, throate, beake, inner part of the wings, and leggs are blacke; the breast-feathers differ from the other: for they [230v] stande furth like short, blacke, and thicke grisles. And bycause of the partycolours in France they call him *Emantelee,* in Greece, *Spodocides Korone,* in Germany *Schiltkrae* and *Naebelkrae,* in Italy *Mulacchia* and *Monacchia,* bycause the colours resemble the attire of Nunnes. They breede not in colde Countreys but passe away from one part of the Continent to another; for avoidinge snowe and colde weather: but in temperate regions, they are founde all the yere longe.

The Blewe Crowe.

This is a very wilde and vntameable fowle called in Misnia *Holzkraey, Galgenregel,* and *Halkregel.* They are founde in the woods of that Countrey. Their beake is blacke, their legs browne and very small in respect of their bodies proportion. The greate feathers of the winges are blacke, the ridge of the backe and of the necke are browne: but the head, wings, taile, and all other the vpper parts most visible are blewe or blewishe mixed with greene. They are taken aliue, and for the varietie of their colours desired in forrayne nations, beinge there called *a Germayne Popin-iay.* And so much for the kindes in this places. ffor Rookes, Night Crowes, and Sea-Crowes shall haue their historye in their proper letter.

All these kindes haue but one voice that I knowe of, which the Graecians call sometymes *Krozein,* and *Eklagra,* the Latynes *Crocitus,* callinge the birde *Rauca Cornix,* and *Stridula Cornix.* All nations make the voice to symbolize with *Cras Cras,* and therefore say it is a type or Hieroglyphicke of hope. *Cornicare* is the latyne worde that signifieth *to singe like a Crowe* as appeareth by this fragment of Persius, *Nescio quid tecum graue cornicaris inepte.*[222] And Agathocles, a pratlinge Kinge of Cicyly, was called a Crowe. The voice is irkesome and vnpleasant accordinge to this olde verse:

[231r] *Tum Cornix plena pluuiam vocat improba voce.*[223]

Then cryes the full Crowe with ill fauoured sound,
That rayne and wett weather will fall on the ground.

They moue or flie verie speedily and nimbly, as Ouid saieth.

Huc leuiter Cornix pennis delapsa per auras.

ffull lightlie came the speedie Crowe
ffrom lofty aer to earth belowe.

They also walke easilie vpon the earth, or leape from place to place, but then are they most nimble, when they feede their younge in the neast or before rayne. They choose their mates and contynue constant vnto them, without chainge, both while they lyve, and after they be dead. They builde their neasts in the tops of trees, and conceiue by treadinge one another like pullen. They lay and hatch about the Sommer Solstice, their egges are speckled and are euer even in nomber: out of which are engendred Males and females: they are not lesse then two, or more then foure, wherefore they are not accompted fruitefull. The reason of their infoecunditie is thus giuen by Alex Aphrod: *Cur animantium alia plura parere, alia pauciora consueuerunt? Censendum* &c.[224] Why some lyvinge Creatures breede many, and other fewe, this is thought to be the reason. God in nature hath so prouided, that those lyvinge Creatures which lyve and last but a litle while, shoulde breede many, that the shortnes of their dayes might be recompenced with the nomber of posteritie. But Rauens, Crowes, and Hartes bringe forth fewe, and breede very slowlie bycause the leingth of their oune life giueth perpetuitie of conseruation to their kind. Therefore also such as lyve a moderate age are also moderatelie fruitfull, both amonge birds, beasts, hearbes, and plants. The female Crowe doth onely keepe the neast and broode the eggs neuer stirringe abroade: but receiueth her foode from the Male: duringe that tyme, which is alsoe a propertie of Rauens. When they are ready to hatch and come forth out of the eggs, they breake not where the head lyeth, but where the feete, for it is saied that the backer parts are first perfected. They are hatched or come out of the eggs blinde, like as swallowes, sparrowes, Ringedoues, and Turtles. The Damme forsaketh not [231v] her neast nor feedeth her younge, till they be feathered, and then she followeth and plyeth them with meate most diligentlie teachinge them to flye, and not forsakinge them till they are past all danger, which thinge caused Greate Basile to write on this manner, *Laudandus est sane Cornicis erga suam prolem amor: Laudanda est diligentia: Hæc suos pullos iam volantes comitatur, suppeditansque alimoniam, aliquamdiu enutrit.*[225] The loue of the crowe to her younge is much to be praised, and so likewise is her diligence, for when they first beginne to flie, the Sires followe them and nourishe them a season and when they sitt and hatch their younge. Isidorus also writeth: *Adeo nidos impense fouent, vt assiduo incubitu plumas exuant. Quare iusta naturæ talione, et decreto quantum temporis impenderint in foetibus educandis, tantum temporis & ipsæ senio confectæ à pullis suis aluntur.* They loue their neasts so well that by daylie keepinge thereon they loose their oune feathers. Wherefore by a iust and deserued recompence, in their olde age they are so longe fedd by their younge as they spent and bestowed tyme in feedinge them. ffor the better preseruation of their younge, they fence their neasts with veruayne against all flyinge wormes, as Zoroaster writeth, wherefore they are helde to be a subtile fowle, which may appeare by many particulars. And first if they finde a nutt or oyster which they cannot open by the streingth of their beakes, they take it in their mouthes, and flie ouer a Rocke, or stone tiles of a house, vpon which they lett it fall, and so breakinge they haue their desires. Wherefore Thranius in Plautus[226] compareth himselfe to a craftie Crowe. They learne to speake especially if the small ende of their tongue be taken of. Of such an one are those wordes of Pliny: *Nam quoque erat in vrbe [Roma] hæc prodente me, Equitis Romani Cornix è Boetica primum e colore admodum nigro, deinde plura contexta verba exprimens, & alia atque alia crebro addiscens.* At this tyme I found in Rome the Crowe of a certeine Knight which coulde expresse many wordes after a man, and euery day learned more and more. Merthes, a

Kinge of Ægipt, had a Crowe that had learned to carry letters to whatsoeuer place he comaunded her. It is a rare instinct of God in nature, whereby the female is fedd by the Male duringe the tyme she keepeth her neast, and [232r] also their perpetuall widowhood when one partie dyeth. Wherefore in olde tyme they were much respected of the wyzards and Augurs. When both appeared it signified a wished desire; but if one alone then it pretended viduitye. Their concorde in marriage is a symbole vnto man; for the Male and female doe neuer fall out or part asunder. Gesner saieth that hee knewe a friende of his that had obserued one paire or couple to haunt his house for meate tenne yeres together. Therefore Mantuan hath this verse:

Concors Nyctimene, Cornix cum coniuge Progne.[227]

As Night Owles lyve in peace togither,
So Crowes from females sieldome seuer.

Of this their Concord, Alciat made the Embleame, *Concordiæ Symbolum,* a match or symbole of Concorde:

Cornicum mira inter se concordia vitæ est,
Inque vicem nunquam contaminata fides.
Hinc volucres hæc sceptra gerunt, quod scilicet omnes
Consensu populi stantque caduntque Duces:
Quem si de medio tollas, discordia præceps
Aduolat, & secum regia fata trahit.

Admired concorde Crowes with themselues doe keepe,
And neuer doe defile each others faith:
Hence fowles beare scepters in their concord deepe,
Consent makes Lords to stand and fall he saieth.
Which once remoued then headlonge discord brings.
The fate of people, and the fall of Kings.

They lyve very longe, ffor Hesiod saieth they lyve, *nouem ætates,* nyne ages of men, vnto whome Iuuenal compareth the life of Nestor.

Exemplum vitæ fuit à Cornice secundæ.[228]

The patterne of his happie life
ffrom Crowes he tooke whose yeres are rife.

ffrom hence Ouid Plutarche and Ausonius say that hee liueth at the least thrice the age of a man, *Trino Cornix viuacior æuo.* Yet all haue not agreed about their age, ffor Aristophanes writeth that hee lyveth but fyve generations, the Ægiptians, (as witnesseth [232v] Orus) foure hundred yeres,[229] and other otherwise: but all say he lyveth very longe, and therefore call him some tymes, *Polygeros* and some tymes *Enneageros*. They love the Storke aboue other fowles: therefore in the Continent they flie with them, and leade them into Asia: which amity is wonderfully praised by sundry Authors. The manners and inclinations of Storkes are not much different from wisedome and reason, for they seeme to warre vnder one standerd, goinge and cominge constantlie vnder one signe; and at one tyme of the yere. And the Crowes of those Countreys whither they goe and come like sergeants and Harbingers make way for them; like suer friends, takinge part both in their good and evill fortune: fightinge for them against their Comon enemyes: which appeareth to the men of those Countreys by a double argument: ffirst bycause they bringe with them markes, signes, and wounds of their skirmishinge: and secondly when the Storkes come, they haue Crowes in aboundance: but when they are gone, there is scarce one to be founde; in a whole Nation. So that nature and naturall amity prescribeth vnto them these lawes of Concomitancy, and bindeth them to the Company and defence of their friendes, like an oath of allegeance amonge reasonable men: which may shame insatiable and hard harted men, who neuer giue countenance or open their gates vnto their oune kinde: but lyvinge onely to themselues, neuer communicate any dram of their happines to them whome God and Religion haue obliged them to respect.

They also love Herons (saieth Aristotle) and together with them fight against Foxes, their common adversaryes. They admire Apes, but for what reason no man can tell: some ascribe it rather to their follie, then to their friendshippe. They also want not their naturall enemyes both amonge beasts of the earth and the fowles of heauen. In the first place, are rancked weasils, *Hæc enim oua & pullos violat & sæpe nidos diripit* (saieth Aristotle),[230] for they clyme vp trees and many tymes spoile their eggs, their younge, their neasts even as they doe vnto pullen and pigeons. They are also in perpetuall hostilitie with night Owles: for in the day time (saieth Ælianus)[231] the Crowes breake the eggs of Owles: and in [233r] the night tymes, Owles sucke the eggs of Crowes, for in the day Owles see not clearely, and therefore the Crowes make advauntage of the light to spoile their enemyes: and likewise in the night the Crowes are silent and dare not stirre, which the Owles vnderstande, and take revenge of them, by renderinge like for like.

Aristotle maketh mention of a birde which he calleth *Tympanus,* a bel or Tympany; peradventure hee meaneth a Hawke. With these also they fight when they heare or see them. They dare meddle with Eagles, who beinge longe prouoked by their importunities teareth them in pieces: ffor this cause also they adventure vpon Falcons, although to their oune detriment. Yet Aristotle writeth that many tymes by watchinge advauntages they harme both Eagles and Haukes. They are also enemyes to Dogs and wolfes, for Mizaldus saieth, that if they chaunce to eate of any Carrion beast that a wolfe hath fedd vpon before, they die through a certeine Antipathy in nature. Concerninge doggs and Crowes I haue reade this Apologue. Vpon a tyme the Crowe preparinge a sacrifice to Pallas, invited the dogg vnto a feast, desirous to curry fauour with hir, but the dog aunsweared that she lost her labour, for the goddesse hated her, and forbade all credit to be giuen her in soothsayinge; and therefore hee wolde not tast of her cheere: the Crowe replied, *Ob id magis* [*ei*] *sacrificabo, vt reconcilietur mihi,* I will therefore the rather sacrifice vnto Pallas, that she may turne my friende, and be reconciled vnto mee. A fitt resemblance of them that serue God for their oune benefitt, such as the deuill obiected to Holy Iob that he serued not God for nothinge. Let such seruants and seruice befitt fowles and fowle deuills, but neuer men of any Religion.

And herein it is not vnorderly to enquire the cause wherefore Crowes were auncientlie fayned to be hatefull to Minerua and the Night-Owle sacred vnto her. Ouid saieth that once Crowes were sacred to Pallas, and shee was pictured in brasse in the Citie Corone, holdinge a Crowe in her hand. But after such tyme as shee had betrayed the three daughters of Cecrops, who kept Erichthonius fast locked vp in a chest, commaundinge them not to open it, nor once to looke into it, Pallas reiected her and tooke the Night- [233v] owle for her seruant. Other make this Allegory hereof. Pallas signifieth study and learninge, and therefore is fayned to be begotten of Iupiters brayne. And bycause the noice and clamour of Crowes especiallie in the morninge which is principallie dedicated to studies hindereth and disquieteth the meditations of the Muses, therefore shee hateth them, and chooseth the Owle, a more silent birde, neither makinge a noice in the day nor yet sleepinge all the night. And hence commeth the warre betwixt Crowes and Owles. One Vrsinus, an excellent Poet, hath disputed and described this matter in these learned vearses:

Cum sim Dux auium, si lecti fœdera seruo,
Cur me Bellonæ non placuisse putant?

An quia garritu pluuiosæ nuntia lucis,
Dicar, & infelix omen habere putar?
Siue quod excerpam baccas pallantis oliuæ
Ohe quid prosunt arma reperta Deæ?
Siue quod Hercæi, quamuis sit nata cerebro,
Nil capiti, cerebro, nil quoque præstet opis?
Mande meum cerebrum, cerebro plus Pallade cruda
Succurret, querulum nec sinet esse caput.[232]

I am the godde of birds obseruinge weddinge knott,
Why then Bellona, please I thinke you not?
Ist for my pratlinge of the morninge light?
Or for ill luck I am mis-iudgd to bringe?
Ist that I plucke of Olive sprigs at night?
And homewarde flyinge in the aër ringe?
Oh earthlie armes availe not heauenly might,
Or if bycause she was bread of Hirces brayne,
And yet nor head nor brayne is better for her.
Who eates[?] crude Pallas shall neuer cease to playne,
A Crowes brayne helpes both head and witt togither.

It was obserued by the olde Athenians that in the woods neere Pallas Temple, *Ab Arcturi sydere, ad aduentum Hirundinum Cornices non conspici.*[233] ffrom the appearinge of the North pole to the Sommer when Swallowes doe first of all come, there neuer appeared any Crowes. And this encreased the superstitious [234r] opinion touchinge the wrath and displeasure of Pallas against Crowes, as if her anger had ben the cause that they forsooke those woods, whereas in truth the true cause lay in the nature of the place, which Lucretius affirmeth sayinge:

Non iras Palladis acris,
Peruigili causa, Graium vt cecinere Poëtæ.
Sed natura loci hoc opus efficit ipsa suopte.[234]

No anger of Dame Pallas grace,
As Greekish Poets to vs fayne,
Make Crowes abhorre Mineruaes place,
But the nature of the same.

Yet Iuno hath made more reckoninge of them, saieth Festus: *Iunonis patrocinio confisa flocci facere Mineruæ odium,*[235] trustinge to the patronage of Iuno, they care not a strawe for the hatred of Minerua. The heathen people did euer attribute very much to this fowle, and at this day both the Kings and people of Calecut doe obserue him as a Creature full of Diuinity, and by publique lawes preserue them from harme and death. ffor Ludouicus Romanus hath left written that the Kinge hath them in singuler veneration. And alwayes after his meate, the Priests come and take away all that hee leaveth, carryinge it to a certeine place and there spread it vpon the bare earth: which beinge so placed they clappe their handes aboue their head: at which signe the Crowes come flockinge, and eate vp all the Princes fragments. The Crowe of the Ægiptian Kinge Merthes, before spoken of, which by signes carried the Kinges letters to Cities was honoured with a buriall. And of her that Embleame of Alciatus may be verified which hath this inscription, *Non tam loquax quam prudens.*[236] But it is suspected by wise men that this Crowe was a diabolicall spirit, for otherwise he coulde not be taught in the life of one man such a qualitie of state and reason.

Hereunto may be added the discourses of the olde superstitions [234v] and idolatries committed with Crowes in Augurismes and Soothsayings, although it was refused, bycause of the blacke colour and not deemed faith-worthie except in evill tidings. ffrom this ground spake Horace:

Hic niger est, hunc tu Romane caueto.[237]

This cole blacke Crowe, O Roman,
Beware, he is good to no man.

And therefore *nigrum* and *improbrum* are many tymes confounded as wee in Diuinity interpret by holy warrant, the workes of darkenes for the workes of impietie. The tyme assigned by Pliny wherein they foreshewed most ominous and vnhappie thinges, was from the solstice, or the first tyme of their layinge vnto the ende of Sommer. And the Soothsayers made spaces or angles with their rods, callinge some of them *Antickes,* some *postickes,* some right and some left Angles. And when the Crowe came flyinge from the Anticke to the lefte angle, they tooke it for a token of destruction of their Cornefieldes by Souldiers. They did also supersticiouslie dread the voice of Crowes, or the meetinge of a single Crowe, bycause it pretended viduitie or losse of wyves. Alsoe the Indians about Narsinga at this day forbeare to ioyne battell with their enemyes if they espie a single Crowe ouer the Armye. But in all their soothsayinges, the greater overcame and blotted out the lesser, although the least be first. As for example, when the Sooth-sayer had made his Diuination by the flyinge of Crowes, if an Eagle chaunced to come after, all the prophecy was dashed out. And in this incerteintie, the poore foules of those tymes were turmoiled, that they must belieue one and the same thinge diuers wayes; for sometymes the voice of a Crowe was happie and sometymes vnhappie: as it pleased the Soothsayer. Whereupon Cicero asketh this quaestion, *Quid habet augur, cur à dextra Coruus, à sinistra Cornix faciat ratum?*[238] What can the Sooth-sayer produce for himselfe, while hee maketh men belieue, that a Rauen perswadeth on the right [235r] hand, and a Crowe on the left. Surely nothinge but as Gamsters which finde chainge of fortune by alteringe their oune seates, and standings at play: so did these deceiuers nowe promise one thinge and then another, by the chainge of the flight in one poore ignorant fowle. ffor I cannot conceale the wordes of Isidorus about this matter: *Cornicem, aiunt augures, hominum curas significationibus agere, insidiarum vias monstrare, futura prædicere. Magnum nefas hoc credere, Deum consilia sua Cornicibus mandare.*[239] The Soothsayers perswade vs that the Crowe taketh care of men, declaringe evills, and foretellinge things to come. It is a greate wickednes to belieue, that God communicateth his Counsailes with Crowes, for both the fight of Crowes in Anno 1484 and the diuination by Crowes which the Indians made before the comminge of the Spanyardes are nothinge else in the opinion of wise men but the workes and illusions of euill spirits.

But wee reade that sometymes Crowes haue spoken. As Aurelius Victor saieth that in Traianes tyme, a Crowe sounded from the toppe of the Capitoll, *Kalos estai,* these two greeke wordes, to signifie the goodnes of the Emperour, and so flewe away. And the like is reported by Suetonius in the life of Domitian of a Crowe speakinge, *estai panta kalos,*[240] a fewe monethes before the Emperour was slayne: vnto which it is thought he alluded, which made these two vearses:

Nuper Tarpeio quæ sedit culmine Cornix,
"Est bene" non potuit dicere, dixit "erit."

The Crowe on Tarpey could not say "All is well":
But "so it shalbe," her *"Cras Cras"* did tell. alludinge to the death of Domitian which followed after. By a Crowe was the sepulcher of greate Hesiod found out, and Iuno gaue signification by the flight of two Crowes: of the meetinge of the two Louers, Iason and Medea. I for my part wonder not at these prodigees: for as they may seeme strainge beinge done by such Crowes (whereof wise men doubt) so their monstrositie ceaseth, when I remember that diuells can chainge themselues into such images and yet retaine their subtilitie to beguile

[235v] men withall. There are also certeine naturall prognostications made of stormes, rayne, faire weather, and such like things by the flyinge and voices of Crowes. And thereupon in Nicander they are stiled, *Vates pluuiae,* the prophets of rayne, and in Horace, *Auis imbrium diuina,*[241] the divine bird for shewinge rayne. This they performe three wayes, first by their voice, then by walkinge about waters, and lastlie by washinge themselues. Their hoarse voices and especiallie in and about the eveninge.

Cum vespertinum Cornix longæua resultat
Tam Cornix plena pluuiam vocat improba voce.[242]

It is englished before, therefore I will here spare it. The accents of this voice are diuers. And I holde it but lost labour to dispute the case, what manner of voice is best to iudge the weather by when the Crowe singeth: for euery Countreyman is a good Astronomer at this facultie. And I will proceede to other grauer and better matter.

Crowes haue ben so beneficiall vnto men, that I finde greate vse made both of their names, witt, fleshe, and imitation. Their name especiallie in Greeke expresseth many things, as the bent bowe, the end of a ploughe, a part of the sterne of a shippe, and Corona the Crowne, which signifieth the toppe of happines, is deriued from *Korone,* a Crowe. ffrom hence Historiographers, Herborists, Mechanicalls, and men of learninge applie the worde to places, herbes, instruments, and sentences. And there was a place in the Riuer of Tyber dedicated to Crowes bycause it was a Sanctuary of Iuno. Touchinge the witt and subtilitie of Crowes I haue alreadie spoken, but I may adde certeine significations that are made vpon them. There was a Prouerbe, *Cornicum oculos configere,* to putt out the Crowes eyes, whereby the Auncients signified the fashion of those men who to gayne credit to themselues doe disgrace Antiquitye, bycause Crowes lyue many mens ages. And when one bad woman reproued another: they were wont to saie, *Sus Cornicem increpat.* the sowe findes fault with the Crowe, the slutt reproues the scolde.

[236r] It was a noble Hierogliphicke amonge the Ægiptians to expresse the vndiuided amitye and loue betwixt man and wife, by a Couple of Crowes, who neuer fall out nor chainge, nor vse copulation, but in the springe, and when they lay egges to breede their younge. Their inviolable concorde was wont to be the cause that they were stamped vpon Coyne with the worde, *Concordia,* written about them: and such was the money stamped by the Empresse Faustina as Pierius

hath left recorded.[243] A dead Crowe did signifie a longe life honorablie buryed. A boy of Athens lost his life bycause hee put out the eyes of a Crowe for the Iudges did thinke it a signe of pernitious spirit and cruell so to punishe a poore fowle, and yet suffer her to lyve. The heathen goddesse hope was pictured like a Crowe sittinge vpon a Tonne or round vessell. A white Crowe signified a rare and extraordinary matter. The ambition of men is described and reproued by Æsop in the examples of the Crowe envyinge the Rauen, and yet takinge vpon hir diuination, and of the Crowe who beinge flattered by the Foxe to haue a good voice, if shee wolde singe; lost her meate whilest shee opened her mouth to singe at the foxes request. I might be infinite in these thinges, but I will conclude the whole discourse with the medicinall a[nd] ciuile vses.

T[h]e Lawe of God forbade all manner of Crowe fleshe to be eaten, bycause it lyueth vpon Carrion and vncleane meates, yet the poore people of Italy doe often feede thereupon. The Phisitians which are the best Counsellors for the bodies health doe vtterlie dislike and improoue the same: *His qui sanitati suæ consultum cupiunt, è culina procul ablegamda est.*[244] Let those which haue care of their healthe keepe the fleshe of Crowes out of the kitchins and bellyes. Yet it is praised for Haukes, especiallie the heart, lyver and braynes, with the brawne of the breast cleared from the bloud: it is salt through their often motion and increaseth thirst which is pernitious to Haukes of all sortes. In the sicknes called *morbi Chronici*, they haue an Apolychronia which they prescribe against longe lastinge evills; and the neasts alsoe bound vnto the body worke a wholesome promulgation of life. Pliny and Marcellus prescribe the brayne to be eaten against headache. Their dunge putt into wyne helpeth against the flixe. The belly and hinde parts boyled three dayes in oyle chainge the haire from blacke to white, if they be annoynted herewithall: whereas in many places [236v] the people are punished with shrewe myce, there is an invention to drive them away by killinge a Crowe and hanginge her vp till it rott and stinke, then remove it into a place neere those mice, and they will so gather about it that they may be easilie killed.

Crowes haue founde fauor to be roosted in the Coate Armes of Gentlemen, And such as I can learne I doe hereafter expresse.

Badbye alias Badly Argent. a Saltier engrailed Gules betwene 3. Crowes. proper.

Baggott of Yorkshire Sab. Semicrossletts Arg. on a Fesse of the second 3. Crowes proper.

Bayly of Shropshire. Arg. a Cheueron Sab. betwene 3. Crowes proper.

Bowdler of Shrosbury. Arg. 3. Crowes proper. 2. & 1.

Cawthorne of Lincolneshire. Arg. a Cheueron. sab. betwene 3. Crowes proper, on a Cheife of the Second, as many Crosse Crosletts Or.

Crathorne A Creste a Crowe proper on a Mount vert, sett vpon a wreathe Arg. & Gules.

Crowe of Kent nowe of Sussex. Arg. a Cheueron Sab. betwene 3. Crowes proper.

Croker of Deuon Arg. a Cheueron engrailed Gules. betwene 3. Crowes proper.

Croche of Oxon. Arg. on a Cheueron Gules. 3. Mullets Or. betwene 3. Crowes proper.

Cromer of Oxon. Arg. on a Cheueron engrailed Gules. 3. Mulletts Or. betwene as many Crowes proper.

Cromer of Kent. Arg. a Cheueron engrailed Sab. betwene 3. Crowes proper.

Crooke of Wilteshire Arg. a Cheueron gules. betwene 3. Crowes. proper.

Croton Arg a Cheueron sab. betwene 3. Crowes proper.

Fremingham of Suffolke. Arg. A Fesse Gules betwene 3. Crowes proper

Mayowe of Wilteshire Arg. on a Cheueron Sab. fyue losinges of the first betwene 3. Crowes proper.

Owen of Oxon Argent. a Cheueron Ermyn betwen 3. Crowes proper.

Pemmerton of Lancashire Arg. 3. Crowes with wings displayed. Sab.

Rowley of Salop. Arg. on a bend. Sab. 3. Escallopes of the first betwene. 2. Crowes proper.

[237r] Tempest Arg. a Cheueron Gules. betwene 3. Crowes proper

Warberton of Cheshire. A Cheueron Sab. betwene 3. Crowes proper.

Warbulton. Arg. a Cheueron. Sab. betwene 3. Crowes risinge. proper.

Warde. Arg. on a Cheueron sab. an runlett betwene 3. Crowes proper.

Wyckliffe Arg. 5. Fusills in Fesse az. betwene 3. Crowes proper.

[XXXVII]

The Cuckowe.

This Comon birde is expressed amonge the Hæbrewes by many names, as *Kaath, Kik, Schalac, Schachaph* and *Schapha.* The Sirians *Coco.* the Arabians *Banchem* and *Euchem.* The Græcians *Kokkyx* and Kokkyzein, to singe like a Cuckowe, the Cretians at this day *Decocto.* The Latynes *Cucculus* and *Cuccus* and the voyce *Cuculare* as in this vearse.

Et Cuculi cuculant fritinit rauca cicada. ffor the name is taken from the voice vttered by the birde, and not from the Greeke or any other language, which the frenche and Belgians sounde *Cocou.* Albertus calleth this birde *Gugulus,* The Italyans *Cucculo, Cucco, Cuco,* and *Cucho.* The [237v] Spanyardes *Cuclillo.* The Frenche *Cocou, Cocul,* and *Coquu.* The Germans *Gucker, Guggauch, Kuckuck,* the Belgians *Kouckouck* and *Kockuut.* Our Auncients called it in olde tyme a *Gouke,* the Illyrians, at this day *ziezgule.* And this though a base and vulgar birde was called *boni ominis auem,* a birde of good lucke, for the olde Germanes so much obserued the voice thereof, as that thereby they chose their wyves and learned to coniecture the leingth of their oune dayes. Wherefore it was sacred to Iuno beinge pictured sittinge vpon her scepter, and Iupiter is supposed to haue vsed the shape of this birde when first he went a wooinge to Iuno, for which cause hee is sometyme amonge the Auncients called *Cuculus*. The honour of this birdes name is applied to many other thinges both in the Greeke latyne and other languages especiallie to fishes, hearbes, garments, medicines, Cities, sports, and mountaynes which I doe but remember and briefelie passe ouer.

It is a birde deryved by no vnlearned Authours from the race of Haukes. ffor Bellonius writeth that his Countreymen the Frenche haue it in a vulgar Prouerbe, *Falco parens Cuculi,* the Falcon is the father of the Cuckoe, althoughe it resemble not the Syre in any thinge besides the colour, beinge otherwise a base and cowardly Creature: although it be sufficientlie armed both with beake and talents. Wherefore Aristotle concludeth more learnedly, that it is neither a bastard nor any true kinde of Hauke, whose wordes doe thus followe: *Cuculus ex Accipitre fieri, immutata figura, à nonnullis putatur; quoniam quo tempore is apparet, Accipiter ille, cui similis est, non aspicitur; sed ita fere euenit, vt ne cæteri quidem accipitres item cernantur* &c.[245] The Cuckoe hath ben thought to be a kinde of Hauke, bycause the Hauke which it resembleth is not seene after the Cuckoe appeareth. But the same may be obiected against all other Haukes for within [a few] dayes after the Cuckoes voice is first hearde, there are none to be founde, the Cuckoe hidinge herselfe in wynter, and the falcons in sommer. So as it cannot bee of the race of Haukes for the former cause, as also bycause neither head nor feete resemble the Haukes, but rather the wood pigeons. The Hauke hath certeine lynes vpon her feathers, the Cuckoe onelie certeine spotts, and neither their flight nor their foode agree, but many tymes Haukes kill Cuckoes, which no fowles vse to exercise vpon their oune kinde. ffor these reasons the frenche prouerbe is iustly exploded, for Cuckoes and [238r] Haukes (saieth Scaliger) agree like the men of Genoa and Placentia or as the Spanyards and the frenche. Neither is Albertus to be credited while hee writeth, *Cuculus componitur ex Niso & Columba vel ex Columba & Asture, habet enim mores compositos. Ex Columba habet quod non prædatur aues, ex Niso siue Asture quod insidiatur nidis aliarum auium debilium.*[246] The Cuckoe is compounded or generated betwixt a Hobby and a Pigeon, and therefore doth imitate both their natures, for hee taketh it from the Doue that hee preyeth not vpon other birdes. And from the Hobby that it destroyeth the egges and neasts of other weaker fowles. So Albertus. But this their diuersitie of manners ariseth not from their next generation which is false and fayned, no more then it may be saied that an Ape is begotten betwixt a woman and a dog, and yet in some members it is like a man.

Albertus maketh two kindes of Cuckoes, a greater and a lesser. And herein hee dealeth trulie, although in the nature of their generation he altogether fableth, while hee saieth that the greater is bredd betwixt the Buzzarde and the Pigeon, and the second or smaller betwixt the Hobby and the Pigeon. There may be other kindes of Cuckoes vnknowen to vs, which I must passe ouer, and followe the description of these before expressed.

The greater is about twelve inches longe, the beake resemblinge the Ringdoues, except that it is a little thicker, sharper, and more crooked: the vpper part beinge longer then the vnder part which is of a horne colour, and the other blacke. The gapinge or passage of the mouth is of a saffron Colour, the nostrills smooth and broade. The iris of the eyes a bright clay and the apples blacke. The vpper part of a white Ashecolour full of transuer[s?]e browne spotts, the quills of the necke, backe, and wings of a rustye yron colour: yet white on the outsides; the longe feathers haue white brymmes, which stretched out at leingth make a white lyne in the winge. Otherwise their colour is blacke, except [238v] in the middle and the ends, which reache to the middle of the tayle. And the tayle hath three colours therein, blacke, white, and a rustye iron colour: all of them so enterlyned and conioyned, as that the middle part, and the extremities are white.

Their leggs are their least and shortest part respectinge the proportion of their bodye, for their thighes are short and slender, their shankes scarce one ynche longe, and the vpper part is coloured with white feathers hanginge downe from the belly beneath the ioynte, the other part of the legge is of a saffron colour, and so are the feete, whereupon God hath onely bestowed two clawes before, and as many behinde. And so much for the description of the former and greater Cuckoe.

The lesser and smaller differeth not much in leingth, but in thother single parts. The beake is longer and more bendinge but not so thicke. The chappes or partes of the beake altogether in colour like the former: but the gapinge and colour within the beake is a clay colour: the eyes are alsoe like the former: The colour of the vpper parts is a white Ashecolour and somewhat Chesnutt vpon the wings: the head, necke, and rumpe are all of ashecolour. The inner parts of the wings are full of white spotts especiallie the longe feathers which reach to the taile disposed in an elegant order of nature. The like beautie is in their taile consistinge of tenne feathers, hauinge white spotts vpon them resemblinge a heart in figure or fashion, and hauinge as much bare space betwixt them as one can lay his finger, in a very beautifull and pleasant manner: beinge also all white in the extremities, and withinside are besett with white spotts. The belly, breast, and rumpe are ashecolour with some transverse blacke lynes as in some kindes of Haukes. Their leggs short and couered with feathers hauinge litle scales or tabletts for their skynne, and their feete yellowe. The Clawes foure as before, and the greatest is somewhat broader, more crooked, and hollowe then the other: beinge so disposed by Almighty God, that the fowle might stande more firmely vpon the trees wheresoeuer it [239r] pearcheth. The younge Cuckoe at the first after it is newly hatched, is blackishe, and in the belly parts is very like a Sparhawke. And so much for the description of both kindes.

The Cuckoe is an idle and lazy birde, neuer buildinge herselfe a neast, but layinge her eggs in the neasts of other birdes as in Wood-pigeons, hedge-sparrowes, wagtayles or such other like. She layeth but fewe eggs. *Parum generat* (saieth Aristotle) *quia naturæ est frigidæ:* And againe, *Maiore ex parte singula, raro bina.*[247] ffor the most part they lay but one egge, and sieldome two: especially in one neast. She neuer layeth them in an emptie neast but therein where shee findeth eggs: bycause shee knoweth that the birde will not forsake her oune eggs for a strainger: but if shee shoulde lay it in an emptie neast the birde that built it wolde leaue it and neuer hatche a Cuckoes egge, or lay her oune vnto it. Authours doe herein much admire at that naturall discretion which the Grand Creator hath bestowed vpon this siely fowle for the propagation of her oune kinde. ffirst it vnderstandeth her oune frigiditie, or coldnes of nature, vtterly disablinge it to hatche her oune kinde. What then is to be done? Must her kinde be extinguished without remedy? Or must not the weakenes of one birdes nature be supported by the streingth of an other. Nature beinge defectiue in one part is wont to supply by another, want of streingth is recompenced with witt, and Cuckoes breede in the neasts of other fowles, bycause they are not able to make their owne. Wherefore in this one poinct of their generation, the worke of God is wonderfull, and his mercy to his Creature magnificent: for by a secreate sagacity and investigation of nature, they discerne betwixt birdes and birds, that is, betwixt birdes agreeinge with them in foode, and other which doe not, least when the younge is hatched it shoulde perishe for want of naturall sustenance. Wormes and flyes are their meate, and not grayne, wherefore they chuse such birdes to be their nurses as feede on wormes and flyes, and not on grayne and berryes, or ells vpon both as Larkes and hedge-sparrowes. Agayne these little birdes cannot finde foode to satisfie two or many Cuckoes, wherefore the fowle layeth but one egge in their neasts least it shoulde miscarry in their hatchinge, or lacke meate after it is out of the shell. The like respect [239v] they haue to the similitude betwene their oune egges, and those amonge which they leaue them, for if they were not like, the Nurse-birde wolde refuse them for spurious and straingers. And therefore when the yonge are growen greate and fullie feathered, they are lefte by their supposed mother, and betake them to their oune parents, who feede and knowe them to be their oune.

Aristotle and Pliny write alsoe, That when the litle birde that hatcheth them perceiueth that the younge Cuckoe groweth greater then her oune naturall younge ones, shee out of her folly forsaketh her oune and onelie feedeth the Cuckoe, beinge more delighted with the beautifull aspect thereof, then with her owne: and so the naturall birds perishe in the neast of their damme; or els are by her cast out as spurious and straingers. Yet some write that the younge Cuckoe beinge too potent and stronge for their foster sisters doe first preuent them, and lurche* them of their foode, and so they perishe through hunger: and last of all they devoure their Nurce, when they are growen greate, and are ready to flie.

Auicen, Albertus, and others affirme, That when a Cuckoe will lay an egge in another birdes neast, shee first suppeth vp and destroyeth the eggs of the naturall birde, and so leaueth her owne in the roome: whereof the birde beinge glad, and ignoraunt of the deceipt, she hatcheth the Cuckoes in steede of her owne. Augustinus Niphus saieth, that the Cuckoe destroyeth not those eggs which shee findeth in the neast wherein shee leaveth her owne, but mixeth them together, And so it happeneth that the Cuckoes are first hatched, and the other neglected die in the shells. The Frenche call the husband of an adulterous woman *Mary Coqu u* as if the Cuckoe nourishe a bastard breede, which is cleane contrary, for not the Cocke but the other Nurse-bird deserueth that name. Acron the greate Grammarian writinge vpon these wordes of Horace, *Magna compellens voce Cuculum,* seemeth to be the Authour of this opinion, that a *Cuckold* cometh of a *Cuckoe*, for he saieth: *Cuculus hoc vitio naturali laborat, vt oua vbi posuerit oblitus, sæpe*

* *lurche* cheat, rob

aliena calefaciat, vnde rustici sibi obiiciunt, quasi alieni curam sustinentes.[248] The Cuckoe is sicke of the disease of forgetfulnes; for she remembreth not [240r] where shee layeth her oune eggs, wherefore shee mistakinge her oune hatcheth another birds eggs, and thereupon Countrey peasants obiect it to one another and call them Cuckolds which father the adulterous bratts of their wyves. But daily experience teacheth the contrary. ffor not Cuckoes but other birds doe hatche Cuckoes and straingers to their kinde. Yet forasmuch as a Cuckoe is a foolishe birde, and respecteth not so much her breede as her egge, it may well resemble a Cuckolde, that watcheth not his wifes dishonestie but for his oune lusts sake (which shee serueth) reteyneth both a whoore and a bastard alsoe. *Iniustus est qui repudiat castam. Impius qui retinet adulteram.* He is not iust which putteth away a chast wife, and hee is vngodly which reteyneth an adulteresse, althoughe with her teares and cryes she ouercome him. And such a one is tearmed by Iuuenal *Curruca,* a Cuckolde or hedge-sparrowe. Satyre. 6.

> *Tu tibi nunc, Curruca, places, fletumque labellis*
> *Exorbes* &c.[249]

> Thou art nowe pleasde o Cuckolde base,
> (Or if thou wilt, hedge-sparrowe milde)
> To suppe the teares of Venus face,
> A foole to father a bastard childe.

Soe that a Cuckolde is not derived of the Cuckoe but of *Curruca,* a hedge-sparrowe that fostereth the Cuckoes breede in steede of his oune. And in Italy such a Cuckolde is called *Cornuto,* a horned man, as if like a beast, hee cared not who couered his wife. The true cause why onely the Cuckoe amonge all other fowles doeth thus putt furth her eggs to be hatched by another is diuerslie disputed amonge Philosophers. One assigneth this: *Cum se ignauum, minimeque opitulandi potentem nouerit, facit quasi supposititios pullos suos, quo seruari possint.*[250] Shee knoweth her oune lazy and abiect infirmitie, to hatche and breede her younge, and therefore is content to putt them to hazard to be nourished by another, bycause shee wolde by some meanes preserue her oune generation. Pliny assigneth another [240v] reason: *Invisum se scit cunctis auibus. Nam minutæ quæque eum infestant auiculæ, ab iisque vellitur, ita vt præ metu earum fugiat. Quare non fore tutum generi suo opinatur, nisi fefellerit, ideoque nullum facit nidum trepidum animal.* The Cuckoe knoweth howe much she is envied of other fowles, for euery small birde doth hunt and annoy her dryvinge her from place to place. Wherefore she thinketh that it is not safe for her to builde a neast like other birds, and therefore by deceipt ouercommeth her foes, makinge those birds to breede her younge that labour to destroy them when they are olde. ffor saieth Theophrastus, *Cuculi genus non extaret, nisi oua sua alieno nido supponeret.*[251] The race of Cuckoes wolde be extinguished vnlesse they were bredd in other birds neasts. Aristotle assigneth no other cause but the conscience of their oune frigiditie, as I haue alreadie touched. And that if any man did euer see a neast of younge Cuckoes (saieth Dr Wootton) I will neither refuse his knowledge nor swearue from this comon receiued opinion, for both may stande together: I will therefore conclude this history of their generation with that Apologue of Plutarke in the life of Aratus,[252] wherein the Cuckoe is set furth complayninge against the other small birdes, bycause they hate and feare her, demaundinge the reason of this their hostilitie, whome they make this aunsweare, *Suspicamur te aliquando futurum Accipitrem,* bycause by the feathers wee suspect thou wilt proue a Hauke.

The voice of this birde is *Coco,* without alteration, and the often reiteration thereof breedeth no delight in the hearer: yet Pliny tearmeth it *Cantum,* a songe, or rather a Cuckoes songe, resemblinge a songe in nothinge, although Martiall say.

Quamuis per multos Cuculus cantauerit annos.[253]

They beginne to singe in the Springe, and ende in Iune, or Iuly, givinge over in the Sommer or hote weather, [241r] bycause (some say) they feare the Canicular dayes; Pliny calleth it therefore *aliter temporariam,* bycause in Sommer, Autumne, and winter they are hidden, and appeare onely in the Springe time. Neither is there any Creature except a Serpent called *Amphisbæna* or double-head (bycause it goeth both wayes) that after it hath lyen close all the wynter, doth so soone apprehend the Springe euen in colde weather: ffor in wynter they lye in hollowe trees or Rockes scabbed and without feathers vnable to flie, and feedinge vpon such wormes and flies as haue there also taken vp their lodginge. Scaliger applieth these vearses of Æschilus made vpon the Lapwinge to the Cuckoe.

τοῦτον δ'ἐπόπτην ἔποπα τῶν αὐτοῦ κακῶν /
πεποικίλωκε[254]

Then did hee make the witnesse of his woe,
The partie coloured bird called the Cuckoe:

Him holdinge fast astonisht all with dread:
Which late was wilde, the bird of Rocke I heed
That in the Springe which vnto colde did yeelde,
Shakes of her rustie feathers in the field.
One [hiewe?]* it hath vntill the Autumne blowe,
And then those feathers of for age doe flowe.

By which vearses wee obserue, that their feathers chainge thrise in the yere, once after the wynter in the beginninge of the Springe: and those againe in Haruest or a litle before the Corne growe yellowe. They are founde in all the places of the worlde except in the West India, and all Æthiopia; in those Countrey[s] (saieth Aluarez) the Spanyard.)[255] they neuer see any Cuckoes. They loue the Rockes and steepe places, and those Cuckoes which loue and haunt the rockes builde neasts for to lay their younge in, but other breede as afore saide. The other race of Cuckoes in the Springe and some part of the Sommer sett vpon the greene boughes and afterwarde creepe into hollowe trees or into Rockes or sometymes in [241v] the bankes of Riuers and ditches, especially those who haue ben bredde in the neasts of ground Larkes. They haue a Tale in Germany That when a Countreyman had layed a hollowe logge on the fire in the wynter tyme, wherein lay a Cuckoe, at the first feelinge of the heate, the bird thinkinge it to be Sommer cried out *Cooco* in his naturall voice. And the like wee haue in England of a younge married couple, who beinge desirous to growe riche by keepinge of Pigeons, bought (as they thought) a paire at the markett, and bringinge them home kept them in a Corner of a benche, not farre from their fire, wherein they beinge extraordinarily warmed one night, and supposinge out of their naturall presage, it had ben Sommer, and that Cinthiaes Sunne had so heated them, began to crye out in their oune voice not *knoo knoo* like pigeons, or Doues, but playne *Cooco* like the fowle wee haue in hand, to the greate discomfort of the newe married folke, *quasi mali ominis auis,* like a birde that foretolde no good fortune to them: ffor here our people doe not either after the olde poeticall fashion nor the Italian fashion nowe at this day in vse take the Cuckoe to be a bird of good fortune sent from Iuno to blesse their marriage, but rather a hatefull prognostication of the husbands hornes, or the wifes death. At this day in some Countreys when a man heareth first the Cuckoe, hee asketh her howe many yeres hee shall lyve, and then after the quæstion hearkeneth to the nomber of the reiterated voices vttered

* [*hiewe?*] color

in that place where hee first heard her, whereby hee maketh his coniecture of the leingth of his oune life, accountinge euery note or sound of the Cuckoe for a yeres life vnto himselfe. And this hee doeth very wisely, as if hee wolde giue the Cockoe a legacye in his will orells leaue him to haue the wardshippe of his Sonne.

Yet trulie and out of nature, they collect some ordinary and reasonable presages from Cuckoes. ffirst they neuer come abroade till the winter be ended. ffor as the Chaffynche sheweth the wynter, so the Cuckoe sheweth the Springe, the Swallowe the Sommer, and the Eatefigge [242r] the Autumne, euery season or quarter of the yeere hauinge a birde to be his Heraulde or Proclaymer, as wee haue already shewed in the History of the Chaffynche. The Cuckoe is also a benefitt to the Husbandmen, for his comminge and goinge sheweth them a newe season accordinge to this olde vearse.

ἦμος κόκκυξ κοκκύζει δρυὸς ἐν πετάλοισι[256]

When Cuckoe doth singe vpon the greene boughe:
Then into the earth let enter your ploughe:

When they come and singe neere a City or enter into it, or Cryinge flye over it, it portendeth tempests and ill weather. Leander in his History of Lombardy[257] telleth an accident that befell Irprandus as hee was in the very action of Crowni[n]ge or inauguration after the death of his father, Liutprandue Kinge of Lombards. ffor at that tyme, as his speare remayned fixed on the grounde, there came a Cuckoe, and sate vpon it, which fell out vnhappilie for him. ffor the people out of that presage helde him vnworthie of his fathers Crown. Some say that when Cockoes singe neere Townes or houses, it presignifieth dearth of Corne: In Germany if they heare a Cuckoe after Midsommer day, they feare the well ripeninge of their grapes, that yere. But I will leave the presages, and proceede to other parts of their History.

They flie but lowe, and in an interrupted strayne risinge and fallinge, bycause of their weakenes: resemblinge (saieth Aristotle) the least kinde of Haukes, and by this kinde of flight shee after deceaueth the Hauke, saieth Oppianus.

Accipitrem cauta cuccus sic decipit astu,
Dum vagus incertas itque reditque vias.[258]

The Cuckoe deceiueth the Hawke her foe:
When goinge and comminge she flieth lowe.

By reason of his weake flight, they cannot crosse the Seas of themselues, (saieth Isidorus) but are carryed vpon the winges of Kytes, least they shoulde fall downe and be drowned. Therefore [242v] they are resemblances of vs weake men whose imperfections are so greate, that euen our most vertuous actions doe waxe and wayne like the Moone or fishe of a Cockle, and rise and fall like the flight of a Cuckoe: but wee coulde neuer passe ouer the longe and wide Sea of this troublesome workinge worlde vpon our oune wings, vnlesse wee were supported by and vpon the wings of our highe flyinge and ascendinge Sauiour. ffor as Moses saieth to the people of Israel, whome God brought out of Ægipt, ouer the redd Sea, into the earthlie Chanaan, hee stretched out his winges like an Eagle, and tooke them vp to carry them vpon his shoulders: so doth our Lord Iesus vpon the wings of Angels carry vs out of the body ouer the red, fiery, and burninge regions vp to the heauenly Canaan: ffor as they passed through water and earth to come to Palestine, so must wee through aer and fire to goe to our heauenly kingdome.

This fowle lyveth vpon wormes, flyes, gnatts, mothes, and other Insects. And therefore they are not rauenous and spoilers of other. Howsoeuer by the receiued opinion of all auncient Authours, they are condemned for murtherers of their fosterers and their issue. But the greatest quæstion is howe they lyve in wynter: when they lye in Rockes or holes of bankes and hollowe trees, without feathers not once able to stirre abroade. Hereunto there are two common and vsuall aunsweares. ffirst although it be not denyed but that like Emmets, they may treasure vp some provision against the wynter, yet it cannot bee but they choose such places of harbour, wherein they finde some foode of wormes, flyes, and other such thinges, and of them they raise their foode in the wynter tyme; vpon which they are maynetained, although in neuer so simple and pernicious manner, yet sufficient to contayne life vntill their tyme of openinge come againe. Secondly it is certeyne that Beares, Tortoyses, and Serpents lyve in the wynter tyme without meate by reason of their colde nature. And therefore also may the Cuckoe, beinge the coldest of all fowles lye still and sleepe in the wynter tyme without foode or naturall nourishment, other then the remaynder of such as shee tooke in the Sommer season. But this is most certeine, that [243r] there be Swallowes in Sarmatia Europia which in the wynter tyme lyve frozen vp in yce, and yet in the Springe when the yce dissolueth they are alyve and fly away. And by the same reason may Cuckooes lyve vnfedd in holes, Rockes, and hollowe trees, where there is lesse colde and more meanes to contynue life, then to the Swallowes lyvinge vnder colde yce.

ffor whosoeuer hath founde a Cuckoe in wynter hath also found with her some things whereof she might eate if famyne constrayned her thereunto, as euery mans experience can readilie witnesse.

These Cuckoes are a base and fearefull Creature, beinge afraide of euery small birde. Wherefore the Authours of Hieroglophickes doe picture a Cuckoe to signifie a Coward and fearefull man. So bycause they lyve vpon gnatts and flies, in the same learninge they signifie the extirpation of such Creatures. In Phoenicia they reape their Corne at the sound and singinge of the Cuckoe, bycause their harvest is much more earely then in any part of Europe. And for this cause also a Cuckoe signified both the Springe and the haruest. The subtilitie of this birde hath sufficientlie appeared in that she layeth her younge amonge her enemyes eggs, euen in the midst, least it shoulde be descryed, and turned out of the neast, *Cuculus semper in alieno nido parit, non bis in eodem,* saieth the Prouerbe. The Cuckoe will neuer deceiue one birde twice, or lay twice in one neast, which is a part of a Craftie foxe, who to avoide the detection of his oune fraude, will not twice vse one shifte, or deceiue one man. *Astutior Coccyge,* saieth another Prouerbe, more subtile then a Cuckoe. When our oune turne is serued by the labour of another without hire or rewarde, euen as the Cuckoe preserueth her race in other birds neasts, without so much as thankes for all their labour and paynes. Vnto this part also belongeth their singuler ingratitude to their fosterers or Nurses, either killinge them orells their other naturall younge: for which cause they are also an Embleame of iniquitie and vnthankefulnes, of all which together Alciatus maketh this Embleme inscribed *Cuculus,* a Cuckoe:

Ruricolas, agreste genus, plerique Cuculos
Cur vocitent? quænam prodita causa fuit?
Vere nouo cantat Coccyx, quo tempore vites
Qui non absoluit, iure vocatur iners.
[243v] *Fert oua in nidos alienos, qualiter ille*
Cui Thalamum prodit vxor adulterio.[259]

Why doe so many call the race of Countrey Clownes
Cuckoes, what is their cause assignd?
In Springe the Cuckoe sends her twise doubled sounds
and blames the hand that hath not prunde his vyne.
Shee leaues her younge in neasts of forreyne breede
like a false spouse defilde with strangers seede.

In olde tyme when a man had not cutt his vynes before the Cuckoe came, the Passengers wolde crye vnto them *Cuckoe,* for saieth Pliny: *Dedecus habetur, opprobriumque meritum falcem ab illa volucre in vite deprehendi, vt ob id petulantiæ sales etiam in primo vere ludantur.*[260] It was accounted a greate shame, that at Cuckoe tyme, men were founde cuttinge and pruninge their vynes, and therefore they were mocked with insolent meryments bycause the Cuckoes voice is not fortunate to vndressed vynes. *Probra canunt seris cultoribus,* saieth Ausonius, they sound out scoffes to the slouthfull and negligent vinedressers.

Cuckoes by reason of their often reiterated voyces are the Moralls of vayne boasters, Thrasonians, and as wee say Braggadocians. for as she scorneth all other notes and voyces, Cryinge nothinge but her oune name even vnto a tædious importunitie: So they loue to talke of nothinge but themselues and their oune acts, envyinge the iust prayses and merits of other men, and extollinge the dunghills of their oune fame, aboue the sweetest mountaynes of the best deseruers. And herein they want not their Complices and Abbettors to sweare their dignitie, and disgrace their enemyes, even as may appeare by this old Apologue which I here expresse followinge.[261] The Cuckoe and the Nightingale come together and at one tyme of the yere vtter their diuers voices; It happened that one day as they mett they fell at varyance and contention about their sounds, which of them sange the sweetest notes. ffor decision whereof they submitted and referred themselues to the vmpire of an Asse bycause they thought by reason of his longe eares, hee was the fittest hearer and discerner of sounds. Who hauinge heard them both pronounced sentence for the Cuckoe [244r] against the Nightingale. But shee appealed to Man, before whome through her diligent and sweete songe, was reuersed the Asses iudgement, and shee recouered her oune credit. Whereby it is evident, that amonge Asses greate talkers are best esteemed, but amonge wisemen sweete songs and wise sayings are better accompted then lowde bablinge and importunate exclamations.

The Cuckoe discordeth with all birdes except the Kite. There is not a little fowle but at birdinge and layinge tyme is at varyance with it; as if by nature they knewe that a Cuckoe is the enemye and Corrupter of their neasts, as Pullen crye out at the sight of a snake. Some assigne the cause of the birdes hatred against the Cuckoe to be her similitude with a Hauke, which is most hatefull to all Fowle, and therefore they take revenge vpon the Cuckoe for hatred to Hawkes. There is also an irreconcileable warre betwixt Cuckoes and Grassehoppers, for it is written that Cuckoes kill them till the Dog-starre arise: but afterwards the grassehoppers creepe vnder the winges of Cuckoes in greate nombers and byte them to death, orells so afflict them with payne that they pyne away through sorrowe and want of rest. And bycause of the Grassehoppers, Cuckoes giue over singinge at Hay harvest, for feare least their oune voyces betraye them to their enemyes.

Isidore writeth a greater wonder, which (if it be true) causeth much matter to magnifie our Creatours greatenes: *Ex Cuculi saliua cicadas gigni quæ mox natæ infenso animo aggrediuntur cuculum, & ad mortem vsque, diuexant sane naturæ lege, vt qui Nutricem suam interemit, ipse quoque ab hiis, quas eius excrementa pepererunt morte mulcetur.*[262] Out of the Cuckoes spittle are Grassehoppers begotten. And they againe so soone as they are able are enraged to the death of the Cuckoe: for it hath pleased the Creatour, that as this bird is the death of his fosterer, so out of her oune excrement shoulde be bredd a siely Creature to putt her to death that had so vnnaturally devoured another. There is a Mountayne in Greece called in olde tyme Thornax or Diccius,[263] where Plutarke writeth there grewe an holme [244v] tree, that like birdlyme ensnareth all kyndes of birdes, that sitt thereupon except Cuckoes. And if our Authour say true in this, then is this tree a friende to Cuckoes and enemye to all other kindes of fowles.

They resemble other ravenous byrdes, bycause in the wynter they deplume and loose their feathers, for by reason of their former foode scabbes growe vpon them, and cast of their feathers, and then they appeare like a naked goose full of sharpe feather rootes. And bycause of this sicknes the Hæbrewes call the birde *Scaphah.* They are also vexed through their colde nature with a perpetuall costivenes: for ease whereof (like Hawkes) they eate wilde prunes, which procure a present loosenesse.

These birdes haue ben supposed to be forbidden by the lawe of Moses to be eaten, yet the olde Græcians in Aristotles tyme, and also the Italians at this day doe eate younge Cuckoes, before they flye and feede themselues, affirminge that there is no fowle sweeter or of more gratefull savour and rellishe. But after the tyme they flie abroade and feede themselues, they are not eaten, no not of the poorest nor meanest people.

They are also vsed for medicine, for Pliny saieth, *Auis cuculus leporina pelle alligatus somnos allicit.*[264] A Cuckoe wrapped vp in a Hares skynne procureth sleepe. The dunge of Cuckoes is prescribed against the perill of death by the bytinge of a madde dogge. The ashes of a Cuckoe burnt with her feathers, and taken in oyle are good against the paynes of the belly and stomacke. Pliny relateth a magicall or superstitious obseruation about Cuckoes, which for a conclusion I will relate, not for the truth thereof but for the strangenes, and to lett my Reader knowe all sorts of devises incident to our story. If a man saieth hee marke the place where his right foote standeth when first hee heareth this birde, and there fashion out the proportion of his saide foote, and afterwarde digge vp the earth within the same and drye it to powder, the same sprinckled abroade killeth gnatts and flies and hindereth their generation that yere. And thus much for the Cuckoe.

[245r] These Birdes followinge doe alsoe beseache your Lordshippe; That they together with the former may haue their Natures emblazoned to the worlde vnder your honorable Name. And their vnworthy Heraulde shall endeauour with his vttermost skill to expresse in them the wonderfull workes of God to his vnspeakeable praise; and the contynuance of your Noble Loue-Learninge-vertues amonge all Posteritye.

D.

Dabchicke. Colymbus
Daker hen. Crex.
Dawe. Monedula.
Didapper. Vrinator
Doue. Columba
Dotterel. Auis Simplex
Ducke & Drake. Anates

E.

Eagle. Aquila
Bastard Eagle. Percnopterus
Eagret. Asterias
Eatbee. Apiaster
Eatecorne. Frugipeta.
Eatefigge. Ficedula
Embriz. Emberiza

F.

Falcon. Falco
Feasant. Fasianus
Feldifare. Collurio
Flaxfinch. Linaria
Flybiters Duditae
Forketayle Biforcata.

G.

Gannet Penelope
Gelgorst. Luteus
Gerfalcon. Girfalco
Globyrd. Lampyris
Goatehead. Capriceps
Goate Sucker. Caprimulgus
Godwitt. Attagena.
Goldfynche. Carduelis
Goose. Anser
Goshauke. Accipiter palumbarius
Greenefynche. Vireo
Gryffon. Gryps
Griglecocke. Grigallus
Gnatt Snapper. Ficedula
Grosbeake. Coccothrauste
Gull. Gauia.

H.

Haggard. Falco gibbosus
Harefoote. Lagopus
Harpyes. Harpyae
Haslehen Gallina Coryllorum
Hawke. Accipiter
[245v] Henharrower. Rubitarius.
Herle. Morillo
Hearne Ardea
Hearonsew. Ardeola
Hickwall. Iynx
Hill-owle. Aluco
Hobby. Nisus fringillarius
Howlett. Vlula
Howpe. Vpupa

I.

Iay. Pica glandaria
Iay of the water Gracculus palmipes

K.

Kernel. Cercella.
Kaiuk. Virginia.
Kestrel. Tinnunculus.
Kingsfisher Alcedo
Krency. Hellorius
Kyte. Miluus.

L.

Lanar Buzzard Lanarius
Lapwinge Capella
Larke. Alauda
Larke of the wood. Acredula
Lynet. Linaria
Loxey Loxia

M.

Manasseneau. Virginia.
Martlet. Cypsellus.
Marten. Riparia.
Maypye. Sitta.
Mauis. Turdus.
Meessenouns. Virginia.
Merlyn. Æsalon.
Murreybyrd. Fasces.
Moore hen. Fulix.
Moore tetter. Rubetra.
Mudwall. Picus martius.
Musket. Percnus.
Muskyn. Parus.

N.

Naffe. Vria.
Night byrde. Scopes.
Nightingale. Lascinia.
Nimurder. Collurio.
Nuttiobber. Sitta

O.

Oedicney. Charadrius
Oester. Tabanus
Olyue. Oliua
Owle. Bubo
Shrich owle. Stryx
Horne-owle. Asio
Eare-owle
Hybris
Osprey. Halyaetus
Owsell. Merula
Ostridge. Struthio camelus
Oxeye. Crepera.

[246r] P.

Parret Psittacus
Partridge Perdix
Peacocke. Pauo
Pelican Pelicanus
Penguyn Pinguizia
Phoenix Phoenix
Pockway } Virginia.
Poucqueo }
Poppogottuweo }
Pochard. Boscas
Pynnocke. Curruca
Pye. Pica
Plouer Pluuialis
Ploides
Plungeon Phalacrocorax
Puet Phalaris
Puffyn Puffinus
Puttocke. Idem quod Kyte

Q.

Quayle. Coturnix
Quayle leader Ortygometra

R.

Rayle. Rallus
Rauen. Coruus
Redfalcon. Rubrifalconus
Redshanke. Porphyrio
Redtayle Fenicurus
Reede byrd
Redstart. Ruticilla
Rhintases. Rinoceros
Ringtayle. Tarquisilla
Ringdoue. Palumbus
Robyn redbreast Rubecula
Rooke Cornix frugiuora
Rowsett. Lussiniola

S.

Sacar. Melanaetus
Seamewe. Cepphus
Seacob. Larus
Seapye. Garrulus
Charadrius
Sheldapple. Idem quod Chaf-
fynche.
Sheldrake. Cataracta
Shoueler. Platalea
Siskin. Ligurinus
Snype. Rusticula minor
Sparrowe. Mistruthium
Hedge sparrowe. Sepiarius
Red sparrowe. Iunco
Speigh. Idem quod woodpecker
Swallowe. Hyrundo
Sea swallowe. Drepanis
Siren. Serinus
Sirenes
Stare. Sturnus
Starre. Stella.
Sterne. Sterna
Stockdoue. Liuia
Stonefalcon Lapidarius
Stubble byrd. Stoporola
Stimphalides
[246v] Sukyus Idem quod Chaf-
fynche
Swanne. Cygnus

T.

Tele. Querquedula
Teauh. Virginia
Thistle lynet. Acanthys
Titlinge. Lingetta
Titmose. Parus
Throstle. Bebriacensis
Thrushe. Idem quod Mauis
Treefalcon. Arborarius
Turkey Cocke. Gallo pauus
Turtle. Turtur.

V.

Vrion. Argatulis
Vyne byrde. Vitiflora
Vultur or Geyre. Vultur

W.

Wagtayle. Motacilla
Watercrowe. Cornix aquatica
Water hen. Tringa
Water swallowe. Cinclus
Westerne. Idem quod Marten
Wigeon. Glaucium
Wittwall. Galbula
Woodcocke. Gallinago
Woodspecker. Picus martius
Sea woodcocke. Trochilos
Wynter Crowe. Cornix Cinerea
Wren. Regulus
Regulialus
Wrynecke. Iynx

Y.

Yelamber. Cittrinella

[247r]

I must craue pardon for these Coates of the chough
Which weare omitted by my writer in their right
order and therefore I thought this last quire to
be the fittest place to conteine them rather
then to conceale them vtterly.

Many and diuers Gentlemen haue made vse of these Choughes in their Coates and Crosts [*sic.*] whose names as many as I coulde gett I will here briefelie describe.

Sir Lawrence Ailmer Maior of London. Arg. on a playne Crosse engrailed Sab. fyne besaunts. betwene foure Cornishe Choughes, proper within a border gobinated Azur & purpur.

Barret of Wilteshire. Arg. a Leopards head. Gules betwene. fyue Cornishe Choughes. proper. 3. in Chiefe. and two in base.

Baynard of Norff Sab. Or. a fesse Or. 3. Cornishe Choughes. proper betwene. 2. Cheuerons. of the Second.

Byscley of Notinghamshire. Or. a Cheueron engrayled Sab. betwene 3. Cornishe Choughes proper.

Caldebecke. or Candebecke. Arg. 3. Cinquepyles in Cheueron betwene 2. Cottises Sab. &. 3. Cornishe Choughes proper.

Carlile of the North Arg. on a Cheueron Sab. 3. Starrs. Or. betwene. as many Cornishe Choughes proper.

Corbin. Or. 3. Cornishe Choughes proper.

Cornwall a Cornishe Choughe proper sett on a Wreathe Arg. &. Gules

Cornwallys of Suffolke Sab. guttye. Arg. on a fesse of the second 3. Cornishe Choughes proper.

[247v] Creyke of Yorkeshire party per fesse. Arg. & Sab. a pale. counterchaingde & 3. Cornishe Choughes proper.

Crowton Arg. a Cheueron Gules. betwene 3. Cornishe Choughes proper.

Danyell. Arg. a Fesse. Sab betwene. 3. Cornishe Choughes proper.

Dawson of Yorkeshire Azur. a Cheueron Ermyn betwene. 3. Arrowes palewayes. Or. attyred Arg. on a Cheife of the fourthe. as many Cornishe Choughes. proper. & a daxster canton gules. charged with one mullet of the thirde.

Drywood of Essex Or. a Lyon passant gardant. Sab. betwene 3. Cornishe Choughes proper.

Dodson of Cornwall. Arg. a bend engrailed Azure. betwene 3. Cornishe Choughes proper

Elrington of Essex Arg. a Fesse dance Sab. bosants. betwene 6. Cornishe Choughes proper.

Ermigle Arg. on a Fesse Gules. 3. Cornishe Choughes proper. betwene sixe bolletts of the second.

Gestwike of Bedf. Arg. a bend Gules betwene 2. Cottises. Sab. & sixe Cornishe Choughes proper One Cheife. Or. charged with 3. mullets vert.

Iones. sometymes Mr. of Paules Schoole. Arg. a Cornishe Choughe. betwene 3. Pheons gules.

Mussenden of Lincolneshire. Or. a playne Crosse engrailed in the dexter quarter a Cornishe Choughe proper.

Offley of London Arg. a Crosse pale. Azure betwene 4. Cornishe Choughes proper.

Prinston of Oxon. Arg. 3. Cornishe Choughes proper

Pector of Deuon. Gules. on a bend Or. one Cornishe Choughe proper. & two Cinquefoyles Azure. betwene as many Escallop shells. Arg.

Pulter of Hartfordshire. Arg. 2. Cottesses. in a bend. Sab. the Cheife part charged with one Cornishe Choughe proper.

Ryse of Wales. Or. a Cheueron. Sab. betwixt three [248r] Cornishe Choughes. proper.

Siluester of Oxon. party per Cheueron. Or & Arg. three Cornishe Choughes proper. 2. in Chiefe &. 1. in base.

The Lord Scrope. two Cornishe Choughes proper for his Supportors.

Stanford Arg. a Cheueron Sab. betwene 3. Cornishe Choughes proper.

Tato Maior of London party por Fesse. Or. &. Gules. 3. Cornishe Choughes proper. & a pale countor chaingde.

Tawyer of Northamptonshire. Or. on a fesse Sab. 3. Mascles. verded. Arg. betwene as many Cornishe Choughes proper.

Tregam of Cornewall Arg. a Cheueron Sab. betwene 3. Cornishe Choughes. proper.

Treheiron of Cornewall Arg. a Cheueron Sab. betwene 3. Cornishe Choughes proper on a dexter canton barre of 8. pieces. Or &. Àrg. a Lion rampant ouer all Gules.

Trenonour of Cornewall. Arg. a Cheueron Sab. betwene 3. Cornishe Choughes risinge proper.

Trywynard of Cornwall. Arg. a Fesse Azure. betwene 3. Cornishe Choughes. with wings displayed proper.

Walthall of London Or. a Cheueron vert betwene 3. Cornishe Choughes proper.

Williams of Dorsetshire. Arg. a Greyhound Current in Fesse Sab. betwene 3. Cornishe Choughes proper. within a border engrailed. Gul. charged. with foure besants. & as many Crosses formy. Or.

Wolsey Cardinall. Sab. on a playne Crosse engrailed. Arg. A Lion Passant. Gul. &. 4. Leopards heads. Azure. a Chiefe. Or. charged with one rose & the third. betwene 2. Cornishe Choughes proper.

Wrytt of Wilteshire. Arg. a fesse Gules. betwene 3. Cornishe Choughes. proper.

Wytman of Middlesex. Arg. on a bend. Sab. 3. Leopards heads Or. betwene as many Cornishe Choughes proper.

[248v—blank]

NOTES

Notes

THE NOTES below pertain mostly to the location of quotations in the text. The text of Topsell's quotations often varies from Aldrovandi's, both often from standard editions. Such liberties, common in Renaissance practice, are here usually disregarded when the text makes sense. Titles and editions used in compiling the notes are abbreviated, but are fully listed in the Bibliography.

Ornithological information is provided in the head note on each bird. As almost all of Topsell's illustrations are copied from Aldrovandi, only exceptions and some unusual variations are noted. Whereas A. often labels his drawings "Mas" and "Foemina," T. copies without distinction, and always the original is debased; sharp outline had to await the metal engraver. Head notes designate locations where the bird is treated in the first editions of Topsell's three main authorities. A. (Aldrovandi, his chief source) and B. (Belon) are listed by book and chapter, G. (Gesner) by page numbers. Identification of the birds must often remain tentative, sometimes impossible. Helpful in this task has been the *Ornithology of Francis Willughby,* 1678, by John Ray, who had frequent occasion to identify the birds of Aldrovandi in the modern vernacular. Use has been made also of *A Dictionary of Birds,* by Alfred Newton, of *A Dictionary of English and Folk-Names of British Birds,* by H. K. Swann, of *Provincial Names and Folk Lore of British Birds,* by Charles Swainson, and of *Key to the Names of British Birds,* by R. D. Macleod. Scientific names follow the most recent order of classification. The notes are listed by italic letters for the Dedication and Prolegomena, by numerals for the text; in each case the location in the original manuscript is indicated parenthetically.

Notes on Dedication and Prolegomena (2r–21v)

a(2r) Judges 5:6, ". . . in the days of Jael, the highways were unoccupied, and the travellers walked through byways" (A.V.).

b(2v) Augustine, *Contra litteras Petiliani Donatistae,* 3.7 (Migne, *P.L.,* 43, p. 352). Below (3r), *Nephalium* (Gr. *nephalion*), an ancient Greek libation of water and mead offered to rustic divinities; or perhaps biblical Nephthalim (Naphtali), sixth son of Jacob, his territory favorable to growing of fruits and olives. *Phelleo* = Gr. *pella,* a cup(?).

c(3r) Aelian, *Variae Historiae,* 4.27, where Diogenes thus thanks Diotimus Carystius.

d(4r) Fulgosus, or Fregosa, Battista, *Factorum* ... (Paris, 1578), 8.8, f. 285v, subheading "De Ocio"; T. adjusted text liberally. The delightful story of John the Evangelist probably appeared in various Renaissance encyclopedias.

e(7v–8v) The "text" is Leviticus 11:13–20, similar to Deut. 14:12ff., in the Vulgate; the "Glose" is Strabus' *Glossa Ordinaria* (Migne, *P.L.,* 113) with additions by Nicolaus de Lyra. T. applies Strabus on the eagle to the goshawk and osprey, and is similarly free elsewhere. But the birds in Leviticus have been translated in various ways. T. cites the Bible from imperfect memory, so that one cannot discover which English version he used.

f(9v) The following argument against augury was well founded in Catholic Europe in view of the prohibition of this practice by the Council of Trent (1545–63).

g(10r) Topsell confuses *faustus* and *nefaustus,* lucky and unlucky, with *fastus* and *nefastus,* good and evil.

h(10v) Plautus, *Epidicus,* II, 2. The source of this "Iambick," added below by T. to his original, has not been found.

i(10v) *Dionysii Halicarnassii Antiquitatvm siue Originum Romanorum Libri X* (Lyons, 1555), Bk. 2, pp. 136–137.

j(11r) Plautus, *Asinaria,* II.1. On *parra,* translated here as "Colmouse," see n. 219 (227r). Below: Cicero, *De Divinatione,* 1.39. sec. 85.

k(11r) *Iliad,* 12.237–240. This is the only Greek passage which is not transliterated into the Roman alphabet.

l(11v) The story of Publius Claudius is elaborated on 172r. On the contrary, instead of "a happie victory," the disastrous defeat of the Romans in this naval battle was attributed to the impiety of their admiral.

m(12r) *Aen.,* 3.88–89. Below: *De Divinatione,* 2.36.

n(12r) Livy, *History of Rome,* 5, 38. In the battle on the Allia the Romans were defeated by the Gauls, in 390 B.C.

o(12v) *Aen.,* 3.359 and 361. Properly, "Ah Trojan, interpreter of the gods who perceivest..." (*sentis*).

p(12v) Livy, *History of Rome,* 6.41.

q(13r) *Iliad,* 12.243 and 241. (Aldrovandi does not thus reverse the lines.)

r(13v) Eusebius, *Preparation for the Gospel,* ed. Gifford, 9.4.

s(14r–v) For thrush, raven, and swallows see Pliny, 59.60 and 53.

t(15r) The Mantuan source has not been found. Above, *Aquileia,* a town at head of Adriatic, is confused with Aquila, birthplace of Sallust, in the Abruzzi.

u(16r) Martial, *Epode,* 13.75 (again quoted, 211r). Below (16v): Pliny, 17.22.

v(17v) More widely known through the Middle Ages was the "Charadrius"

(Stone Curlew *Burhinus oedicnemus*), which, confronting a sick man, looked at him if he was to recover, away if he was to die. A wealth of lore concerned knowledge of how birds cured themselves, chiefly by means of herbs.

w(18r) Aelian, *De Anim. Nat.*, 17.22, describes the "orio," heron-sized, red-legged, blue-eyed, and burning with a love song which Siren-like draws the hearer. Below (18r): Diodorus, *Library of History*, 2.4.

x(18v) Jeremiah 15:3, "... the sword to slay, the dogs to tear, and the fowls ..." (A.V.).

y(18v) Theophrastus, *Enquiry into Plants*, Minor Works, *Concerning Weather Signs*, sec. 17 (Loeb, II, 401).

Notes on Text

1(22r) King Henry IV to Robert Cecil, ambassador to France and later Earl of Salisbury: "I am censured amongst you, to be sold over to idleness and delight . . . and, as I know my frailty is a scar in my forehead, so . . . I doubt not but I may be numbered (if not amongst the better sort) yet not among the vilest rank of Princes," 23 March, 1597 (Birch, *An Historical View of the Negotiations* ..., p. 110).

2(22v) Thus Topsell wholly disregards any classification of birds. Aldrovandi, following Belon, had grouped them according to habitat—water and land.

3(22v) T.'s folio numbers apply to the 1606 ed. of Ramusio's *Navigationi e Viaggi, Terzo Volume*, which includes part of *De Orbe Novo* by Peter Martyr (folios 1–36), Oviedo's *Sommario . . . della sua Historia* (folios 37–60) and Oviedo's *L'Historia generale, & naturale dell' Indie occidentali, diuisa in libri xx* (folios 61–186), besides other works. Oviedo's descriptions of the Alcatraz occur on folio 49 B–D and folio 136 B–D. R. Eden translated Martyr and Oviedo in part in 1555, STC 647, but T's second passage on the Alcatraz occurs only in the expanded version by Lok, 1612, STC 650. T.'s odd spelling "Alcatrax" is found only in Eden's 1555 text, folio 191r, as a marginal gloss.

I. Alcatraz (22r)

Alcatraz or *Alcaduz* is from Gk. *Kados*, water pot, bucket, applied to Pelican from resemblance to its pouch (Newton, p. 6). A.19.2, B.3.2, G. pp. 241 (Alcatraz) and 605 (Onocrotalus). European White Pelican *Pelicanus onocrotalus* and West Indian Brown Pelican *Pelicanus occidentalis occidentalis*. On the different manner of fishing of the two species, see 24v–25r and note. This bird affords all writers ample scope for the fabrications on the capacity of the pouch; see notes.

4(23r) Turner's accounts of the Pelican appear pp. 124–126 and in letter to Gesner, pp. xii–xiv (ed. Evans); from the latter come Topsell's allusions here and later (25r).

5(23v) See Perottus, *Cornucopiae* (Venice, 1513), p. 691, where he states he has witnessed this sight, though his account is only a variation of Pliny's (10.66); cf. note 9(24v).

6(24r) Odoric, contained in Ramusio, Vol. 2, thus describes the geese of South China ("Manzi"), near Canton ("Ceuscala") folios 248v–249; see also *The Journal of Odoric*, text from Hakluyt, 1599 (*Travels of Sir John Mandeville*, ed. Pollard) ch. 8, p. 341. Taking their cue from Hakluyt's marginal gloss T. and A. identify the "geese" as pelicans, alcatrazes, which are described as West Indian by Peter Martyr in *De Orbe Novo*, 1530 and 1587, in Ramusio, Vol. 3; see further, n. 10 (24v–25r).

7(24r) Albertus, *De Animalibus*, 23.131 and 132, states only that there are two genera of pelicans, water and land. These include two species of Onocrotalus and two of Pellicanus. T. abbreviates the Albertus quotation from A.3.51.

8(24v) Martial, *Epigrams*, 11.21.10.

9(24v) Pliny on the Pelican (10.66), here garbled, states that the bird has a kind of second stomach in its throat. The full pouch is disgorged into the beak, then received in the true stomach.

10(24v–25r) Peter Martyr (*De Orbe Novo*, 1587, Decade 7, chapter 8, pp. 510–511) describes the fishing of the New World Brown Pelican, which plunges from the air, whereas the European White Pelican fishes indeed "like a swanne," as Gesner states.

11(25v) This method of capture of pelicans by "Spaniards" is recounted by Horapollo (Horus Apollo), *Hieroglyphica*, 53 (Lyons, 1621), p. 62, who writes of Egyptians. The same emblem is continued on 27r.

12(26r) The work by Kiranides has not been accessible. Such account of the enmity and battles of birds is believed to have an astronomical origin, according to Thompson, Preface to *Glossary of Greek Birds*; see further 232v–233r.

13(26v) This sentence has not been located in the *Hexaemeron* of Ambrose; for birds see 5.12–24 (Migne, *P.L.*, 14), pp. 235–255.

14(27r) Orus; see n. 11(25v).

15(27v) For first quatrain see Alciati, Emblem 90 "Gula"; for that below, Emblem 95 "In garrulum gulosum." The translations typify the free hand of Topsell who, improvising a quatrain, often does violence to the Latin text.

16(27v) The proverb reads "leg," not "winge" (Tilley, pp. 375–376).

II. Alchata

A.15.7–8, B.6.21, G. p. 294. Stock Dove *Columba oenas*, which, however, was often confused with Rock Dove *Columba livia*, ancestor of the domestic pigeon.

17(28v) Gesner on Alchata is paraphrased. "Potissimum," thus mistranslated, means *chiefly*.

18(28v) Athenaeus, *Deipnosophists* 9.394 explains the dissemination of "mistletoe" (ἰξίας) by means of birds. Pliny, 22.21, calls the plant chameleon (pine thistle, *Atractylis gummifera*) and relates *Ixia* with viscidity.

19(28v) Topsell's reference to Turner's ignorance of Alchata (*Vinago* or Rock Dove, Evans, p. 62) is rare evidence of direct acquaintance with Turner's work, for neither Gesner nor Aldrovandi mentions this odd lapse.

III. Artennah (29r)

A.19.3, B.3.2, G. p. 367. A Shearwater, perhaps Cory's *Procellaria diomedia.*

20(29r) For entire account see Strabo, *Geography*, 6.9.

21(29v) Aelian, *De Anim. Nat.*, 1.1.

22(29v) Silenus is described by Aldrovandi (19.3) as a teller of fabulous stories; Comutas is "filius Steneli, vel . . . Cyllabari," see Catalog of Proper Names. For the metamorphosis see Ovid, *Met.*, 14.447–511.

23(30r) First two lines, Ovid, *Met.*, 14.508–509; latter two, *Met.*, 14.502–503.

24(30v) Pliny, 10.61, supplied most of the entire account.

25(31r) Shearwaters have many nests in their colonies, but only *one* egg in each. Their moaning notes have often, as below, been compared to "the cryinge of children" (see Robert Murphy, *The Oceanic Birds of South America*, II, 660, 676, 687). Albertus states that the Diomedean bird "fovet in hyeme" (6.18), but (23.42) writes nothing on "Gurguliones."

IV. Virginia Birds (31v–32r)

The four "Virginea" birds (31v–32r), three arranged vertically on f. 31v, are drawn and colored from copies tracing to lost originals executed by John White, who in 1585 accompanied Thomas Hariot to the New World. These birds, bearing Algonquin Indian names have been identified as follows: *Aushouetta*=female Red-eyed Towhee *Pipilo erythrophthalmus erythrophthalmus* (the male being pictured under another name on 85v); *Aupseo*=Eastern Bluebird *Sialia sialis sialis*; and *Aiussaco*=Yellow-shafted Flicker *Colaptes auratus*. The fourth bird, *Artamokes*=Blue Jay *Cyanocitta cristata,* described, however, in terms more applicable to the Mockingbird *Mimus polyglottos polyglottos*. For full account of these and six more North American birds (81v, 85r–v, 86r, and 206v) see Harrison, *John White and Edward Topsell.*

V. Barnacle (32v)

Drawing combines two blocks from A. and presents adult bird above four chicks swimming but lacks A.'s overhanging tree, reeds, and distant mountain.

A.19.23, B. (lacking), G. p. 107. Barnacle *Branta leucopsis*, or Brent Goose *Branta bernicle.* The legend of the generation of Barnacle Geese, rejected in the thirteenth century by Albert the Great and occasionally questioned in later centuries, was popularized further by John Gerard in his *Herball*, 1597, and continued on every hand to be spread abroad, even in verse. Sylvester's translation of Du Bartas (1605, Week 1, Day 6, p. 22) elaborately describes "those Goslings hatcht of Trees." Michael Drayton, well acquainted with recent scientific authority, devotes a full passage in *Polyolbion* (Song XXVII) to the trees:

> . . . from which those Tree-geese grow,
> Call'd *Barnacles* by us, which like a Jelly first
> To the beholder seeme, then by the fluxure nurst,
> Still great and greater thrive, until you well may see
> Them turn'd to perfect Fowles, . . .
> Which well our Ancients did among our Wonders place.

For a full consideration of this "wonder" see Edward Heron-Allen, *Barnacles in Nature and Myth*, London, 1928. T.'s translation from A. stands as the most comprehensive review to date in English of the myth which with other evidences of spontaneous generation was soon to become obsolete.

26(33r) For the "Hollanders" see Ramusio, III, 408v, or Gerritt de Veer, *A True Description of Three Voyages . . .* (i.e., 1594, 1595, 1596), Hakluyt Soc. Publication XIII, 1853, pp. 79–81. The *Voyages,* translated into English in 1609 by Wm. Phillip, marks the first true account of the nesting of the Barnacle Goose.

27(33r) Albertus, *De Animalibus,* 23.31: "Et hoc omnino absurdum est quia ego et multi mecum de sociis vidimus eas et coire et ovare et pullos nutrire sicut in antehabitis diximus."

28(33v) Aeneas Sylvius, *Historia de Europa,* ch. xlvi (*Opera quae extant omnia,* Basle, 1561), p. 443. Below: Hector Boece, *Scotorum Historiae* (Paris, 1574), fol. 8v–9, or *Description of Scotland,* ch. 11 (Holinshed's *Chronicles,* 1577).

29(33v–34r) This account of the sodden ship mast which Topsell examined on the Sussex coast appears to be from direct observation. It is advanced as evidence linked with Turner's that barnacles "are bredd in moe places than one," that is, in Ireland as well as Scotland.

30(34r) Turner (ed. Evans), p. 26.

31(34v) Not from Isidore but from Vincent of Beauvais, *Speculum Quadruplex* (1624), vol. 1, 16.40. For account of error and full quotation see Heron-Allen, p. 30 and notes, pp. 132–133, 146.

32(34v) T. (and A.) would have it both ways: Barnacles "breede by copulation who were begotten by putrefaction."

33(34v) On Ephemeros see Aristotle, *H.A.,* 5.552b, 18–23 and Turner, p. 28. The Latin quote is Aldrovandi's alone; Aristotle says nothing of putrefaction or ships.

34(35r) J. C. Scaliger, "Ata," *Poemata . . .* (Heidelberg, 1591), Pars Altera, Ee lv, p. 66.

VI. Bat (35r)

A.9.1, B.2.39, G. pp. 733–739. Although the bat had been recognized as a mammal since Aristotle, flight put it among birds, "wherein appeareth the power and wisdome of the blessed Trinitie who without feathers and quills causeth this Creature to mount aloft in the aer." No question here is involved for Topsell, who later (71v–72r) blithely accepts as bird a West Indian firefly found, among other sources, in Moffet's *Theatrum . . . Insectorum.*

35(35r) Varro, as quoted by Nonius, *De Compendiosa Doctrina,* 1.46–47 (ed. Lindsay, I, 67), and by N. Perotti, *Cornucopiae* (Basle, 1532), column 1205, ll. 57–58.

36(35v) Nonius (see n. 35). Below: Ovid, *Met.,* 4.415 and Albertus, *De Anim.,* 23.142.

37(35v) Aristotle, *De Part. Anim.,* 4.697b, 1–3.

38(36r) Plato, *Republic,* 5.479, alludes to riddle of eunuch; Scholiast gives entire riddle as above (*Scholia Platonica,* ed. Greene, p. 235).

39(36r) The Sempronius riddle has not been located.

40(36r) Ovid, *Met.,* 4.389–390, states that the three women were changed respectively into a crow, a bat, and an owl.

41(37r) Pliny, 10.81.

42(37v) Ovid, *Met.,* 4.414.

43(37v) Alexander Aphrodisiensis' *Problemata,* translated into Latin by T. Gaza (Rome, 1475), Bk. 1, Sec. 66, fol. 260; for the present passage Aldrovandi cites Bk. 1, ch. 66). For the sense of the passage see *The Problemes* of Aristotle (1595, S.T.C. 763), Sec. xx, sig. K3v–K4.

44(38r) Petrarch, *Rime,* 19.1–4.

45(38r) Athenaeus, *Deipnosophists,* 6.238. T.'s liberties in translation are obvious.

46(38r) Lucian, *A True Story,* Bk. 2 (ed. Loeb, I, 337).

47(38r) Ovid, *Met.,* 4.412–413, and below, 407–408.

48(38v) *Odyssey,* 12.434 and, below, 24.6.

49(38v) Peter Martyr, *De Orbe Novo* (Paris, 1587), Decade 2, ch. 4, and Decade 3, ch. 6.

50(38v–39r) "One prince Herodotus," mistranslation of "principsque Herodotus" (Pliny, 12.42), that is, first of all, Herodotus. Cited by Pliny, Herodotus (3.110) writes of Arabians, not East Indians.

51(39r) 1 Samuel 17:7: "and the staff of his spear was like a weaver's beam: . . ." (A.V.).

52(39v) Basil, *Commentarius in Isaiam Prophetam.* Cap. II (Migne, *P.G.*, 30, p. 278).

53(40r) This, not from Aldrovandi, has not been identified.

54(40r) Basil, *Homilia VIII* in *Hexaemeron* (Migne, *P.G.*, 29, p. 182), where the Latin text differs considerably from that followed by A. and T.

55(40r) Alciati, Emblems 62 "Vespertilio" and (last four lines) 61. The translation seems to regard neither punctuation nor meaning of the original.

56(40v) Strabo, *Geography*, 16.1.7. Below: J. C. Scaliger, *Exoter. Exercit.* (Frankfurt, 1601), 15.36.3, p. 754. These are the *Pteropodidae*, or Fruit-eating Bats.

57(40v) Aldrovandi, 9.1, legend: "Monachus moribundus a Vespertilione sanatur."

58(41v) Serenus, XXIV entitled "Pilis quibus (cum) que internecandis," 11.663–664 (*Corpus Medicorum Latinorum*, ed. Vollmer, II, pt. 3).

VII. Bergander (42r)

Drawing is the only one from Belon. A.19.19, B.3.5, G. p. 155. Shelduck *Tadorna tadorna*. Except for its size and nesting habits, the description only loosely fits this beautiful duck with its conspicuous chestnut breast band. As a rare addition, T. notes its presence on the Thames and Sussex coast.

59(42r) Contrary to T.'s etymology, *Bergander* derives from M. E. *berz*, shelter or burrow, plus *gander*. German *bergente* means "mountain duck." But the old name *burrow* or *burrough* duck derives from the bird's habit of nesting in rock crevices or rabbit burrows.

60(42v) Aelian, *De Anim. Nat.*, 5.30 (15.51, in ed. P. Gillius, Lyons, 1535).

61(42v) Pliny, 10.29. Below: Aretaeus, 8.13, 8 (*Corpus Medicorum Graecorum*, ed. Hude, II, 169).

VIII. Bramlyn (43r)

A.18.7, B.7.29, G. p. 374. Brambling *Fringilla montifringilla*. Topsell knew this bird as only a winter resident in England. As a cage bird and mimic, the Brambling makes only "as good musicke as dry chippings doe good meate." When birds are thus forced upon his attention, the author is at his best.

62(43v) Alciati's Emblem 100, "In quatuor tempora anni," is later applied to the Chaffinch (78r), also a fringillid.

IX. Bullfynche (44r)

A.71.31, B.7.9 (only mentioned), G. pp. 701–702. Bullfinch *Pyrrhula pyrrhula*. The excellent description here traces to the observations of Turner, but see note below.

63(44v) Turner's account of the summer and winter habitat of the Robin (ed. Evans, p. 156) is here transferred to the Bullfinch, which "nec locum mutat" (p. 160). Otherwise Topsell (and A.) follows Turner closely.

X. Bunting (45r)

A.17.29, B.5.23, G. pp. 628, or 614, 697. Sky Lark *Alauda arvensis.* Turner had identified the English "Bunting" as the Stonechat *Saxicola torquata* as distinct from Linnet *Carduelis flavirostris* (ed. Evans, p. 158). Topsell is wide of the mark in his equation with Sky Lark, and so later, following A., in describing the "Cenchram" kinds (76v–77r).

XI. Bustard (45v)

A.13.12, B.5.3, G. pp. 466–472. Great Bustard *Otis tarda.* No longer present in Britain, this handsome fowl, not uncommon in Topsell's day, was described even as late as Wordsworth, who ("Guilt and Sorrow," 1791–94, ll.106–108) on Salisbury Plain saw this "shy tenant" which

> . . . gave a mournful shriek,
> And half upon the ground, with strange affright,
> Forced hard against the wind a thick unwieldy flight.

The bird's interest in horses, so aptly explained by Plutarch (see note 70 below), became well known to emblematists and writers like Oppian.

64(45v) Isidore, *Etym.*, 12.7 (Migne, *P.L.*, 82, p. 460).

65(45v–46r) The word *Bustard* or *Bistard* is anglicized Spanish *avutarde,* Italian *ottarda,* French *bistarde*, all from Pliny's *avis tarda*, a misnomer for a bird so swift on foot and in flight.

66(46v) Athenaeus, 9.390.

67(46v) Hector Boece, *Scotorum Historiae* (Paris, 1574), f. 7v, or *Description of Scotland,* ch. 8 (Holinshed's *Chronicles,* 1577).

68(47r–v) Aelian, *De Anim. Nat.*, 6.34 or *Opera omnia,* ed. Gesner (Zurich, 1556) 2.28, p. 39, or ed. P. Gillius (Lyons, 1535), 7.28, p. 210.

69(47v) Oppian, *Cynegetica,* 2.407 and 432, mentions only love of bustard for horse and partridge for deer. The entire passage appears in this author's *De Aucupio* with paraphrase by Eutecnius (Zurich, 1776), Bk. 3, sec. 8, p. 340.

70(47v) Horapollo (Lyons, 1621), Bk. 3, p. 79, writes of a bustard, "Haec enim equo conspecto protinus auolat," which signifies, "Debiliorem hominem, quem validior ac potentior, insectetur, volentes designare, otidem & equum pingunt." So T.'s account. Plutarch (*Moralia,* 981 B) states aptly that this bird is attracted to horses by the food in their dung.

71(48r) Unlike Athenaeus, 9.390, Pliny does not confuse *Otis* (bustard), 10.22, and *Otus* (owl), 10.23.

XII. Bald-Buzzard (48v)

A.5.8, B.2.12–14, G. pp. 48, 192, 199. Marsh Harrier *Circus aeruginosus,* correctly identified by Turner as "Balbushard," Bald Buzzard (ed. Evans, p. 32), quoted by Gesner, p. 192, and called by the French "Hobreau." Aristotle's "Subbuteo," Turner believes, is the bird "quem Angli ringtalum appellant" (p. 18) or Ringtail, French "Blanchequeue," namely, the female Hen Harrier *Circus cyaneus*. The Bald Buzzard was identified by even later writers with Osprey *Pandion haliaetus*, exclusively a fish eater.

72(48v) Aristotle, *H.A.*, 9.620a.19 and Gaza's text (Turner, ed. Evans, p. 15), which Topsell freely adapts.

73(49v) Belon, 2.12. The combat below (50r) engages a Bald-Buzzard (*Hobreau*) and a Ringtail (*Blanchequeue* or *Oiseau saint Martin*).

74(49v) Collaboration of dog and bird is described by George Turberville, *Booke of Faulconrie* (1575), f. 54. Cf. Spenser, *The Faerie Queene*, 3.8.33:

> Like as a fearefull partridge, that is fledd
> From the sharpe hauke, which her attached neare,
> And fals to ground, to seeke for succor theare,
> Wheareas the hungry spaniells she does spye,
> With greedy jawes her ready for to tere; . . .

75(50r) Plutarch, *Life of Pelopidas*, sec. 1 (Loeb, *Lives*, V, 341), states only that Antigonus' soldier suffered from a secret disease. The story is borrowed by John Fletcher in *An Humorous Lieutenant*, where the title character has the pox.

XIII. Buzzard (50v)

A.5.7, B.2.9, G. p. 45 Buzzard *Buteo buteo*. The French Buzzard, from Belon, seems to be the Rough-legged *Buteo lagopus*, pictured in A. examining a captured snake which is omitted from T.'s drawing; in neither illustration, however, are the legs feathered all the way. Alternative to Rough-legged would be Short-toed Eagle *Circaëtus gallicus*, which unlike the former is a breeding bird in Central Europe. The Italian bird may be the Honey Buzzard *Pernis apivorus*.

76(50v) Not Terence, but Catullus, 86.3. Below: Festus, *de Verborum Significatione*, Bk. 1, closely followed by A.: "vastitatis est causa, quae intraverit, ut Bubo . . ." Topsell's text often varies.

77(52r) Belon, 2.9, pp. 100–101.

78(52v) This lone German proverb A. found in Gesner.

79(52v) *Oppiani et Nicandri quae supersunt*, in *Poetae Bucoli et Didactici* ed. Lehrs, et al., Paris, 1862), Part 2, Bk. 1, sec. 6, p. 109.

80(52v) Athenaeus, 7.299c. Topsell omits "from the Maeander."

81(53r) Festus, 1: "Buteo genus avis, quae ex eo se alit, quod accipitri eripuerit . . ."; for continuation see n. 76(50v).

82(53r) Pliny, 10.69.

83(53v) Albertus, 23.29.

84(53v) Pliny, 10.9. The augur is Phoemonoe, priestess at Delphi. Below: G. B. Porta, *Phytognomonica* . . . (Frankfurt, 1591), 3.44, p. 218 and 4.19, p. 278. For Leah and mandrakes see Genesis 30:14–16.

XIV. Bittour (54r)

Drawing shows snake in bill and coiled about neck. A.20.16 and 17, B.4.4, G. p. 208. Bittern *Botaurus stellaris*. The "lesser" is the Squacco Heron *Ardeola ralloides*, the "Crested" more clearly the common Heron *Ardea cinerea*. The "fourth with a ringe about his necke" is completely unidentifiable. Methods of fishing and means of "roaring" were fair game for mythographers. Chaucer's bittern "bombleth in the myre" (Wife of Bath's Tale, 972). And Drayton (*Polyolbion*, Song XXV):

> . . . in some small Reedy bed, . . .
> The Buzzing Bitter sits, which through his hollow Bill,
> A sudden bellowing sends, which many times doth fill
> The neighboring *Marsh* with noyse, as though a Bull did roare.

85(54r) "De Philomela," title of three poems of unknown authorship (*Poetae Latini Minores*, ed. Baehrens), V, no. LXI, l.42.
86(56r) On Phoix, see Pausanias, *Description of Greece*, ch. 29, "Phocis," which tells of wife of Ocnus and of ass.
87(56r) Alciati, Emblem 83, "Ignaui." Below: Apollonius, in *Life of Apollonius*, by Philostratus, 1.7.
88(56v) Passage unidentified.

XV. Blackbird (57r)

A.16.6–18, B.6.25–28, G. pp. 579–584. Blackbird *Turdus merula*. Of the thirteen further kinds the first three may be dismissed as albinos or part-albinos. Ray-Willughby state that white Blackbirds are encountered in Apennines and Alps, that a parti-colored one was seen in a Roman poulterer's shop, and that such alterations are due to effects of cold and snow (see further, Thompson, *Glossary*, p. 101). The "Mountayne blackbird" (58v) = female Ring Ouzel *Merula torquata*, the following bird being the male, "a ringe about his necke." The "rose coloured blackmacke" (60r) = Rose-coloured Starling *Sturnus roseus*. The "Black-macke of Brasilia" (and perhaps the footless one following) = the Brazilian Scarlet-breasted Tanager *Lamprotes loricatus*. Finally, the Alpine "nutbreaker" (61r) = Nutcracker *Nucifraga caryocatactes*. The author is more interested in the lore of their capture and fattening for the table than in their songs, on which he is content to quote Aelian.

89(57v) For Arcadian White Blackbirds, see Aristotle, *H.A.*, 9.617a, 19. Below: Varro, *Rerum rusticarum*, 3.9.17.
90(61r) Aelian, *De Nat. Anim.*, 8.24, notes the sweet singing of blackbirds, but not in these words. Below: *Fringultire*, to twitter, is good Latin, Topsell's *frindulciere*, a coinage.
91(61r) "De Philomela," ll. 13–14; see n. 85(54r).
92(61v) Albertus, 23.128.
93(61v) Theocritus, *Epigrams*, 4.9–10.

94(61v) Varro, *Rerum rusticarum,* 3.3.
95(62r) Aristotle, *H.A.*, 5.544a, 27.
96(62v) *Ibid.*, 9.609b, 8–12 (cf. n. 12).
97(63r) *Ars Poetica,* 457–459. Below: *Satires* II, 8.89–91.
98(63r) For Nicostratus see *Comicorum atticorum fragmenta* (ed. Kock), II, 219–229.
99(63v) Cure of spots is based upon the doctrine of signatures, that, in the shapes of leaves, for example, plants bear the secrets to their medicinal use.

XVI. Birds of Paradise (64r)

A.12.21–26, B.1.24 (only mentioned), G. pp. 611–614. Birds of Paradise *Paradisidae.* Chief of the authors who repeated the fictions concerning Birds of Paradise was Jerome Cardan, in *De Subtilitate* (1553), whose opinions were refuted by J. C. Scaliger, in *Exotericarum Exercitationum* (1557). As the legs, and, frequently, wings and head were removed prior to shipment from the East, the birds were supposed to live and breed in the air, never alighting upon earth. Belon identified them with the mythical Phoenix; Antonio Pigafetta, who had seen them in the Moluccas, described the legs (1536); Aldrovandi refuted both Belon and Pigafetta, Topsell adds chiefly denial of the Earthly Paradise as the home of Birds of Paradise (see further Harrison, "Phoenix Redivivus," pp. 173–180). The only comparable marvels are the birds of Ethiopia and Hispaniola, here appended, which the author found in Uretta and Ramusio.
100(64v) Sir John Harington, *Orlando Furioso* (ed. 1607).
101(64v) A.'s "upupa," the hoopoe, is misconstrued as "lapwinge," as often in biblical translation; (see n. *e*).
102(65r–v) This awkward sentence renders Aldrovandi, 12.21: "Manucodiatis omnibus certam magnitudinem assignari non posse, satis e[x] iis, quae iam dicta sunt, constare arbitror."
103(68r) Luis de Urreta, *Historia eclesiastica* . . . , Valencia, 1610 (see Introd.). Having read Aldrovandi, Urreta transfers the Birds of Paradise to Ethiopia under another name (p. 257): "la aue que aca llamamos del Parayso, o como llaman en la Etiopia Camenios, que quiere dezir Cameleon del ayre."
104(69r) "The Mountayne Amara" replaces Aldrovandi's "in maria Moluchis Insulis" (12.21). There is, in Ethiopia, a Mt. Amara which Urreta describes as the haunt of Birds of Paradise (see n. above).
105(69r) Belon, *Les Observations de Plusieurs Singularitez* . . . (Paris, 1553), 1.25, pp. 190–191, and *Histoire . . . des Oyseaux* (1555), 6.35, pp. 329–331. Janissaries are Turks, not "Indians."
106(69v) According to A. (12.21), this emblem is by Luca Contile; see *Ragionamento* . . . , Pavia, 1574, 77v–78r, where he provides the Impresa of Alessandro Farra with a bird in flight, the motto being "Sine Pondere Svrsvm."

107(69v) By "Indian" the author means West Indian, from account by Peter Martyr and Oviedo in Ramusio, Volume III.

108(69v–70r) With these original comments on the incredible cf. Spenser, *Faerie Queene,* Proem, Bk. 2, Stanzas 2–3:

> But let that man with better sence advize,
> That of the world least part to us is red;
> And daily how through hardy enterprize
> Many great Regions are discovered, . . .
> And later times thinges more unknowne shall show.
> Why then should witlesse man so much misweene,
> That nothing is but that which he hath seene?

and also *Cymbeline* 3.4.139–140:

> Hath Britain all the sun that shines? Day, night,
> Are they not but in Britain?

109(70r) Of the Suhayo Urreta writes (p. 96): "Los Persianos y Turcos las estiman para poner y aderiçar sus turbantes, en tanto, que acontece dar de vna de estas plumas hallandola a comprar, quatro y cinco, y a vezes seys zequies, o escudos, tan bellas y lindas son; tiene por nombre Suhayo."

110(70r) The bird with no "excrementary" except upon the back is T's addition of a Bird of Paradise fiction; "in the water" is surely a slip for "in the air." Below: the "Cancancello," apparently lacking in Urreta, provides Topsell with discourse upon flatterers (70r).

111(70v) The Catalinitas, writes Urreta (p. 268), people take "por tan grande castigo y flagello de Dios." The account of the Ruc, below, which Urreta acknowledges he took from Paulus Venetus (Marco Polo) and Joseph Acosta, includes the usual features which T. takes over (p. 350): "la hechura y forma como Aguilas . . . las plumas de las alas tienen cada vna doze passos de largo . . . de tal suerte, que agarra de vn Elefante, y se lo sube y lleua bolando por los ayres . . ."

112(71r–v) The Supiniminis, which tends the flower Ghoyahula, delights both Urreta (pp. 291–292) and T., who renders the entire account: "Quando la flor est à abierta, . . . se pone encima de la flor, tecogiendo en si todo su olor y perfume; y hecho esto se pone a cantar suauissimamente, . . ." This is a fanciful description of one of the African Sunbirds (*Nectariniidae*).

113(71v) The account of the Nesir derives, not from Urreta, but closely from Leo Africanus, whom Topsell read either in the translation by John Pory (1600), *A Geographical Historie of Africa,* Bk. 9 (Hakluyt Soc. Repr. vol. 94, p. 956) or in Ramusio, vol. I (6 edd. 1550–1713); T.'s "Buett" is Italian *buettere,* a rapacious bird (probably a vulture). Below: The Indian "Night-birds," are freely adapted from Oviedo, in Ramusio, vol. III, 14.7.

114 (71v–72r) From Ramusio "Volume 3, fol. 140" Topsell draws Peter Martyr's account of the "Cucuie," a West Indian Firefly, which he terms "a birde"

(in the Projected List he calls it *Globyrd*). This firefly had been drawn by John White, of the Ralegh expedition to Virginia, the drawing sent to Thomas Penny in England who pictured and described this insect for *Theatrum . . . Insectorum,* edited after Penny's death by Thomas Moffet (London, 1634), English translation by John Rowland, 1658 (see Raven, *English Naturalists,* p. 223). Instead of "eyes vnder his wings" this insect has "two golden studs or bosses hard by the neck, out of which the glittering rayes, especially when it flies and the wings are opened, do issue with marvellous glory" (*Theater of Insects,* p. 977). Topsell's error is curious, for he knew the work of Penny and Moffet in manuscript. Du Bartas thus describes this wonder (Fifth Day, First Week) tr. Sylvester, London, 1605, pp. 179–180:

> New-Spaynes Cucuio, in his forhead brings
> Two burning Lamps, two vnderneath his wings:
> Whose shining Rayes serue oft in darkest night, . . .
> The Vsurer, to count his glistring treasures:
> The learned Scribe, to limne his golden measures.

115(72r) The "Amphibion" is simply another name for the Osprey *Pandion haliaetus,* whose webbed and taloned feet are traditional and account for this newly fabricated name. William Harrison (*Description of Britain*, Holinshed, *Chronicles,* I, 382) writes that he has never seen an Osprey and hence, as regards the feet, "whether it be so or not, I refer to the further search and trial thereof to some other."

XVII. Canaries (74r)

A.18.4–5, B.7.14, G. pp. 1, 248, 249. Greenfinch *Chloris chloris.* The wild Canary *Serinus canarius,* native in the Canaries, Madeiras, and Azores and imported into Europe early in the sixteenth century, was first described by Gesner as reported by two men, one of whom was Turner. The Siskin, he writes, is "huius generis, quas Anglia aues canarias uocat" (ed. Evans, p. 108). George Gascoigne, in "Complaint of Philomene," 1.33, names "Canara byrds." In addition to Turner's account of Greenfinch, Topsell draws also from Turner's notes on Siskin *Carduelis spinus* and Yellowhammer *Emberiza citrinella,* all being relatives of the imported kind. The imported "Indian Canary" (76r) may be the Chinese Greenfinch *Chloris sinica.*

116(74r) Not "greate doggs," but harmonious sounds, "ex canorarum genere, quas a loco vnde afferuntur, Passeres Canarienses, vel Canarios" (A.18.5). Pliny, 6.37, citing authority of Juba, states *canaria* derives "a multitudine canum ingentis magnitudinis." A.'s *canorarum* is used as substantive, "singing (birds)"; *canarius* = pertaining to dogs.

117(74v) The Epigram, states A.(18.5), was written by a certain German "periti Germani cuiusdam." In the translation *Maxima moles* (greatest weight or might) becomes "Eagle great!" The final sentence literally translated: Therefore, lyre and strings of the cithara, do you declare our (bird) silent or, if it is right, without the muse.

XVIII. Cenchram (76v)

A.13.24, B.5.20, G. p. 366. Corn Bunting *Emberiza calandra.* Of this one bird, Gesner's *Emberiza alba*, wrote Willughby-Ray (p. 268), "Aldrovandus makes four, giving us the Bunting under the title of *Emberiza alba:* of *Alaudae congener;* of *Cenchramus Bellonii;* also (if we be not much mistaken) of *Calandra;* all of which he exhibits for distinct species." The Cenchram was associated with *Ortygometra*, or Corncrake *Crex crex*, truly "Quail-leader," for this bird is now known to accompany quails in migration.

118(77r) Varro, *Rerum rusticarum*, 3.5.2.

119(77r) Aristotle, *H.A.*, 8.597b, 15–18 (Gaza's translation in Turner, ed. Evans, p. 128). Below (77v): Pliny, 10.33. Here Aristotle's *Glottis*=Gaza's *Lingulaca* (Turner, p. 104); Topsell translates "Linguacula" as "Crane"! The bird is unidentified, but is possibly the long-tongued Wryneck *Jynx torquilla* (see Thompson, *Glossary*). Aldrovandi follows Turner (p. 128) in tentatively identifying Ortygometra with Scrica or "Schreeke" (Owl or Swift) or, as Turner adds, with Daker Hen (the Corncrake).

XIX. Cercyon (77v)

Source of T.'s drawing has not been found. A.20.57, B.1.24 (only mentioned), G.p.593. For this bird from Aelian Gesner suggests *Tringa*, *Cinclus*, or *Junco*, that is, Water Rail, Sandpiper, or Reed Sparrow. More likely it is one of the Mynahs *Gracula.*

120(77v–78r) Aelian, 16.3.

XX. Chaffinch (78r)

A.18.6, B.1.23, G. p. 373. Chaffinch *Fringilla coelebs* The capture and care of this popular cage bird engages the author for the most part.

121(78v) Alciati, 100 "In quatuor tempora anni." T. quotes directly from Alciati, whose lines are lacking in A. For *ficedula* as "Eat-figge" see Projected List (Appendix I).

122(78v) Plautus, *Casina,* III.2.49.

123(79v) Gesner first observed that in winter chaffinch sexes live apart.

XXI. Chalander (79v)

A.18.13, B.5.24, G. p. 76. Calandra Lark *Melanocorypha calandra.* This songster, "being of very good taste & nourishment," has the advantage over the Chaffinch.

XXII. Chough (80v)

A.12.7–9, B.6.5–6, G. pp. 501–509. Chough or Cornish Chough *Coracia pyrrhocorax,* correctly described except for "clay colour head, & backe," which are black; and the bill is decurved. The "mountaine Chough," or Alpine *Coracia gracculus,* has a straight, yellow bill, not "crooked like a halfe bowe, of a red colour like a pomegarnett" (82r). The two birds were often confused; see Turner below. The "Barbarian Chough" (81v), space for the drawing left blank, is the North American Common Grackle *Quiscalus quiscala.* The author names only the commonest of all, the Jackdaw, "Cad-dawe," *Corvus monedula,* then adds three others.

124(80v) Festus, Bk. 7. A.12.6: ". . . vel quod ex oliuetis cubitum sese recipientes binas baccas pedibus, ore vero tertiam ferant." The word *baccas* is taken by A.'s engraver to mean *sprigs* and hence so translated and pictured by Topsell; *bacca* is the fruit or berry. Above the description of the Crow (*coracias*), 82r, stands the figure holding a sprig in its bill, none in feet.

125(81r) Turner (p. 90) equates Cornish with Alpine Chough, which alone has the straight, yellow bill. Even Longolius, a foreigner, had described the Cornish "rubro rostro" (G2r), which is decurved.

126(82v) Described only as "nostri aeui poeta" (A.12.6).

127(83r) The latter two proverbs appear in Erasmus' *Adagia,* 43A and 164B respectively (Tilley, pp. 620, 621).

128(83r) Encelius, *De re metallica,* Frankfurt, 1551, 3.54, p. 243.

129(83r) *Iliad,* 17.755–757.

130(83v) Aristophanes, *Birds,* 86, where, however, the bird has *flown away* in fear.

131(83v) This is not a translation from Pindar, but see *Olympian,* 2.87, where the eagle may stand for Pindar, crows for Bacchylides and Simonides. The account, below, of snaring cranes does not appear in the *Cynegetica* of Oppian.

132(84v) Theophylactus Simocatus, "Epist. Them. ad *Chrysip.*" (A.) has not been available. For the verse below on the Aesopian Chough A. designates "doctissimam aeui poetam."

133 The story of devils as choughs has not been found in Athenaeus.

XXIII. Virginia Birds (85r–86r)

Four North American birds are here pictured, two of which are described: *Chuquareo,* "resemblinge our owsell" = (male) Red-wing *Agelaius phoeniceus; Chuwheeo,* the "Virginian pye" = (male) Red-eyed Towhee *Pipilo erythrophthalmus erythrophthalmus; Chawankus* = Baltimore (?) Oriole *Icterus galbula;* and *Chungent,* "a Virginia water bird" = Common Loon *Gavia immer.* See also 31v–32r and head note IV.

XXIV. Colmouse (86v)

A.12.45, B.4.27, G. pp. 575–578. Bee-eater *Merops apiaster.* "Gnatsnapper" is an old name for this bird; the other is clearly erroneous. *Colmouse,* from Ger. *kohlmeise,* Turner (p. 130) rightly identifies with the Great Tit *Parus major;* later the name was applied to the Coal Tit *Parus ater.* After A., T. describes as a "second kinde" the Blue-cheeked Bee-eater *Merops superciliosus,* an African and Asian species.

134(86v) On confusion over the identity of "parra" see n. 219 (227r).

135(87v) Albertus (24.128) writes nothing on the note of the Bee-eater. The couplet is from "de Philomela" ll. 43–44; see n. 85 (54r).

136(88r) *Georgics,* 4.13–14.

137(88r) Aristotle, *H.A.,* 9.615b, 24–26; cf. also Turner, p. 112.

138(88v) Last two lines of Alciati, Emblem 186 "Dicta septem sapientum."

XXV. Corlieu (89r)

A.20.21, B.4.12, G. pp. 215–216. (Greater) Curlew *Numenius arquata* and Whimbrel *Numenius phaeopus.* This bird is less accurately defined as "a water fowle," the first line, than as a lover of "the meddowes and sea sydes," last line. Drayton describes the bird as "scratching in the Oose and Ore" (*The Man in the Moone,* 206).

XXVI. Cormorant (90r)

Of eleven drawings four and all but head of fifth appear to be fabricated by the English artist: "another C.," "Daucher," body of "Great Goose" C. (96r), C. "Shildrake," and "Great Goose" C. (98r). A.19.56–59, B.3.7–10, G. pp. 118–131. The true cormorants are, as the author indicates, the sea c. or Shag *Phalacrocorax aristotelis* and the inland Cormorant *Phalacrocorax carbo.* Though the family includes also the Divers *Colymbi,* Grebes *Podicipidae,* and Mergansers *Mergi,* the following species, tentatively identified, are mostly ducks and geese *Anatidae*:

1. Cormorant of Rhyne or White Nonne (90v) = male Smew *Mergus albellus;* Ise Cormorant (93r) = female Smew; the Weasel Cormorant (93v) = immature Smew.
2. Daucher (92r) = male White-headed Duck *Oxyura leucocephala.* Uncommon north of southern Italy.
3. "Long bild Cormorant" (94v) = Goosander *Mergus merganser.* "His head as *Ebon* blacke, the rest as white as snow" (Drayton).
4. Herle or Harle (96v) = Red-breasted Merganser *Mergus serrator.*
5. Tiers (97r) = female Pochard *Aythya ferina* (see note 141 below).
6. Cormorant morfex (97v) and Great goose Cormorant (98r–99v) = Cor-

morant *Phalacrocorax carbo.* The "lesser" (98r) = Shag *Phalacrocorax aristotelis.*

Needless to say, both drawings and descriptions are often wide of the mark.

139(90r–v) This does not appear in Wotton, *De Diff. Anim.* For Albertus on the cormorant see 7.39 and 23.129. The "horned *Cormorant*" of Sulpitius is probably the widespread Great Crested Grebe *Podiceps cristatus.*

140(94v–95r) This renders A.: "Eiusdem coloris & collum est aliquantisper; caetero extrinsecus cinereum, vt & dorsum cum cauda, alisque." *aliquantisper,* meaning gradually, T. appears to render as "but afterward the same"; back, wings, *and tail* are ash-colored, writes A. Below: ". . . They keep . . . high," is further confusion of the original: "nidulari inter arundines: sub aqua diutissime omnium se continere: . . . caput inter natandum sublime attolere" (19.62), where the erect heads apply to swimming posture, not nesting. There may be confusion here with habits of grebes as also in the description of the "Beuer Cormorant" (95v).

141(97r) "Nostre vulgaire recognoist Tiers à ce qu'il est Tiers entre Morillon & Cane" (Belon, 3.10, p. 165), that is, between Pochard and Mallard.

142(98r) Albertus, 7.39, "carbo aquaticus." Ovid, *Met.,* 11.793, 794, and 753 (with variations from Loeb text). The Latin prose below is from A.19.49.

143(98v) Ovid, *Met.,* 11.795, in reference to Aesacus, who is referred to below (99v).

144(98v) Virgil, *Aen.,* 5.124–128. The "winter bird," etc., is T.'s invention; Virgil's "tranquillo silet" means that in calm weather it (the rock) is silent. The illegible word, supplied, is probably *haunsed,* lifted or raised (OED), reference being perhaps to the halcyon, which was supposed to nest during the winter solstice.

145(99r) *Odyssey,* 5.336–337.

146(99v) Ovid, *Ex Ponto,* 1.6, "To Graecinus," 51–53.

147(99v) For fishing with Cormorants see Ramusio, Vol. II, or *The Journal of Friar Odoric,* chapter 9 (*Mandeville,* ed. Pollard, p. 343) and J. C. Scaliger, *Exoter. Exercit.,* CCXXXII, p. 729.

148(100r) Wotton, *De Diff. Anim.,* Bk. 7, 129v.

149(100v) Virgil, *Geor.,* 1.360–362. Below: Isidore, *Etym.* (Migne, *P.L.,* 82), 12.7, sec. 54.

150(100v) Horace, *Satires,* 2.2.51–52.

XXVII. Corrier 102r)

A.19.65, B.7.5, G. pp. 681–682. Either Spur-winged Plover *Hoplopterus spinosus* or Crocodile Plover *Pluvianus aegyptius.* Known as *Trochilos* to Herodotus, this bird was often described, by the encyclopedists among others, for its service to the Nile crocodiles (see Newton, p. 733), a notable instance of symbiosis.

151(102r) "Tabellaria," not a bird name, is thus explained by A.: "Corriram, hoc est, tabellariam," that is, courier, or modern courser, applied to certain plovers because of their swift running.

152(102r) This fable of the sacred bees was originated by Antoninus Liberalis, *Transformationum congeries* (Basle, 1568); in a later edition, Greek and Latin (Amsterdam, 1674), ch. XIX, "Fures," pp. 123–126.

153(102v) Paraphrase of Oppian by Eutecnius (see n. 69), 2.3., p. 116.

[The section mostly on domestic fowls, 103r–205r, omitted from the present edition, consists of an abridgement of Book 14 of Aldrovandi, freely rearranged in thirteen chapters ("cap 3" by error designating two of these) as follows: 1. The Cocke and Henne (104r–111r). 2. The Vulgar Dunghill Cock Hen & Chickens (111v–114v). 3. Of seuerall kindes (115r–129v). 4. The voyce and crowing of Cockes and other misticall accidences (130r–136r). 5. The salacitie of Cockes and Hens & layinge of Egges (136r–142r). 6. Of the hatchinge of Chickens (142r–153v). 7. Of the education breedinge and feedinge of pullen (153v–158v). 8. Of the naturall disposition of Cockes and Hens (158v–165v). 9. Of Cocke fightinge (165v–169v). 10. Moralls or superstitious vses of Pullen (169v–176v). 11. The Diseases of Pullen & their Cure wth the meanes how to take them speedily (176v–186r). 12. Medicines out of Pullen (186r–195r). 12. Forrayne Ciuill and promiscuous applications of Pullen (195r–198r), and coats of arms (198r–205r). The chapter above on "kindes," however, includes members of three genera of wild birds: Indian cock and hens, 119r–120r; Heathcock, 122r–v; and Moorcock and Hen, 122v–123r, which follow below.]

XXVIII. Indian Cock and Hens

A.14.9–12. These fowls, brought to Italy undoubtedly from Mexico or South America, all belong to the *Cracidae*. The cock, pictured and described, is a male Great Curassow *Crax rubra*, a gallinaceous bird possibly brought alive to Ferdinand, Duke of Florence, for it is easily domesticated. The "Hens," presumably Guans, as pictured look like Francolins *Tetraonidae.*

XXIX. Heathcock (122r)

A.13.7, B. lacking, G. p. 461. Black Grouse *Lyrurus tetrix.* Turner (pp. 42–44) first distinguished and described this species as Blackcock (male) and Greyhen (female). Topsell (and A.) follows closely, but later (201v–205r) identifies these same birds as *Tetrao* or *Urogallus minor* and *Grygallus minor* respectively. Capercaillie or Wild cock of the wood is "Gallus sylvestris," properly *Urogallus major* (male) and Nemesian's Tetrax, *Grygallus major* (female). The two species were finally rectified by Ray-Willughby in 1676.

XXX. Moor-Hen and Moor Cock (122v)

A.13.9 and 20.54, B. (lacking), G. pp. 223, 225, 461, 483. The Moor-hen (Turner's "mot hen") *Gallinula chloropus* does not dive; "Dab-chicke" is locally applied to this bird but more commonly is a synonym for Little Grebe *Podiceps ruficollis,* the diver described by Topsell and, in verse, by Drayton (*The Man in the Moone,* 189–190) as "Dive-dopper,"

> That comes and goes so quickly and so oft
> As seemes at once both under and aloft.

The "Myrcocke," or Moor Cock, namely Red Grouse *Lagopus scoticus,* is indigenous to Britain and distinct from Black Grouse already described. T.'s last two sentences on this bird apply to grouse, not grebe or Moor-hen; the drawing is copied from the Red Grouse of Gesner, p. 225.

XXXI. Wilde Cock or Cock of the Wood (201v)

A.13.6, B.5.11, G. pp. 159, 459, 472–475. Male Capercaillie *Tetrao urogallus,* the female described (204r) as the "fourthe kynde."

XXXII. Smaller Wild Cock (202v)

See Heathcock, above. The figure of the "Smaller" is copied from Gesner's, a dead specimen, p. 476.

154(203r) Olaus Magnus, *Historia de gentibus* . . . 19.33–34, probably describes the Ptarmigan *Lagopus mutus.*

155(203r) "Aristotle's wonders . . ." or *De Mirabilibus Auscultationibus,* 835a15 (*The Works of Aristotle,* tr. Ross, VI). T. mistranslates *neque excernant* as "blinde, see not"; correctly, they do not void excrement.

156(203v) Longolius, sig. E6r–v. This identifies the "Birkhun," the Black Grouse, a bird unknown in Greece, as the classical Attagen, which more exactly was the Francolin *Tetrao francolinus:* see Thompson, *Glossary,* p. 37.

157(204r) Nemesian's fragment was discovered from its first appearance in Longolius (sig. E2r–v), the passage later quoted by Gesner and Aldrovandi.

158(204v) Encelius, *De re metallica* . . . 3.54 (pp. 245–246).

XXXIII. Crane (206r)

A.20.5–7, B.4.1, G. p. 509. Crane = European C. *Megalornis grus;* Balearian C. (207r) = African Crowned Crane *Grus balearica;* Crane of Japan (207v) = Japanese C. *Grus japonensis.* The "Crane of Virginia" (206v), the Sandhill C. *Grus canadensis,* is the tenth and last North American bird; see IV. Virginia Birds (31v–32r). Since the days of Jeremiah and Homer, the sight of migrating cranes has been a most impressive phenomenon of bird life. Like his authority, T. gives it full scope (210r–218v) in a careful analysis of the mysteries of migration on which even today the final word has not been said.

159(206v) Paulus Venetus (Marco Polo), in Ramusio, vol. 2, as in *Travels of Marco Polo the Venetian*, 1.56 (ed. Masefield), pp. 143–144, where cranes and other birds are described as resorting to Cianiganiorum (Changanor) in Tartaria. Below: For P. Martyr see Decade 1, Bk. 3, tr. Richard Eden (1555), p. 16.

160(207v) Pliny, 30.52: "gromphenam . . . avem in Sardinia narrant grui similem, ignotam iam etiam Sardis, ut existimo . . ."

161(208v) Gellius, *Attic Nights*, 19.2.

162(208v) Festus, *De Verb. Sig.*, 7.

163(208v) Attributed by A. to Mantuan's "in Grue," which has not been found.

164(208v) Virgil, *Aen.*, 10.262–266, with omissions.

165(209r) *Inferno*, 5.46–49, the latter two lines badly misconstrued in the translation.

166(209r) Unidentified.

167(209v) Hesiod, *Works and Days*, 448–450; the rest of the Hesiod line from A., "tempusque inducit arandi."

168(209v) The "Greeke Poet" is Aristophanes, *Birds*, 712–714.

169(209v) See n. 163(208v).

170(210r) Oppian, *Halieutica*, 1.620–621.

171(210r) *Helena*, 1479–1481.

172 (210v) *Orlando Furioso*, 2.49, ll. 1–6, in translation of Harington, 1607.

173(210v) Though from time to time they alight to feed, cranes do indeed "flie night and day."

174(211r) *De Deorum Natura*, 2.49.125 with variation. Cf. Milton, *Paradise Lost*, 7.425–431.

> Part loosly wing the Region, part more wise
> In common, rang'd in figure wedge their way,
> Intelligent of seasons, and set forth
> Thir Aierie Caravan high over Sea's
> Flying, and over Lands with mutual wing
> Easing their flight; so stears the prudent Crane
> Her annual Voiage, born on Windes.

175(211r) *War Against Gildo*, Bk. 15. ll. 476–478. Below: Martial, *Epode*, 13.75 (quoted above, n. 28, 16r).

176(211v) This is not in Virgil.

177(211v) Cassiodorus, *Variarum* . . . , Bk. 8, *Epistola* 12 (Migne, *P.L.* 69, p. 745).

178(212v) Aristotle, *H.A.*, 8.597a, 30–31 and 597b, 1–3, states that cranes fly *against* the wind, or as Gaza translates, "volant flatu secundo," with a favoring wind. Topsell earlier (212r) had explained why they fly against the wind.

179(212v) Albertus, 23.24.
180(212v) Pliny, 10.23.
181(213r) Aristotle, *H.A.*, 9.614b, 21–23 and Turner, p. 96. "The Greeke sayinge," below, A. assigns to Joannes Tzetzes, a native of Constantinople, 12th century. Cf. Pliny, 10.30, Aelian 3.12, and Arist. *H.A.*, 8.597a. 12–14.
182(213v) Albertus, 23.113.
183(213v) Ennius, *Annals*, Fragment 556 (ed. Vahlen, p. 102). Virgil, *Geor.*, 3.76, "de equo loquens," has imitated the line.
184(214r) Mantuan, *de Calamit. tempo.* (1499), Bk. 1, approximately l. 380. T. does not translate last line.
185(214r–v) Albertus, on nesting of domestic crane, 23.11; accounts below of crane and parrot and cock are apparently lacking in Albertus.
186(214v) Petrarch, *De remediis utriusque fortunae libri duo*, Bk. 1, Dialogus 57, "De Fertilitate terrae" (Bern, 1605), p. 208.
187(215r) Suidas on cranes here does not correspond to the text of standard editions. Below, Claudian, *Shorter Poems*, 31, "Epistula ad Serenam" 11.13–14. *Rubri* is omitted by T., who mistranslates second line: "They gathered in their mouths the precious pearls of the Red Sea." *Germina* means offspring, or figuratively pearls.
188 (215v) Aristotle, *H.A.*, 8.597a, 2–8; see Turner, ed. Evans, p. 94.
189(215v) Philostratus, *Life of Apollonius*, 3.45. For Basilis and Menecles, below, see Athenaeus, 9.390.
190(215v) For Eustathius, on *Iliad*, see *Commentarii*, 3.6 (ed. Olms, 11, 301–302).
191(216r) *Batman on Bartholome*, 12.15, where, however, there is nothing about pygmies. Below: Augustine, *De Civitate Dei*, 16, 8 (cited in margin of MS).
192(216r) Strabo, *Geography*, Bks. 1, ch. 2, and 7, ch. 3 (cited in margin of MS).
193(216v) Calaber (or Quintus Smyrnaeus), *The Fall of Troy, Posthomerica,* 13.101 ff.
194(216v) *Orlando Furioso*, 1.77.
195(217r) Ambrose, *Hexaemeron*, 5.14 (Migne, *P.L.* 14, p. 239).
196(217r) Aristotle, *H.A.,* 9.615b, 16–18.
197(217v) *Geor.*, 1.307 and *Aen.*, 11.579–580 (with variations). Below: T. translates A's "gruarium" as "Girfalcon," "Crane-Falcon." The prefix *gir* probably derives from L. *gyro*, to circle, from the Gerfalcon's habit of circling its prey before swooping.
198(219r) Paulus Jovius, *Elegia Doctorum Virorum*, translated by Gragg, *An Italian Portrait Gallery*, p. 129.
199(219r) For the Greek, Plutarch, *Moralia*, "Concerning Talkativeness," 509F (Loeb, VI, 438). Gregory Nyssenius (Migne, *P.G.*, 44–46) includes no title "de Providentia" (A's gloss).
200(219v) Sidonius, Ausonius, *Idyl de Hist.*, 12.12 (*Anthologia Palatina*

(Paris, 1864), I, caput 7, no. 745). For classical allusions to "The Cranes of Ibycus" see Thompson, *Glossary*, pp. 43–44. For the Greek adage below, see Suidas, *Ibycos*.

201(220r) N. Reusner, *Emblemata* (Frankfurt, 1581), Bk. II, Emblem 34.

202(220v) Philostratus, *Life of Apollonius*, 4.16, states only that Homer neglected to name Palamedes to avoid shame of Odysseus, whose whim caused his death.

203(220v) This unidentified quotation is not in Aldrovandi.

204(220v) Ambrose, *Hexaemeron*, 5.15 (Migne, *P.L.*, 14, p. 242) includes also the further sentence quoted below.

205(221r) Excerpted with variations from Cassiodorus, *Variar.* 9.2, "Edictum Athalarici Regis" (Migne, *P.L.*, 69, p. 767); for the corresponding passage which follows, from Theodoric, see *ibid.*, p. 640. Theodoric was predecessor, not "successor" of Athalaricus; see Catalog of Proper Names.

206(222r) "Hoc enim epithetum inter schedas meas reperio sine authore" (A.20.5).

207(222v) Gellius, *Attic Nights*, 6.16.

208(222v) Plutarch, *Moralia*, "On the Eating of Flesh," Bk. 2, 997F (Loeb, XII, 564).

209(222v) Ovid, *Fasti*, 6.173–178.

210(223r) Statius, *Silvarum*, 6.8–9.

211(223r) Aelian, 13.25: "Pindels" are from A.: "Pindulos (aves Attaginum similes)," that is, like Godwits; "Bocales" from "Boccalidas (alias Barcalides)," T.'s "Bareballs" (?)

212(223v) Platina, *de re Culinaria* (Lyons, 1541), 6.2, p. 55.

213(224v) Pliny, 37.72.

XXXIV. Coot (225r)

Original drawing of "seconde kinde" not found. A.19.13 and 14.51; B.3.24, G. pp. 374–377. Coot *Fulica atra.* The "seconde kinde" = Crested Coot *Fulica cristata,* restricted mostly to S. Spain. The *diable de mer* is no other than the common coot.

214(225r) In Psalm 104:17 Hebr. *chasida* = stork (A.V.).

215(226v) Mantuan, *Trophaei Francisci Gonzagae, Opera omnia* (Antwerp, 1576), vol. 3, Bk. 2, f. 125v. Mintus = the River Mincius, near Mantua.

216(226v) Aelius Julius Crottus, "Cyresium," in *Opuscula,* Ferrara, 1564, p. 56. "alisque sub ipsis, Unda latet," that is, the wave hides under their wings, not, as T. has it, "to wings they sproote."

217(226v) Alciati, Emblem 169 "Obnoxia infirmitas." *Orata,* vulgar form of *aurata; giltheads,* goldeneye or perhaps the golden wrasse (*O.E.D.*).

218(227r) Antoninus Liberalis, *Transfor. cong.*, ch. XIV, "Munichus," pp. 99–103. (Cf. also n.152, 102r).

219(227r) Not Ausonius, but Paulinus of Nola, in a verse epistle to Ausonius, his preceptor; see Poema XI (Migne, *P.L.*, 61, p. 462). The passage of Paulinus ends with "me compone tibi" which accounts for Topsell's strange predication "are comparable." *Parra* (Horace, *Od.*, 3.2 and 7.1, and Pliny, 18.69) has been identified with Barn Owl, Green Woodpecker, and Lapwing; T. is uncertain.

XXXV. Crex (227v)

A.19.64, B. (lacking), G. p. 225. Avocet *Recurvirostra avosetta.* Aldrovandi's "Avosetta" is confused in name with his Crex (20.23), properly the Corncrake *Crex crex.*

220(228r) Aristophanes, *Birds*, 1133–1141.

XXXVI. Crow (228v)

A.12.22, B.6.1–4, G. pp. 308–319. Carrion Crow *Corvus corone*; Rook *Corvus frugilegus*; Roiston or Hooded C. *Corvus cornix,* called "Royston" because common about Royston and Newmarket; "Blewe" C., Roller *Coracias gracculus.* This chronicle of the lore of crows—battles, hieroglyphics, etc.—involves more misinformation than Topsell (and A.) presents about any other bird.

221(230r) This, attributed to Possidippus, is not in the *Greek Anthology.*

222(230v) Persius, *Satire*, 5.12.

223(231r) Virgil, *Geor.*, 1.388. Rather, the ill-favored crow with full sound. Below: Ovid, *Amores*, 3.5.21; *venit*, last word of sentence omitted.

224(231r) Alexander Aphrodysaeus, *Problemata* (Rome, 1475), Bk. 2, sec. 64, fol. 269v.

225(231r) Loosely from Basil, Homily 8, ch. 6 (Migne, *P.L.* 29, p. 182). Lines below are not from Isidore, on the crow, *Etym.* 12.7. (Migne, *P.L.*, 82).

226(231v) Plautus, *Mostellaria*, III. 832–840, Tranio the speaker. Below: Pliny, 10.43.

227(232r) The Mantuan line has not been located. Below: Alciati, Emblem 38, "Concordia."

228(232r) Juvenal, *Sat.* 10.247. Below: Ausonius, "A Riddle of the Number Three," Bk. 16. l. 12 (Loeb, I, 360).

229(232v) Horapollo, *Hieroglyphica* (Lyons, 1621), Bk. 2, p. 84, states that the Egyptians believed the crow lives 100 years, adding: "Constat autem Aegyptiacus annus quattuor vsitatis & communibus annis."

230 On crow and weasel see Aristotle, *H.A.*, 9.609a, 7–18.

231(232v–233r) See Aelian, 3.9, and Aristotle, *H.A.*, 9.609a, 10–12. On the hostilities of birds see n.12(26r).

232(233v) Johannes Ursinus, *Prosopopeia* . . . (Vienna, 1541), a book of poems on animals and birds with annotations by author; see "Cornix," p.

50, or "Cur Mineruae inuisae," according to A. (12.2). A literal translation of the final lines: Eat my brain, it will help a brain more than raw wisdom, and does not allow a head to be complaining.

233(233v) Pliny, 10.13.

234(234r) Lucretius, *de rerum natura,* 6.753–755.

235(234r) Festus, 3, "Corniscarum . . . quod in Junonis tutela esse putabantur."

236(234r) Alciati, Emblem 19, "Prudens magis, quam loquax."

237(234v) Horace, *Serm.*, 1.4.85, refers not to a crow but to a man who commits this or that crime; "est niger," is a bad character.

238(234v) Cicero; see Prol., n.*j* (11r).

239(235r) Isidore, *Etym.*, 12.7.44 (Migne, *P.L.*, 82).

240(235r) Suetonius, *Lives of the Caesars*, "Domitian," ch. 23.

241(235v) Horace, *Od.*, 3.27.10.

242(235v) First line unlocated; for second line see note 223 (231r).

243(236r) Valerianus, *Hieroglyphica* (Lyons, 1621), 20.28, p. 205.

244(236r) This is by A. himself (12.2).

XXXVII. Cuckowe (237r)

A.5.17, B.2.28, G. pp. 348–355. Cuckoo *Cuculus canorus.* The two drawings of the cuckoo are among the best in the MS. Topsell notes truly (239v) that the eggs of this bird vary in size and coloration to simulate those of the victim host. Fledglings do not, however, desert their foster parents for their own nor do "they devoure their Nurse, when they are growen greate, and ready to flie" (239v), a belief surviving in *King Lear* (1.4.205–206):

> The hedge-sparrow fed the cuckoo so long,
> That it had it head bit off by it young.

Finally, to this mixture of true and false Topsell has added the mild anecdote of the young married couple who mistook cuckoos for pigeons (241v).

245(237v) Aristotle, *H.A.*, 6.563b, 14–16 and Turner, p. 66. The confusion of hawk and cuckoo is still current in parts of England.

246(238r) Albertus, 23.38.

247(239r) Aristotle, *De Gen. Anim.*, 3.750a, 12–14 and *H.A.*, 6.563b, 30–32 and 564a, 1–2; and Turner, p. 68.

248(239v) On Horace, *Sat.*, 1.7.31, see Acron, ed. Keller, II, 93.

249(240r) Juvenal, *Sat.*, 6.276–277. Loeb text reads *uruca*, a dolt, a cuckolded husband who is deceived by his wife's tears. The Hedge Sparrow (*curruca*) is a frequent victim of the Cuckoo.

250(240r) See n. 247 (239r). Below (240v); Pliny, 10.11.

251(240v) Theophrastus, *De Causis Plantarum*, 2.17.9 (*Opera*, ed. Wimmer, p. 216). Below: Wotton, *De Diff. Anim.*, ch. 135, 121v, states only that "pullos cuculi fere nemo se ait uidisse."

252(240v) Plutarch, *Life of Aratus,* ch. 30, attributes the fable to Aesop.
253(240v) This line is not in Martial, cited by A. Below: (241r) Pliny, 10.11, "occultatur caniculae ortu." T.'s phrase following is lacking in Pliny.
254(241r) Aeschylus, Fragment, No. 304 (*Tragicorum Graecorum Fragmenta,* ed. Nauck). *Epops,* properly Hoopoe, was often translated as Lapwing.
255(241r) See "Viaggio nelle Ethiopia," in Ramusio, vol. 1, or Alvarez' *Narrative of the Portuguese Embassy to Abyssinia During the Years* 1520–27, edited and translated by Lord Stanley of Alderney (Hakluyt Soc. Pub. LXIV, 1881).
256(242r) Hesiod, *Works and Days,* 486.
257(242r) Leandro Alberti, *Descrittione di tutta Italia* . . . , f. 383v.
258(242r) This couplet is not in Oppian. Below: Isidore, *Etym.*, 12.7, 57 (Migne, *P.L.*, 82).
259(243r–v) Alciati, Emblem 60, "Cuculi."
260(243v) Pliny, 18.66. *Below:* "Mosella," 167.
261(243v–244r) The source of the story of Cuckoo and Nightingale has not been found.
262(244r) Isidore, *Etym.* 12.7.67 (Migne, *P.L.*, 82), states only, "Horum salivae cicadas gignunt."
263(244r) Plutarch (and A) names the mountain *Coccygius,* not *Thornax* or *Diccius;* see *Of Rivers and Mountains,* ch. 18, "Inachus."
264(244v) Pliny, 30.47.

VARIANT READINGS

Variant Readings

IN THE LIST below, all textual readings adopted and variant readings are provided in roman, irrespective of the hand in the original. Readings are identified by reference to the signature of the manuscript, followed by page and line of the text. The reading placed first is that adopted in the text, followed by the source of the reading in italics, and by a semicolon; alternative readings then follow. Abbreviations: *T.* = Topsell's MS of "The Fowles of Heauen"; *G.* = Gesner (in sixteenth-century Latin texts); *A.* = Aldrovandi (first edition, unless date is also provided); *ed.* editorial emendation. Emendations are usually not "justified" here except in a few instances where there seemed special reason —in those cases they are added in italics and in parentheses. Topsell's transliterated Greek quotations, often garbled, appear verbatim as in the MS.

(3r) 4. 23 Carystius *Aelian*; Carysnis *T.*
(11r) 13. 32 επι δεξι προς εεοσι εελιοντε ειτ επι ἀρισερα οντι ἀλεγιζω *T.*
(11v) 14. 9 velint *ed.*; volunt *T.*
(12r) 15. 6 auspicato *A.*; auspicio *T.*
(12v) 15. 16 Troiugena *Virgil*; Troiugenae *T.*
16 Diuum *Virgil*; Deum *T.*
(13r) 16. 19 Eis oioonos aristos amnuesthai peri patres, Hemeis megaloio deos &c. *T.*
(13v) 16. 27 Mosolam *Eusebius*; Mosoman *T.*
(14v) 17. 38 Mutina *ed.*; Mutimum *T.*
(15r) 18. 30 Fortia *ed.*; Sfortia *A.* and *T.*; Sforza (*proper Italian*).
(17r) 21. 1 fabras *ed.*; fabros *T.*
(18v) 22. 26 15.3 (A.V.); 15.4 *T.*
(20r) 25. 21 macrescunt *ed.*; marcescunt *T.*
(21v) 27. *col.* 1. *l.*2 Onocrotalus *A.*; Onocratolus *T.*
1. 5 Aiussaco *ed.*; Aiussiaco *T.*
1. 7 Artamokes *ed.*; Artomakes *T.*
2. 12 Chuwheeo *ed.*; Chuwheo *T.*
(22r) 29. (Heading) Alcatraz *ed.*; Alcatrax *T.* (*see note*).

(22v) 30. 10 Alcatraz *ed.*; Alcatrax *T.*

(23r) 21 Onocrotalus *A.*; Onocratalus *T.*

29 Onuogel *ed.*; Onuoget *T.*

(23r) 30 Kropffuogel *G.*; Kropffuoget *T.*

30 vanetna *G.*; vawetna *T.*

31 Surpesi *G.*; Sucpesi *T.*

(24r) 32. 30 Manzi *Ramusio*; Nanzi *T.*

31 Ceuscala *Ramusio*; Censcala *T.*

32 Onocrotalus *A.*; Onocratalus *T.*

33 cum *ed.*; tum *T.*

(24v) 33. 7 Port Hercule *ed.*; port. Hercule *T.*

17 imponet *ed.*; imponat *T.* and *A.*

27 Miluorum *Martyr*; Miluoram *T.*

27 petulantum *Martyr*; petulantiú *T.*

28 eleuatae *Martyr*; eleuati *T.*

28 circumrotant *Martyr*; circumcrotant *T.*

(25v) 35. 19 roboratur *ed.*; roboretur *T.*

(26r) 36. 9 pelagi *ed.*; pelargi *T.*

9,10 *Words in brackets supplied from A.*

(27r) 38. 4 Heraclea *ed.*; Heracles *T.*

(27v) 12 Gula *Alciati*; Gulae *T.*

14 gestat *Alciati*; gestit *T.*; gestet *A.*

14 onocrotalum *A.*; onocratalum *T.*

25 multiforisque *Alciati*; multiformisque *T.*

(28v) 39. 27 Filacotona *G.*; Filacatona *T.*

28 Monspessulum *A.*; Montpessulan *T.*

33 praedura *A.*; perdura *T.*

41. 12 cuius *A.*; cuis *T.*

(30r) 43. 37 pedum *Ovid*; pedis *T.*

37 digitos . . . cornu *Ovid* and *A.*; digites . . . corum *T.*

(33r) 48. 38 vidimus *Albertus*; videmus *T.*

(33v) 49. 22 Pethslege *Boece* and *A.*; Pethelege *T.*

(34v) 51. 30 Hypanis *A.*; Hypanus *T.*; Hyppanis *Gaza's Aristotle.*

37 laetae *Scaliger*; laeta *T.*

(35r) 38 Qui *A.*; Quae *T.*

52. 1 quiritratrix *Scaliger*; quiritatrix *T.*

3 corpore et *A.*; corpore e *T.*; corpore. at *Scaliger.*

(35v) 30 Leuit. 11 *A.*; Leuit. 12 *T.*

31 Anseb. *A.*; Ansohe *T.*

53. 1 volatum *Perrotti, Nonius,* and *A.*; volandum *T.*

1 proferat *Perrotti* and *Nonius*; praeparat *T.*

3 volat *T.*; volant *Ovid.*

3 tenet *T.*; tenent *Ovid.*

11 Murziegalo *A.*; Murciegalo *T.*
12 Vlermuys *A.*; Vlermys *T.*
(36r) 26 talictro *A.*; talitro *T.*
54. 4 Alcithoe *ed.*; Alciothoe *T.*
4 Minyas *Ovid*; Meneus *T.*
7 Minyeia *Ovid*; Meneia *T.*
(37r) 55. 40 Nycterin *A.*; Nycteres *T*
(37v) 57. 25 videant *Gaza's Alexander* (*of Aphrodisias*) and *A.*; vident *T.*
(38r) 38 si *Petrarch*; se *T.*
38 difende *Petrarch*; defende *T.*
58. 9 dio *A.*; die *T.*
(38v) 59.4,7 oute sterixai oute epibenai. . . . Ote Nycterides mycho antroa. *T.*
(40r) 62. 27 alas *Alciati* and *A.*; ales *T.*
32 & *Alciati*; vt *T.*
(42r) 65. 31 Ceramides *G.*; Ceramida *T.*
66. 3 Ciccus *A.*; Cicco *T.*
3 Oca sterna *A.*; Deasterica *T.*
(42v) 67. 13 Epanetus *ed.*; Epinetus *T.*
16 facie *Aretaeus*; facici *T.*
(44r) 69. 15 Suffuleno *A.*; Saffuleno *T.*
18 Gutfinck *G.*; Gutfinch *T.*
18 Bollebick *G.* and *A.*; Bollebuk *T.*
19 Hail Goll *G.*; Haill goll *T.*
20 Blutfincke *G.* and *A.*; Blutfinche *T.*
22 Laubfincke *G.*; Lobfincke *T.*
23 Gumpel *G.* and *A.*; Gumpfell *T.*
23 Quetschfyncke *ed.*; Quetchfyncke *T.*; Quetschfinck *G.* and *A.*
24 Dlask *G.*; Dlasken *T.*
(44v) 70. 12 buds *ed.*; birdes *T.* (*buds, food of bullfinches*)
(45r) 26 rubetra *A.*; rubetta *T.*
71. 2 Heidlerch *G.*; Bludlerch *T.*; Bleidlerch *A.*
2 Himmellerch *G.* and *A.*; Himmelerch *T.*
2 Holtzlerch *G.*; Boltzlerch *T.*
14 Himmellerche *G.*; Himmelerche *T.*
16 aer then *ed.*; aer; then *T.*
(46r) 72. 29 Gustardes *A.*; Guestards *T.*
31 Outarde *A.*; Otarde *T.*
31 Drofa *A.*; Drufa *T.*
73. 24 lesser *ed.*; moderne *T.*; minor *A.*
(46v) 74. 3 gracili *A.*; gracilique *T.*
13 Merchia *Boece* and *A.*; Marchia *T.*

(47v) 75. 38 accedunt *Aelian 1535* and *A.*; accedant *T.*
38 capiat *Aelian 1535*; capit *T.*
76. 22 eques *Oppian* and *A.*; equus *T.*
23 possit *Oppian* and *A.*; potest *T.*
23 ostendit. Sequuntur *Oppian*; ostendit sequuntur *T.*
31 ensnared and *ed.*; ensnared; and *T.*
(48v) 78. 4 Hawke and *ed.*; Hawke; and *T.*
8 Subbuteones *Gaza's Aristotle* and *A.*; Subbuleones *T.*
(49r) 23 Hypotriorchos *G.*; Hypotrarcha *T.*; Hypotriorchis *A.*
23 Gypotriorchos *G.*; Gypotriorcha *T.* and *A.*
79. 2 Hobreau *ed.*; Hobrean *T.*; Hobraeu *A.*
4 crooked and *ed.*; crooked; and *T.*
(49v) 80. 7 they finde *ed.*; they growe hungry, then they flie alofte vntill *T.* (*words repeated unintentionally*).
(50v) 82. 8 Aieta *G.*; Aiera *T.*
(51r) 10 Bussahrn *G.*; Busahrn *T.*; Busarhn *A.*
11 Busshen *G.*; Bushen *T.*
11 Rüttelwye *G. subst.* (*without final e*); Ruttellwye *T.*
12 Masshuw *G.* and *A.*; Masshun *T.*
12 Masswy *G.* and *A.*; Massiry *T.*
20 beake to *ed.*; beake; to *T.*
(52v) 85. 7 Busshart *G.*; Bushard *T.*
13 ignauos *A.*; ignaues *T.*
23 Erodios gar Egchilen Naiandrenen
Triorchon euroon esthionta apheileto *T.*
(53r) 86. 20 Aruergne *A.*; Arnergne *T.*
(53v) 23 [as] *so the catchword on 53r of MS.*
38 Phoemonoe dedit. *ed.*; Phoemonoe dedit phoemonoe. *T.*
87. 16 for *ed.*; from *T.*
(54r) 88. 16 Trombono *A.*; Trombone *T.*
18 Vrrind *G.*; Vorid *T.*
18 Meerrind *G.*; Merrid *T.*
18 Masskuh *G.*; Maszku *T.*
19 Moszreigel *G.* and *A.*; Moszriegel *T.*
(54v) 22 Lorrind *G.*; Lorread *T.*; Lorriad *A.*
22 Wasserochs *G.*; Wasser Ochs *T.*
23 Erdbuell *G.*; Erdbull *T.*
25 Pickart *G.*; Pickurt *T.*
27 Domphorn *G.*; Somphorne *T.*
27 Geluae *G. subst.*; Gelne *T.*
(55r) 89. 38 Larynx *ed.*; Laryme *T.*
(56r) 91. 31 coeuet *Alciati 1551*; ceuet *Alciati 1608* (*with gloss:* "alas agitat, & volare contendit"); coenet *T.*

(57r) 93. 10 Cossifos *G.*; cossisos *T.*
11 Pro Archi *A.* (*opening words of a sentence*); Proarchi, *T.* (*misinterpreted as a proper name*)
11 Echus *A.*; Echas *T.*
11 Edulcus *G.* and *A.*; Edulchas *T.*
11 Ethida *G.* and *A.*; Ethedia *T.*
17 Merulum *G. subst.*; Meruleum *T.*
21 Merle *G.*; Milre *T.*
23 feluek *G.*; Eeluek *T.*
(57v) 31 Naeuius *A.*; Maenius *T.*
33 Cyllene *ed.*; Cyllena *T.*
(58r) 95. 4 but . . . feete *ed.*; *words repeated in MS.*
(58v) 12 Birckamsel . . . Birckamsslen *G.*; Bukhamsell . . . Birghamsslen *T.*
96. 10 Waldamsel *G.*; Waldramsel *T.*; Waldtamsel *A. 1610.*
(59r) 19 Collier *G.* and *A.*; Collierr *T.*
(60r) 97. 13 back *ed.*; bagge *T.*
(61r) 99. 10 Cariocatactes *G. subst.*; Cariocatacti *T.*
11 Nussbrecher *A. subst.*; Nussbrescher *T.*
11 Nusshaeher *G.*; Nusshaher *T.*
12 alpadic *G.*; alapadien *T.*; alapadie *A.*
(61v) 100. 21 E'arinnoi de liguphthoggoisin aoidas.
Kossiphoi acheusin poi chilo traula mele. *T.*
34 Testudines *A.* and *Varro*; Testitudines *T.*
101. 14 smaller corne *ed.*; smaller the corne *T.*
(62v) 102. 18 e'l *A.*; e'il *T.*
32 ipsi *ed.*; ipse *T.*
(63r) 103. 13 decidit *Horace* and *A.*; decipit *T.*
20 ut *Horace*; & *T.*
21 edit *Horace*; edat *T.*
23 Hare *ed*; Hart *T.*
(64v) 105. 25 nones *Harington, 1607*; nonce *T.*
29 sweet *Harington 1607*; sweetely *T.*
(65r) 106. 3 Phison *A.*; Phision *T.*
(66v) 108. 17 Cauallerio *A.*; Caualerio *T.*
(68r) 110. 12 Camenios *Uretta*; Camoemos *T.*
(69v) 113. 36 petat *A.*; petit *T.*
(70r) 114. 23 credib(le?) *ed.*; credibe *T.* (*MS reading blurred*).
31 Suhayo *Uretta*; Suchayo *T.*
(71v) 117. 11 Nesir *Leo Africanus in Ramusio*; Nefr *T.*
(75r) 122. 2 verdeyre *A.* and *G.*; verdire *T.*
3 Gruenfinck *G.*; Grunfinck *T.*
3 Gruenling *G.*; Grunlinge *T.*

	4	Rappfincke *G. subst.*; Rapfincke *T.*
	5	Assarandos *G. subst.*; Asarandes *T.*
(77r) 125.	11	has alunt *ed.*; has alant *T.*; (quidam alunt *A.*)
	25	Tirtertirteriiz *A.*; Tirtirtictirijz *T.*
	26	Teriz *A.*; Tiriz *T.*
(78r) 127.	8	franguello *A.*; franguelle *T.*
	11	Pinkawa *G.*; Pinkaua *T.*
	11	Slowick *G.*; Slouuicke *T.*
(78v) 128.	16	redit *Alciati*; venit *T.*
(79r)	33	quaerelas *A. subst.*; quaerulas *T.*
(80r) 130.	15	Chalandra *A.*; Clalandra *T.*
(80v) 131.	17	Anapha *G. subst.*; Anapa *T.*
	17	Oreb *G.*; Orab *T.*
	18	Koloios *A.*; Kolaios *T.*
	19	Pola *G.* and *A.*; Polo *T.*
132.	1	Kaycke *G.*; Kaeyke *T.*
	2	Cau *G.*; Canu *T.*; Kauu *A.*
	2	Talhe *G.*; Talche *T.*
	2	Doel *G. subst.*; Dol *T.*
	3	Hannckyn *G. subst.*; Hannekyn *T.*
	3	Kawka *G. subst.*; Kauuka *T.*
	6	iacta *Festus* and *A.*; iactu *T.*
(81r)	27	Bergdoel *G.*; Bergdol *T.*
	27	wilde Tul *G.*; wildtul *T.*
(82v) 134.	24	Quodcumque *A.*; Quodcunque *T.*
(83r) 136.	20	Toon de w̄ste psaroon nephos erchetai ee koloion Oulon keklegontes ote proidoosin iontai Kirkon ote smikroisi phonon pherei ornithessin *T.*
	23	crowes or *ed.*; crewes of *T.*
(84r) 138.	10	immortalem excolas. Haec *A.*; imortalem excolas haec *T.*
	11	immortalis *A.*; imortalis *T.*
(84v)	31	Athenaeus *A.*; Æthænus *T.*
(86v) 140.	21	Darda *A.*; Dardo *T.*
	21	Melissophagos *A.*; Melissophagus *T.*
	24	Neapolitans *A.*; Neopolitans *T.*
	25	dell' api *A.*; dell api *T.*
(87v) 142.	22	wrurull *T.*; ururul *A.*
	25	prognis *Carmen de Philomela*; Progne *T.*
	26	sciunt *Carmen de Philomela*; solent *T.*
(89r) 145.	2	Charlot *G.*; Charlor *T.*
	5	Wettervogel *G.* and *A. subst.*; Mettervogel *T.*
	6	Corlis *G.* and *A.*; Cortis *T.*
	7	Hanikens *G.*; Bunikens *A.*; Barikens *T.*

		7	Gruey *G.*; Gruy *T.*
		7	Schrye *G.*; Schye *T.*
		8	Schryck *G.* and *A.*; Schyek *T.*
		9	Macrimito *A.*; Marcrimito *T.*
(90r)	146.	8	Schalac *G.* and *A.*; Scalac *T.*
		10	poynges *A.*; poyngs *T.*
		10	Bunge *A.*; Binge *T.*
		12	plonget *G.*; plongent *T.*
		13	Daucher *G.*; Sucher *A.* and *T.*
		14	Teucher *G.* and *A.*; Tewcher *T.*
		14	Duchent *G.*; Suchent *A.* and *T.*
		14	Dueckeckin *G.*; Sickeckin *T.*
		18	non *A.*; nan *T.*
(90v)		24	Dytini *A.*; Dytimi *T.*
	147.	1	Rhynenten *G.* and *A.*; Rhymunten *T.*
		1	yszenten *G.* and *A. subst.*; yzenten *T.*
		2	Duchenten *G.*; Suchunten *T.*
(91r)		5	Merch *G.*; Merech *T.*
		6	Nunnen *G.*; Nonnen *T.*
(91v)		26	Morgon *G. subst.*; Mergon *T.*
		26	Gyuen *G.*; guien *T.*
(92r)	148.	9	Daucher *G.*; Saucher *T.*
(92v)	150.	10	diuarication *ed.*; dmarication *T.*
		13	& transparent *ed.*; *words repeated in MS.*
(94r)	151.	23	Wiselgen *G.*; weiselgen *A.* and *T.*
		30	Schwartzer Teucher *G.* and *A.*; Sclwartzer Tucher *T.*
(94v)	152.	10	Pylstert *G.* and *A.*; pylstret *T.*
(95r)	153.	1	ashe colour. But *ed.*, as *A.*; ashe colour but *T.*
		13	deuourers *ed.*; dedeuourers *T.*
(95v)	154.	6	stayned *ed.*; strayned *T.*
(97v)	156.	7	Aelguess *G.*; Aelguss *T.*
		7	Scholucheren *G.*; Scholecherez *T.*
		8	Aelguess *G.*; Algusa *T.* and *A. subst.*
(98r)	157.	11	corpore longe *Ovid, Loeb ed.*; tergore longum *T.*
		12	substricta *Ovid*; Substrata *T.*
		12	guttura *Ovid.*; guttere *T.*
(98v)	158.	9	quia *ed.*; q'a *T.*
		17	procul *Virgil*; procull *T.*
		18	tunditur *Virgil*; conditur *T.*
(99r)		33	Ter oduse eleese alomenon alge echonta Aithnis de eikui a pote *T.*
(99v)	159.	23	ferae *Ovid*; fera *T.*
		34	guttur *A.*; gutter *T.*
(100v)	160.	28	aequore *Virgil*; equore *T.*

161. 7 edixerit *Horace*; eduxerit *T.*

(102r) 162. 9 Steganpodem *A.*; Steguzapodio *T.*

(122v) 168. 2 Myrcocke *ed.*; Wyrcocke *T.*

(201v) 171. 1 Erythrotao *G.* and *A.*; Erythratao *T.*

2 Stolzo *G.* and *A.*; Stultzo *T.*

2 Stolcho *G.*; Stolco *T.*

4 Birkhuener *G.*; Birkhaner *T.*; (Birkhuner *A.*)

4 Pirkhuener *G.* and *A.*; Pirkhaener *T.*

5 Tetrez *G.* and *A.*; Tetriz *T.*

5 Tetrzeuu *G.* and *A.*; Tetrizun *T.*

(202r) 31 backe *ed.*; Cocke *T.*; (dorso *A.*)

(202v) 173. 3 Orhan *G.*; Orhaen *T.*

4 Laubhan *G.*; Laubhaen *T.*

5 Fasiano *A.*; Faciano *T.*

(203v) 174. 6 Birkhun *G. subst.*; Birkhan *T.*

6 Betula *A.*; Betulae *T.*

15 Spilhan *G.*; Spilhaen *T.*

(204r) 175. 2 Coeperunt *Nemesian* and *A.*; Coeporunt *T.*

5 adductos *Nemesian* and *A.*; adiutos *T.*

20 Peltinnum *A.*; Pentinnum *T.*

(205r) 176. 15 [Germans] *ed.*; *blank space in MS*; Germanis *A.*

15 vrhanschlangen *A.*; Vrhansclangue *T.*

15 Birgschlangen *A.*; Birgschangen *T.*

20 ryver Tangera *ed.*; ryver. Tangera *T.*

(206r) 177. 16 Sus *A.*; Sennith *T.*

16 Senuit *A.*; Sennit *T.*

33 Palamedes *ed.*; Palamaedes *T.*

(206v) 38 Zoraw *G.*; Zoraus *T.*

178. 2 kleine *A.*; klein *T.*

3 Fru *A.*; gru *T.*

3 Ml'odzi zorawie *G.*; Ml'ozio rawze *T.*

15 Lordeste *A.*; Lordesta *T.*

(207v) 180. 24 Gromphena *ed.*; Gomphena *T.*

(208v) 181. 31 gruere. *ed.*; gruere *T.*

182. 5 quales *Virgil* and *A.*; qualis *T.*

(209r) 14 come *Dante* and *A.*; como *T.*

15 Facendo *Dante* and *A.*; Face udo *T.*

15 di sè *Dante* and *A.*; dice *T.*

20 dalla *Dante* and *A.*; dala *T.*

183. 7 Leonicus *A.*; Leoninas *T.*

(209v) 37 Sperein otan men geranos krooizein eis ton libaen meta chore
Kai pedalion tote Nauclero phrazei kremasanti katheudrei,
Eita de oresee chlainan vphanein limaner rigeon apodue *T.*

184. 4 takes *ed.*; stakes *T.*

9 Hadrianopolis *A.*; Hadrionopolis *T.*
(210r) 185. 18 Lybuis oionoi storchades lipousai Cheimeroon *T.*
(210v) 186. 10 Lambda *G.*; Eamed *T.* (*possible MS reading*: Lamed).
(211r) 33 vnam *A.*; inuicem *T.*
(211v) 187. 16 Epicharmus *ed.*; Epicarmus *T.*
(212v) 189. 12 abeunt *A.*; adeunt *T.*
35 petere *A.*; pellere *T.*
36 transierint *Pliny* and *A.*; transirent *T.*
39 Criumetopos *A.*; Criumelopos *T.*
(213r) 190. 17 Ekousi de kai phulakas Kai ouragous prodous *T.*
(214r) 191. 33 Gruis *Mantuan* and *A.*; grues *T.*
35 ferat *Mantuan* and *A.*; feret *T.*
38 Paulatimque *Mantuan* and *A.*; Paulatinque *T.*
193. 19 Manucodiata *A.*; Mann. codriats *T.*
(214v) 194. 23 &c. *A.*; sata *T.*; *not in Petrarch*
(215r) 26 Geranoi georgou katenemonto choran epis esparmeuen neoosti purinoo sitou *T.*
choran episparmenen neosti purino *ed.;*
chorun esparmeuen neoosti purinoo *A.*
195. 12 geranomachian *ed.*; yeranomachia *T.* (y=Gr. gamma)
(215v) 33 life *ed.*; like *T.*
196. 5 pugme *ed.*; peugme *T.*
(216r) 41 ipse *A.*; esse *T.*
197. 6 fabulis *A.*; fabula *T.*
9 credulitate *ed.*; credulitatis *T.*
10 historicae & poeticae *A.*; historica & poetica *T.*
(216v) 39 solum longo *A.*; longum longo *T.*
198. 9 e *Ariosto* nad *A.*; et *T.*
(219r) 203. 4 Hai Ibykou ekorkoi pareesin *T.*
(219v) 20 Cur *A.*; Cui *T.*
21 Quando nec *A.*; Quando me *T.*
22 Eumenidum *A.*; Eumenidem *T.*
29 thieues, "loue gayne" youre taught: *ed.;*
thieues,– loue gayne youre taught *T.*
(220r) 204. 15 Stat *A.*; Stal *T.*
16 Scilicet *Reusner* and *A.*; Scicilet *T.*
19 Commoda *Reusner* and *A.*; Comoda *T.*
(221r–v) 207. 11 leade *ed.*; leade leade *T.*
(223r) 210. 1 Phasidis *Statius* and *A.*; Phasidus *T.*
22 (undecipherable) ; uyse(?) *MS.*
(224v) 212. 34,38 Geranitis *Pliny*; Geranites *T.*
37 Scarites *Pliny* and *A.*; Scaretes *T.*
37 Triglitis *Pliny* and *A.*; Trigleditis *T.*

(225r) 213. 7 called *ed.*; called called *T.*
9 Schachaph *A.*; Schacaph *T.*
9 Chasida *A.*; Chaseda *T.*
10 104 *A.*; 105 *T.*
12 Fulix a furuo *A.*; Fulor a furno *T.*
19 Boellhinen *G.*; Bellhinen *T.*
22 Rorhennle *G.*; Rochermle *T.*; Rothennle *A.*
23 Schwartztaucher *G.*; Zwartlawcher *T.*
(225v) 24 Meercoote *A.*; Meerecoote *T.*
(226r) 215. 5 and *ed.* (from *A.*); in *T.*
(226v) 33 vlua *Crotti*; aluo *A.* and *T.*
35 Coerula *Crotti*; caerulea *T.*
216. 12 Eheu *Alciati*; Heu *T.*
(227r) 21 Mynichus *Ant. Lib.*; Mymichus *T.*
21 Dryan *Ant. Lib.*; Oryas *T.*; Oryan *A.*
23 Lelanta *A.*; Loelas *T.*
23 Alcandrus *A.*; Alcander *T.*
24 Hyperippa *A.*; Hyperhippa *T.*
217. 2 aequas *Paulinus*; aeques *T.*
(228r) 218. 2 Crataz. *ed.*; Crataz *T.*
14 Beccostorta *G.*; Beccostorto *T.*
15 Beccoroella *G.*; Beccoroello *T.*
15 d'acqua *A.*; de acqua *T.*
(228v) 24 Kurka *A.*; Churka *T.*
220. 2 Hacha *A.*; Hacho *T.*
2 Barositis *A.*; Barosiris *T.*
7 Corneilleau *A.*; Cornellaie *T.*
7 Kraee *G.*; Crae *T.*
7 Krahe *G.*; Krah *T.*
Hausskraee *G.*; Heuskrah *T.*
7 Schwartzkraee *G.*; Swartzkrahe *T.*
(230r) 221. 9 Pundterkrae *G.*; Boutekrey *T.*
(230v) 21 Naebelkrae *G.*; Nabelkrae *T.*
27 Holzkraey *G.*; Holzkraba *T.*; Holzkraha *A.*
28 Galgenregel *G.* and *A.*; Galganregel *T.*
222. 6 Krozein *A.*; krazein *T.*
6 Eklagra *A.*; Eilagra *T.*
(231r) 18 delapsa *Ovid* and *A.*; dilapsa *T.*
(232v) 225. 31 Haec . . . violat . . . diripit *A.*; Hae . . . violant . . . violant *T.*
(233v) 226. 39 foedera *Ursinus* and *A.*; faedera *T.*
40 putant *Ursinus* and *A.*; putent *T.*
227. 2 putar *Ursinus*; puter *T.*
5 quod *Ursinus* and *A.*; quud *T.*

5 quamuis *Ursinus*; quod vis *T*.

7 Pallade *Ursinus* and *A*.; pallada *T*.

8 sinet *Ursinus*; sinit *T*.

(234r) 28 acris. *Lucretius*; acres *A*. and *T*.

30 suopte *Lucretius*; suapte *T*.

36 Mineruae *A*.; Moneruae *T*.

(234v) 228. 35 Narsinga *A*.; Nersinga *T*.

(236r) 231. 24 Apolychronia *A*.; Apolychromia *T*.

(237r) 233. 4 Schachaph *G*.; Schacaph *T*.

5 Euchem *G*. and *A*.; Enchem *T*.

5 Kokkyx *G*. and *A*. *subst*.; Kokyr *T*.

6 Kokkyzein *A*. *subst*.; Kokkyzim *T*.

7 Cuccus *G*. and *A*.; Cullus *T*.

9 fritinit *A*.; futiuit T.

11 Cocou *G*.; Coucouc *T*.

(237v) 13 Cuclillo *A*.; Cuchillo *T*.

15 Kouckouck *ed*.; Kockock *G*.; Konchout *T*.

15 Kockuut *G*. *subst*.; Koikuunt *T*.

234. 19 est *Gaza's Aristotle* and *A*.; is *T*.

19 aspicitur *Gaza's Aristotle* and *A*.; cernatar *T*. (*see* cernantur *in following line*)

23 [a few] dayes *ed*.; *space blank in MS*; paucibus diebus *A*.

(239v) 237. 32 an *ed*.; and *T*.

238. 1 sustinentes *Acron*; sustinentibus *T*.

(240r) 12 repudiat *ed*.; repudiens *T*.

30 possint *A*.; possunt *T*.

(240v) 35 auibus. Nam *A*.; auibus, nam *T*.

37 trepidum *A*.; trepidal *T*.

(241r) 239. 25 aliter *ed*.; alitem *T*.

35 Tou toon oon epopten epopa toon autou kakoon Pepoikiloke &c. *T*.

(242r) 241. 14 Emes Kokkyx kokkizei dryos hen petaloisi *T*.

(243r) 243. 30 vocatur *Alciati*; notatur *T*.

(244r) 245. 9 sane *A*.; ea *T*.

10 mulcetur *ed*.; mulctetur *A*. and *T*.

(The following emendations of the projected list are based mainly on Aldrovandi and Gesner. Topsell's garbled spelling follows the correct one.)

(245r) 247. *col*. 1. *l*.8 Anates; Anatis *T*.

1. 20 Collurio; Colario *T*.

1. 21 Flaxfinch. Linaria; Flaxflius. Linipha *T*.

2. 1 Girfalco; Grifalco *T*.

2. 8 Accipiter; Accipitor *T*.

2. 9 Vireo; Vereo *T*.

(245r)	247. *col.*	2.*l.*11	Griglecocke; Greglecocke *T.*
		2. 12	Ficedula; Picedula *T.*
		2. 13	Coccothrauste; Cocko thraste *T.*
(245v)		2. 25	Iynx; Linx *T.*
		2. 26	Aluco; Alucon *T.*
		2. 27	fringillarius; feingellarius *T.*
	248.	1. 2	Pica; peca *T.*
		1. 6	Kernel; Karnel *T.*
		1. 21	Cypsellus; Gypsellus *T.*
		2. 3	Sitta; Citta *T.*
(246r)		2. 28	Curruca; Corruca *T.*
		2. 30	Pluuialis; Pluuiarius T.
	249.	1. 4	Rubrifalconus; Rubrifalconius *T*
		1. 8	Ruticilla; Ruticila *T.*
		1. 9	Rhintases; Rhintase *T.*
		1. 19	Garrulus; Garulus *T.*
		1. 24	Platalea; Platalia *T.*
		1. 25	Ligurinus; Legurinuo *T.*
(246v)		2. 14	Treefalcon; Threefalcon *T.*
		2. 19	Vitiflora; Vitae florus *T.*
		2. 22	Motacilla; Motocolla *T.*
		2. 27	Glaucium; Glaucca *T.*
		2. 30	Picus; Peccus *T.*
		2. 32	Cinerea; Cineria *T.*
		2. 37	Cittrinella; Cittrinula *T.*
(247r)	250. 13		Wilteshire *ed.*; Witteshire *T.*

APPENDIXES

I. Identification of Birds in Author's Projected List

II. Glossary of Heraldic Terms

III. Catalog of Proper Names

APPENDIX I

Identification of Birds in Projected List

Dabchicke. Colymbus: see 122v.
Daker hen. Crex: Corncrake *Crex crex*, after Turner, p. 70; but see 227v–228r, where illustration and description of "Crex" apply to Avocet.
Dawe. Monedula: see 80v.
Didapper. Urinator: "Dabchick."
Dove. Columba: Family *Columbidae;* see 28v.
Dotterel. Auis simplex: Dotterel *Charadrius morinellus.*
Ducke & Drake. Anates: Family *Anatidae.*
Eagle. Aquila: Genus *Aquilae.*
Bastard Eagle. Percnoptorus: *Percnopterus* (Aristotle, 618b33, and Turner, p. 34) probably Egyptian Vulture *Neophron percnopterus* (Thompson, pp. 146–147).
Eagret. Asterias: Little Egret *Egretta garzetta* (Swann)
Eatbee. Apiaster: see "Colmouse," 86v.
Eatecorne. Frugipeta: Frugilega, see 229r.
Eatefigge. Ficedula: It. *beccafigo*, Blackcap *Sylvia atricapilla* (or one of fly-catchers).
Embriz. Emberiza: Ger. *embritz*, Genus *Emberizae*, Buntings; see 45r.
Falcon. Falco: Family *Falconidae.*
Feasant. Fasianus: Pheasant *Phasianus colchicus*
Feldifare. Collurio: Fieldfare *Turdus pilaris* (Turner, p. 58).
Flaxfinch. Linaria: Ger. *flasfinc* (Turner, p. 158). Linnet *Carduelis cannabina.*
Flybiters. Dudita: Family *Muscicapidae*, Flycatchers.
Forketayle. Biforcata: Kite *Milvus milvus.*
Gannet. Penelope: Gannet *Sula bassana.*
Gelgorst. Luteus: Ger. *geelgorst,* Yellowhammer *Emberiza citrinella.*
Gerfalcon. Girfalco: Gyr Falson *Falco rusticolus.*
Globyrd. Lampyris: lampyris, firefly (Aristotle, *H.A.* 551b24); see 71v–72r.

(Italics designate birds previously dealt with in the text, as well as families and genera)

Goatehead. Capriceps. Godwit, snipe, or error for *caprimulgus* (Newton p. 365).
Goate sucker. Caprimulgus: Nightjar *Caprimulgus europaeus.*
Godwitt. Attagena. Bar-tailed Godwit *Limosa Lapponica.* Godwit as Attagen, Turner, p. 44.
Goldfynche. Carduelis: Goldfinch *Carduelis carduelis.*
Goose. Anser: Genus *Anser.*
Goshauke. Accipiter palumbarius: Goshawk *Accipiter gentilis.*
Greenefynche. Vireo: see 75r–75v.
Gryffon. Gryps: Griffon Vulture *Gyps fulvus.*
Griglecocke. Grigallus: see 203v–204v.
Gnatt snapper. Ficedula: see 86v.
Grosbeake. Coccothrauste: Hawfinch *Coccothraustes coccothraustes.*
Gull. Gauia: Genus *Larus.*
Haggard. Falco gibbosus: Peregrine *Falco peregrinus.*
Harefoote. Lagopus: Genus *Lagopus,* Grouse and Ptarmigan.
Harpyes. Harpyae (fabulous).
Haslehen. Gallina Coryllorum: Hazel Hen *Tetrastes bonasia.*
Hawke. Accipiter: Genus *Accipiter.*
Henharrower. Rubetarius: Hen Harrier *Circus cyaneus.*
Herle. Morillo: Fr. *morillon.* Red-breasted Merganser *Mergus serrator,* 96v.
Hearne. Ardea: Heron *Ardea cinerea.*
Hearonsew. Ardeola: "Hearne."
Hickwall. Iynx: Green Woodpecker *Picus viridis* (Swann). (Wryneck is *Jynx torquilla.*)
Hill-owle. Aluco: Tawny Owl *Strix aluco,* "Hill Hooter" (Swann).
Hobby. Nisus fringillarius: Hobby *Falco subbuteo;* see Bald-buzzard, 48v–49r.
Howlett. Vlula: Little Owl *Athene noctua* or Barn Owl *Tyto alba* (Swann).
Howpe. Vpupa: Hoopoe *Upupa epops.*
Iay. Pica glandaria: Jay *Garrulus glandarius.*
Iay of the water. Gracculus palmipes: Picus marinus is Halcyon (Gesner).
Kernel. Cercella: Kernel or Cercella (Gesner) is Garganey *Anas querquedula* (Ray).
Kaiuk. Virginia: N. American Indian name of a Gull.
Kestrel. Tinnunculus: Kestrel *Falco tinnunculus.*
Kings fisher. Alcedo: Kingfisher *Alcedo atthis.*
Krency. Hellorius: Gr. *Helorius,* a water-bird (Thompson, p. 53), identified with "Crex" or Avocet, 228r.
Kyte. Miluus: "Forketayle."
Lanner Buzzard. Lanarius: Lanner Falcon *Falco biarmicus.*
Lapwinge Capella: Lapwing *Vanellus vanellus.*
Larke. Alauda: Genus *Alauda;* see "Chalander," 79v–80r.
Larke of the wood. Acredula: Wood Lark *Lullula arborea.*

Lynet. Linaria: see "Flaxfinch."
Loxey. Loxia: Crossbill *Loxia curvirostra.*
Manasseneau. Virginia: N. American Indian name of Brown Thrasher *Toxostoma rufum rufum* (?).
Martlet. Cypsellus: Gr. *Gypsellus.* House Martin *Delichon urbica.*
Marten. Riparia: Sand Martin *Riparia riparia.*
Maypye. Sitta: Ger. *meyspecht.* Nuthatch *Sitta europaea.*
Mauis. Turdus: Song Thrush *Turdus ericetorum.*
Meessenouns. Virginia: N. American Indian name of Cardinal Grosbeak *Richmondena cardinalis cardinalis.*
Merlyn. Aesalon: Merlin *Falco columbarius.*
Murreybyrd. Fasceas: "Feasant"? Murry = reddish brown.
Moore hen. Fulix: Moorhen *Gallinula chloropus,* but cf. "Moore hen," 122v, for Little Grebe.
Mooretetter. Rubetra: "Mortetter" (Turner, p. 158) or Moor titling is Stonechat *Saxicola torquata.*
Mudwall. Picus martius: Woodwall = Green Woodpecker *Picus viridis;* Picus martius = Black Woodpecker *Dryocopus martius.*
Musket. Percnus: Sparrow Hawk *Accipiter nisus.*
Muskyn. Parus: a Tit *Parus?*
Naffe. Vria: "Vria, a bird called a naff (*mergus cirrhatus*)" OED; see "Herle."
Night byrde. Scops: Scops owl *Otus scops.*
Nightingale. Luscinia: Nightingale *Luscinia megarhynchos.*
Nimurder. Collurio: "Nyn murder" (Turner, p. 168). Red-backed Shrike *Lanius collurio.*
Nuttiobber. Sitta: see "Maypye."
Oedicney. Charadrius: "Oedicnemus" (Belon). Stone Curlew *Burhinus oedicnemus.*
Oester. Tabanus: "oistris," ostridge (Turner, p. 164); Tabanus: "biting oxe flie" (Cooper, *Thesaurus,* 1578).
Olyue. Oliua: Essex name of Oystercatcher *Haematopus ostralegus* (Swainson), or Belon's *cane petiere,* namely, Nemesian's *Tetrax* (204r).
Owle. Bubo: Eagle owl *Bubo bubo.*
Shrich owle. Stryx: Probably Barn owl *Tyto alba* (Swainson).
Horne-owle. Asio: Long-eared Owl *Asio otus,* (Swann).
Eare-owle. Hybris: Same as "Horne-owl."
Osprey. Halyaetus: Osprey *Pandion haliaetus;* see Bald-buzzard, 48v–49r.
Owsell. Merula: see 57r.
Ostridge. Struthio camelus: Ostrich *Struthio camelus.*
Oxeye. Crepera: Great Tit *Parus major.* "Crepera" (Turner, p. 52) is Tree Creeper *Certhia familiaris.*
Parret. Psittacus: Genus *Psittaca,* Parrot.
Partridge. Perdix: Partridge *Perdix perdix.*

Peacock. Pauo: Peacock *Pavo cristatus.*
Pelican. Pelicanus: Spoonbill *Platalea leucorodia;* true Pelican is *Onocrotalus,* "Water Pelican," or *Alcatraz,* 23r.
Penguyn. Pinguizia: Great Auk *Alca impennis* (Ray-Willughby).
Phoenix. Phoenix (fabulous).
Pockway, Poucqueo, Poppogottuweo } Virginia: Unidentified N. American Indian names.
Pochard. Boscas: Pochard *Aythya ferina.*
Pynnocke. Curruca: Dunnock or Hedge Sparrow *Prunella modularis.*
Pye. Pica: Magpie *Pica pica.*
Plouer. Pluuialis ploides: "Lapwing."
Plungeon. Phalacrocorax: Cormorant, 90r.
Puet. Phalaris: Black-headed Gull *Larus radibundus* (see Turner, p. 76, and for *Phalaris,* p. 92); Puet is also the Lapwing.
Puffyn. Puffinus: Puffin *Fratercula arctica.*
Puttocke. Idem quod Kyte.
Quayle. Coturnix: Quail *Coturnix coturnix.*
Quayle leader. Ortygometra: Properly Corncrake *Crex crex,* but equated with *Cenchram,* 77r–77v.
Rayle. Rallus: Water Rail *Rallus aquaticus.*
Rauen. Coruus: Raven *Corvus corax.*
Redfalcon. Ruberfalconus: Red-footed Falcon *Falco vespertinus.*
Redshanke. Porphyrio: Redshank *Tringa totanus.*
Redtayle. Fenicurus: Redstart *Phoenicurus phoenicurus.*
Reede byrd: Reed Bunting *Emberiza schoeclus* ("rede sparrow," or junco of Turner, p. 104).
Redstart. Ruticilla: "Redtayle."
Rhintases. Rinoceros: *Rhintaces* is Phoenix or Bird of Paradise (Belon); "Rhinoceros" is a Horn-bill *Buceros rhinoceros.*
Ringtayle. Tarquisilla: see 48v.
Ringdoue. Palumbus: Wood Dove *Columba palumbus.*
Robyn redbreast. Rubecula: Robin *Erithacus rubecula.*
Rooke. Cornix frugiuora: "Eatcorne."
Rowsett. Lussiniola: "Roussette," a frugivorous bat *Pteropus vulgaris* (O.E.D.); see Bat, 35r.
Sacar. Melanaetus: Sacar Falcon *Falco cherrug.*
Seamewe. Cepphus: Common Gull *Larus canus* (Swainson).
Seacob. Larus: "Gull," "Seamew."
Seapye. Garrulus Charadrius: Oystercatcher *Haematopus ostralegus.*
Sheldapple. Idem quod Chaffynche: see 78r.
Sheldrake. Cataracta: see Bergander, 42r.
Shoueler. Platalea: "Pelecan."

Siskin. Ligurinus: Siskin *Carduelis spinus.* "Ligurinus" is Greenfinch, "luteola" is Siskin (Turner, pp. 104, 108).
Snype. Rusticula minor: Snipe *Capella gallinago.*
Sparrowe. Mistruthium: Genus *Passer.*
Hedge sparrowe. Sepiarius: "Pynnocke."
Red sparrowe. Iunco: "Reede byrd."
Speigh. Idem quod woodpecker: "Hickwall." Properly "Wood-spite or Wood-speck" (Swann).
Swallowe. Hyrundo: Swallow *Hirundo rustica.*
Sea-swallowe. Drepanis: A Tern: Common *Sterna hirundo,* Arctic *Sterna macrura,* or Little *Sterna albifrons* (Swainson). *Drepanis* is the Swift *Apus apus* (Thompson).
Siren. Serinus. Sirenes (fabulous).
Stare. Sturnus: Starling *Sturnus vulgaris.*
Starre. Stella. [?]
Sterne. Sterna: Black Tern *Chlidonias niger.* Turner's "stern," p. 78.
Stockdoue. Liuia: See "Alchata," 28v, but possibly also Rock Dove *Columba livia.*
Stonefalcon. Lapidarius: "Merlyn" (Swainson).
Stubble byrd. Stoporola: Grey Lag Goose *Anser anser,* "Stubble Goose," Swainson).
Stimphalides (fabulous).
Sukyus. Idem quod Chaffinche: "Eatfigge. Ficedula." See *Sukalis* (Turner, p. 70 and Thompson, p. 163); "linnets or Sukyus" (79r).
Swanne. Cygnus. Genus *Cygni.*
Tele. Querquedula: Teal *Anas crecca.*
Teauh. Virginia: N. American Indian name.
Thistle lynet. Acanthys: "Goldfynche."
Titlinge. Lingetta: Meadow Pipit *Anthus pratensis* (Swainson).
Titmose. Parus: Genus *Pari.*
Throstle. Bobriacensis: "Mauis."
Thrushe. Idem quod Mauis.
Treefalcon. Arborarius: "Hobby" (Swann).
Turkey Cocke. Gallo pauus: Turkey *Meleagris gallopavo.*
Turtle. Turtur: Turtle Dove *Streptopelis turtur.*
Vrion. Argatulis. [?]
Vyne byrde. Vitiflora. Wheatear *Oenanthe oenanthe.*
Vultur or Geyre. Vultur: Family *Aegypiidae.* "Ger. *eyn geyr*" (Turner, p. 176).
Wagtayle. Motacilla: Genus *Motacillae.*
Water crowe. Cornix aquatica: Dipper *Cinclus cinclus* (Turner, p. 22).
Water hen. Tringa: "Moore hen."
Water swallow. Cinclus: "Water crowe."
Westerne. Idem quod Marten.

Wigeon. Glaucium: Wigeon *Anas penelope.*
Wittwall. Galbula. Golden oriole *Oriolus oriolus.* Vireo or "witwol" (Turner, p. 172).
Woodcocke. Gallinago: Woodcock *Scolopax rusticola.*
Woodspecker. Picus martius: "Mudwall. Picus martius."
Sea woodcocke. Trochilos: Bar-tailed Godwit *Limosa lapponica* (Swainson); namely, Aldrovandi's "Corrier," 120r (Ray-Willughby).
Wynter Crowe. Cornix Cinerea: "Royston Crowe," 230r.
Wren. Regulus Regulialus: Wren *Troglodytes troglodytes.*
Wrynecke. Iynx: Wryneck *Jynx torquilla.*
Yelamber. Cittrinella: "Gelgorst."

APPENDIX II

Glossary of Heraldic Terms

Arg. argent white
bar horizontal line less wide than a fesse
battelle, imbattelle embattled, crenellated, having an edge shaped like a battlement
bend ordinary drawn from the dexter top to the sinister base of the shield
besaunts gold roundels
bollet probably billet, a rectangle twice as high as it is wide
bosants byzants, gold roundels
canton small square division occupying upper right of shield
Chiefe, Chief top
Cheueron a charge on the escutcheon shaped ∧
cinquepyles probably error for *cinquefoils*
Cottises, Cotteses detached hems of any ordinary
countercharged the tinctures interchanged or reversed
dance a fesse or band shaped like a very wide M
daxster dexter, right
engrailed the edge indented with curvilinear notches
Ermyn heraldic fur, black spots on white
Escallopes series of segments of circles or leaves forming a scalloped edge
Fesse horizontal band across the shield, one third from top or bottom, fairly wide
Fusills bearings in the form of an elongated lozenge (see under *losinges*)
gardant having the full face towards the spectator
gobinated divided into alternate areas of two colors
Gules red (as basic color)
guttye from *gutté,* besprinkled with drops
heads erased heads represented with a jagged edge, as if torn off
losinges lozenges, plane rectilineal figures with 4 sides, two acute and two obtuse angles

memberd bird whose legs are of a different tincture from the body
Mulletts stars with five or more straight points
ordinary major plain charge on shield
pale an ordinary consisting of a wide vertical stripe in the middle of the shield
paleways palewise, in the direction of a pale (see above)
party divided into parts of different tinctures
passant walking, looking towards right side with the right forepaw raised (OED)
Pheons broad barbed arrows, or heads of javelins
proper represented in its natural color
runlett cask or vessel
Sab. sable, black
Second second color previously mentioned (in heraldic idiom, colors are never mentioned twice)
Semicrossletts small half crosses
Torteaxes from French *torteaux*, small red circular figures representing cakes of bread
whilke whelk, kind of mollusc.

APPENDIX III

Catalog of Proper Names

ACRON, HELENIUS, Roman grammarian, 2d cent. A.D., wrote commentaries on Terence and, as supposed, upon Persius and Horace.

ACRONIUM, modern Lake Constance, N.E. Switzerland.

AEGIALIA, Aegiale, wife of Diomedes, Greek hero at Troy.

AEGOLIUS, transformed into an owl (Thompson); see n. 152 (102r).

AELIAN(US), CLAUDIUS, 3d cent. A.D., Roman author of *De Animalium Natura* and *Variae Historiae*.

AELIUS JULIUS (CROTTUS), 16th cent. Latin poet of Ferrara, his collected work entitled *Opuscula*, Ferrara, 1564.

AEMILIUS PAULUS LUCIUS (229–160 B.C.), Roman consul and general.

AENEAS SYLVIUS (PICCOLOMINI, 1405–1464), Italian emissary to England and later Pope Pius II, whose *Opera quae extant omnia* appeared at Basle, 1551, 1561, and 1571.

AESACUS, son of Priam, enamoured of Hesperia, whose death caused him to throw himself into the sea and who was then changed by Thetis into a cormorant.

AETIUS (fl. 1st or 2d cent. A.D.), Greek medical writer who compiled *Sixteen Books on Medicine*.

AGATHOCLES (361–289 B.C.), tyrant of Syracuse, warred against the Carthaginians.

AGRIPPINA, city in the country of the Daunians, perhaps Argyripa, formerly Argos Hippium, founded by Diomedes.

ALBERTUS MAGNUS, Albert the Great (1206–1280), bishop and scholar, whose *De Animalibus* is distinguished as a realistic treatise on animals.

ALCANDER, son of Munichus, King of Molossa, according to Nicander.

ALCIATI, ANDREA (1492–1550), native of Milan, Professor of Law at Avignon and at Bourges and at various universities in Italy, author of notable legal works and *Emblemata*.

ALCITHOE, see Meneus.

ALEXANDER AB ALEX(ANDRO), (1461–1523), Italian author of *Dies*

Geniales (Rome, 1522) and *Dissertationes Quattuor de Rebus Admirandis quae in Italia nuper contigere, id est, De Somniis . . .*, Rome? 1525.

ALEXANDER APHRODISIENSIS (of Aphrodisias), 3d cent. A.D., Greek commentator on Aristotle, author of *Problemata*, Venice, 1488, 1501, etc.

ALTHÆUS, brother of Daunus, mythical king; see 29v.

ALVAREZ, FRANCISCUS (*c.* 1465–1541), Portuguese missionary and explorer, wrote account of embassy to Ethiopia, 1520–1527, his chief work being *Ho Preste Joam da Indias* (Coimbra, Portugal, 1540?); his writings included by Ramusio in *Primo Volume delle Navigationi e Viaggi*, 1554.

AMBROSE (ST., A.D. 337–397), Bishop of Milan and one of great Fathers of the Church, wrote a Hexaemeron.

AMBROSIUS NOLANUS (of Nola), Leo Nolanus, Leone Ambrogio, Italian physician, fl. at Venice *c.* 1532, annotated works of Averroes, wrote *Emblemata.*

AMBRACIA, Greek city in Epirus, n. of Bay of Actium.

ANTIGONUS (II, *c.* 320–239 B.C.), Greek philosopher and soldier, reestablished Macedon as a nation.

APALIA, properly Apulia, a region of S.E. Italy from Mt. Garganus to S.E. extremity, modern Le Puglie, comprising provinces of Foggia, Bari, Brindisi, Taranto, and Lecce.

APHRODYSAEUS, see Alexander Aphrodisiensis.

APICIUS, M. GABIUS, celebrated Epicure in time of Tiberius.

APOLLONIUS or Appolonius (of TYANA), Greek philosopher of Neo-Pythagorean school, lived a few years before Christian era, subject of marvelous stories as told by his biographer, Philostratus.

AQUILEIA, Italian city at head of Adriatic, T. confuses with Aquila, which is near Amiternum, where Sallust was born.

ARETAEUS, 2d cent., physician of Cappadochia, contemporary of Galen, author of work in 8 books on causes, symptoms, and cure of acute and chronic affections.

ARGUENTORATE (Argentoratum), modern Strasbourg.

ARIOSTO, LODOVICO (1474–1533), Italian poet of Ferrara, famed author of *Orlando Furioso,* translated into English by Sir John Harington, London, 1591 (revised 1607).

ARISTIPPE, see Meneus.

ARISTOPHANES BIZANTINUS (*c.* 257–180 B.C.), edited Hesiod, Homer, the Greek dramatists.

ARNOBIUS, *c.* A.D. 305, Christian writer and teacher of rhetoric in Numidia, author of *Aversus Nationes,* attacking paganism.

ARNOLDUS, Arnaldus de Villa Nova (*c.* 1235–1313), famous European alchemist, astrologer, physician, student of Arabian philosophy, his works repeatedly issued during the 16th century.

ARSINOE III, born *c.* 235 B.C., Ptolemaic Egyptian princess who married her brother, Ptolemy IV Philopator.

ASTOLPHO, the famous hero of the *Orlando Furioso* by Ariosto.
ATHALARICUS (A.D. 516–534), King of Ostrogoths (526–534), grandson of Theodoric the Great.
ATHAMAS, son of Aeolus, husband of Ino.
ATHENAEUS, Greek rhetorician and grammarian of Egypt, fl. *c.* A.D. 200, author of *Deipnosophistae*, a storehouse of miscellaneous information.
AUGUSTINE (ST., A.D. 354–430), Bishop of Hippo and famous theologian, his greatest work *De Civitate Dei*, in 22 Bks.
AUGUSTINUS NIPHUS (1473–1546), Italian physician and philosopher, among many works wrote a translation and commentary on Aristotle (Venice, 1537), collected works issued in 1559, 6 vols.
AURELIUS VICTOR, SEXTUS, 4th cent. A.D., African governor of Pannonia Secunda, a moralizing historian interested in prodigies.
AUSONIUS, DECIMUS MAGNUS (*c.* A.D. 310–395), Roman poet, best known piece the *Mosella*, describing the Moselle River.
AUERGNE, Auvergne, ancient Arvernia, formerly a French province, now corresponds to the Departments of Cantal and Puy-de-Dôme.
AUICEN, AVICENNA (979–1037), greatest of Arabian philosophers, whose *Canon of Medicine*, in Latin translation, was for centuries a standard textbook.
AZALIUS (AZALUS), POMPILIUS, a Portuguese lawyer, supposed author of *Liber . . . de omnibus rebus naturalibus*, Venice, 1544.

BABILON, ancient capital of Babylonia, on the Euphrates River.
BACCHILIDES, Greek lyric poet, fl. *c.* 450 B.C.
BALEARES, BALEARICS, group of four islands in Mediterranean, off E. coast of Spain.
BARBARY, N. African area comprising Morocco, Algeria, Tunis, and Tripoli.
BARTHOLOMEUS (ANGLICUS), great English encyclopedist of 13th cent., author *De Proprietatibus Rerum,* widely translated, into English by Trevisa (ed. Berthelet, 1535) and, with additions, by Stephen Batman, *Batman on Bartholome*, London, 1582.
BASIL (ST., *c.* A.D. 330–379), Bishop of Caesarea, famous preacher and theologian, author of a Hexaemeron.
BASSILES, a personage quoted in Athenaeus.
BELON or BELLONIUS, PIERRE (1517–1564), French naturalist, author of *L'Histoire de la Nature des Oyseaux* and *Les Observations de plusieurs singularitez et choses mémorables trouvées en Grèce, Asie . . .*
BEUCEPHALA (Bucephala), a city on the Hydaspes, in India, built by Alexander the Great honoring his horse so named.
BISTONIA, a city in Thrace, the Bistones a people mentioned by Strabo and Pliny.
BOEDROMION, the name of the third Attic month, corresponding to latter half of September and beginning of October.

BOETIUS (BOECE), HECTOR (*c.* 1465–*c.* 1536), Scottish historian, professor at University of Paris, priest at Tyrie, Aberdeenshire, and first principal of University of Aberdeen, author of *Scotorum Historia* . . . in 19 Bks. (1526–1527), enlarged ed. Paris, 1574, translated into English by William Harrison and included in Holinshed's *Chronicles of England and Scotland,* 1577.

BOLLEN, modern Boulogne-sur-Mer, city in N. France on the English Channel.

BONHAM, THOMAS (d. 1629?), English physician, Edward Topsell's friend who, he says, gave him descriptions of several North American birds.

BONONIA, Bologna, commune N. Italy, native city of Aldrovandi.

BORSIPPA, a city on the Euphrates, in Babylonia, according to Strabo, who alludes to edible bats found there.

BRABANT, central province of Belgium, part of an ancient duchy.

BRITHELINSTON, ancient Bristelestune, modern Brighton, on Sussex coast, in England.

BRUTHE, a Scottish castle in N. Aberdeenshire.

BUDAEUS (BUDÉ), GUILLAUME (1467–1540), French scholar and lexicographer, friend of Erasmus and More.

BUTHQUHAN, Buchquhan, the Scottish parish of Buchan, Aberdeenshire, Scotland.

CADMUS, founder and ruler of Thebes, believed to have introduced the alphabet.

CAELIUS, LODOVICUS (RODIGINUS or L. C. RICHERIUS, *c.* 1450–1525), Italian philologist, Professor of Greek and Latin at Milan, chief work *Antiquae Lectiones* (Ancient Readings), 1516.

CALABER (QUINTUS SMYRNAEUS), Greek epic writer, 4th cent. A.D., author of *Posthomerica.*

CALECUT, Calcutta, capital of Bengal, in India.

CARAMBIS, a promontory on the Black Sea, in Paphlagonia, modern Turkey.

CARDAN, GIROLAMO (JEROME, 1501–1576), voluminous Italian writer on astrology and natural magic, most popular works *De subtilitate* and *De rerum varietate.*

CARYSTIUS (DIOTIMUS CARYSTIUS), in Aelian; see note *c*(3r).

CASSIODORUS, FLAVIUS MAGNUS AURELIUS (*c.* A. D., 490–585), Roman senator and scholar, author of *Variarum Libri XII* and other works, popular through the Middle Ages.

CASSIUS, Casius, a mountain in N. Syria, now called Jebel-Okrab, near Seleuceia.

CATIGAN, Chattigan, modern Chittagong, chief port of modern E. Pakistan, opening on Bay of Bengal.

CAVALERO, Cavalleriis, Jo.-Bapt. de, Roman antiquary, 16th cent., author of *Antiquarum statuarum urbis Romae primus et secundus liber,* Rome, 1585.

CAYSTER, or Caystrus, a river in Lydia, its mouth on the Asian plain in Turkey, a resort of wild fowl.

CELEUS, transformed into the Green Woodpecker, first identified with this name by Gesner (Thompson); see fable of sacred bees, 102r.

CEUSCALA, or "Ceuskalon" (Hakluyt), a town in the province of "Mancy" (India or Burma; but possibly Canton in China); see Nanzi below.

CERBERUS, transformed into unidentified bird (Thompson); see above on Celeus.

CHAEREPHON, Greek philosopher, born *c.* 480 B.C., friend of Socrates and noticed favorably by Plato.

CHALCIDONIA, Chalcidon, Calchedon, ancient maritime town of Bithynia, in Asia Minor, almost directly opposite Byzantium.

CHALDEES, Chaldeans, or Babylonians.

CHRISIPPE, Chrysippus, Athenian Stoic, *c.* 280–205 B.C.

CITHEREUS, PHILOXENUS, a glutton described by Gellius.

CLARONA, Clarenna, modern Kirchheim or Rain, a small German town in Bavaria.

CLAUDIANUS, CLAUDIUS, Roman poet, fl. A.D. 395–404, author of the epic *Rape of Proserpine.*

CLAUDIUS, PUBLIUS (PULCHER), Roman admiral in First Punic war, consul in 249 B.C.

CLEARCHUS, father of Dionysius of Heraclea (*c.* 328–248 B.C.).

CLEOPATRA EPIPHANIUS, wife of Ptolemy V. Epiphanes, ruler in Egypt, 201–181 B.C.

COLLEN, modern Cologne, Germany, city on the Rhine, associated with the name of Albert the Great.

COMUTAS, properly Cometes, son of Sthenelus, enamoured of Aegiale, wife of Diomedes.

CONSTANCE, after Lake Geneva, the largest lake in Switzerland, on the N.E. border, formed by the Rhine.

CONSTANTINOPOLITANUS, a name applied to many Byzantines, chiefly theologians; here an unidentified physician.

CORONE, city in S.W. Peloponnesus, named after Coronis, daughter of Phlegyas, got with child by Apollo and killed by him on discovery of her marriage to Ischys; see Ovid, *Met.*, II, 542 ff.

CORTYNA, properly Gortyna, an ancient city in Crete.

COTYS, COTIIS, a Thracian king who warred against Athenians, 356 B.C.

CRASSUS, JUNIUS PAULUS, doctor of Padua and professor of medicine, translated and annotated Theophrastus and other classics, d. 1574.

CRIUMBTOPAS, a great southern headland overlooking Euxine to a promontory of Casambis, in Asia Minor.

CUKMAN (CULMANUS), JOHN, unidentified Netherlander, correspondent of Gesner.

CYCLADES, a group of islands in the Aegean Sea.

CYDNUS, see Tarsus.

CYLLABAR(US), properly Cylarabes, a king in Argos, who succeeded his father Sthenebus, their graves in Corinth (Pausanias, *Corinth*, XXII)

CYLLENA, Cyllene, an Arcadian city mentioned by Aristotle, *H. A.* 617a.19.

CYROPOLIS, city built by Alexander the Great in Media Atropatene between the rivers Cyrus and Amardus.

CYRUS (the Great), famous commander, founder of Persian Empire, 559–529 B.C.

DAUNUS, King of Dauni, whose daughter married Diomedes; see Ovid, *Met.*, XIV, 458 ff.

DEIMACHUS, Syrian ambassador to India, sent by Antiochus I Soter, 280–261 B.C., left account of India, which, with that of Megasthenes, is said to be full of lies; see Strabo, *Geography*, II.i.9.

DELACHAMPIUS, JACOBUS (Dalechamps, Jacques, 1513–1588), scholar and editor, author of *Historia Generalis Plantarum in libris XVII . . .*, Leyden, 1586–1587.

DEMETRIUS, (1) D. of Apamea, Greek physician of unknown date, or (2) D. Pepagomenus (fl. 13th cent.), author of work on gout, printed in Greek 1558.

DEMETRIUS (fl. 15th–16th cent.), Italian teacher of Greek, a disciple of L. Tomaeus.

DEMOCRITUS, a physician and geoponic writer.

DENTATUS, JUNIUS PARTHENOPAEUS (that is, of Naples), fl. 16th cent. and, though called "an old writer before Alex. ab Alex.," is termed by him a lifelong friend.

DEUCALION, son of Prometheus, saved from flood, landed after nine days and nights on Mt. Parnassus.

DIODORUS (SICULUS), Graeco-Roman historian, author of World History *c.* 60–30 B.C.

DIOMEDES, son of Tydeus and Greek hero at Troy.

DIONISIUS COLAN (1402–1471), D. the Carthusian, or Lewis de Rickel, German author of *Contra vitia superstitionum.*

DIONYSIUS, (*c.* 328–248 B.C.), philosopher of Heraclea, on the Pontus.

DIONYSIUS HALICARNASS (of Halicarnassus), rhetorician, historian, taught at Rome 30–8 B.C., author *On the Arrangement of Words, On the Ancient Orators,* and other critical works.

DIONYSUS or Bacchus, god of wine, emblem of gluttony.

DOMINICUS, LUDOVICUS, Italian emblem writer born at Placenza, author of *Facetie et Motti arguti di alcuni eccellentissimi ingegni* (Florence, 1548, and 8 further edd. before 1600). Died at Pisa, 1564.

DOMITIAN(US), TITUS FLAVIUS, Roman emperor, A.D. 81–96.

DRYAS, father of King Munichus.

ECBATANE, ancient Agbatane, later Hamadan, a city of Media, on the Iranian plateau, its supposed founder Semiramis.

ENCELEIUS (ENTZELT), CHRISTOPHORUS, early 16th cent. German scholar, born in Saalfeld, in Thuringia, author of *Tractat de Re Metallica* . . . , Frankfurt, 1551.

ENNIUS, QUINTUS (239–169 B.C.), termed "father of Roman poetry."

EPICHARMUS, (5th cent. B.C.), Sicilian writer of comedy.

EPINETUS, properly Epanetus or Epaenetus, a culinary author referred to by Athenaeus, who states that he wrote a treatise on fishes and another on the art of cooking.

ERICHTHONIUS, mythical Athenian king, called son of Vulcan, father of Pandion.

EUIPPA, or Evippe, daughter of King Daunus, second wife of Diomedes.

EUCHERIUS (d. *c.* A.D. 450), native of Gaul, Bishop of Lyons *c.* A.D. 434, author of several religious works.

EUSEBIUS (*c.* A.D. 264–340), Christian scholar of Caesarea, in Palestine, the father of church history, author of *Praeparatio Evangelica* (15 Bks.), concerned with evidences of Christianity.

EUSTATHIUS (12th cent. A.D.), Bishop of Thessalonica, author of commentaries on Homer and of polemics.

FABIUS, Q. FABIUS MAXIMUS, Roman admiral mentioned by Livy as augur.

FACHINETTI, LUDOVICI (16th cent.), Italian marquis, member of distinguished family of Bologna, friend of Aldrovandi.

FARRA, ALEXANDER (16th cent.), born in Alexandria, in Italy, prominent in the Academy of the Affidati in Pavia, Governor of Ascolti and Casal, author of *Della divinità dell' huomo* and *Miracoli d' amore*.

FAUSTINA, (1) the Elder, (A.D. 105–141), wife of Emperor Antoninus, and (2) the Younger, wife of Emperor Marcus Aurelius, d. A.D. 176.

FESTUS, SEXTUS POMPEIUS (2d cent. A.D.), Roman grammarian, author of *De verborum significatione*, 1471, 1510, 1511, 1565, etc.

FEZ, capital of Morocco, N. Africa.

FRIZLAND, the Frisian Islands, a chain along coast of Holland and Germany.

FULGOSUS, or FREGOSO, Battista (1509–1587), Duke of Genoa, author of *Baptistae Fulgosii Genuensis Factorum et Dictorum memorabilium* (Cologne, 1541, Antwerp, 1565, etc.).

GALEN (*c.* A.D. 130–200), Greek physician born at Pergamum, in Asia Minor, founder of experimental physiology, certain of his vast writings reaching West in Latin translations from Arabic.

GALLOWAY, ALEXANDER, 16th cent. parson of Kinkell (or Kilde), an ancient parish of Aberdeenshire, in Scotland.

GELLIUS, AULUS (*c.* A.D. 123–165), Roman author of *Noctes Atticae.*

GEMMA, CORNELIUS (1534–1579), Frisian philosopher, mathematician, and physician, author of *De naturae divinis characterismis*, Antwerp, 1575.

GERANEA, or Megara, a city, a district, a mountain chain; territory comprises great part of Greek Isthmus from Mt. Cithaeron to the Acrocorinthus.

GESNER, CONRAD (1516–1565), the great German-Swiss linguist and naturalist, his greatest work *Historia Animalium* (4 vols., Zürich, 1551–1558): Book III, *De avium natura*, was chief source of Aldrovandi's *De Avibus*, translated and adapted by Edward Topsell in *The Fowles of Heauen.*

GNOSUS, properly Cnossus (Knossus), ancient city in Crete.

GOATELAND, far northern lands referred to by Olaus Magnus as "in Septentrione (in Noruegia & finitimis regionibus)," Bk. XIX, ch. 33–34; he may have meant the Swedish island in the Baltic.

GRATAROLUS, GULIEL (1516–1568), Italian physician and editor of works on medicine and natural science, corresponded with Gesner, author of *Prognostica naturalia*, Basle, 1552.

GREGORIUS NYSSENUS, St. Gregory of Nyssa, (died *c.* A.D. 385), author of several exegetical and theological works.

HADRIAN (A.D. 76–138), Publius Aelius Hadrianus, Roman Emperor A.D. 117–138.

HAKLUYT, Richard (1552?–1616), famous English geographer, collector of travels, translator, editor, author *The Principall Navigations, Voiages, and Discoveries of the English Nation*, London, 1589, later enlarged edd. H. furnished Topsell with drawings of N. American birds; see 85v, p. 139.

HALY (ABBAS), Ali ibn al Abbas (d. A.D. 994), Persian author of *Liber Regius,* medical work translated into Latin by Constantine the African, brought to the West a view of Greek medicine.

HARLEM, HAARLEM, a town in province of N. Holland, W. of Amsterdam, surrendered to Spanish after siege, July, 1573.

HEBRUS HADRIONOPOLIS, ancient Thracian city on banks of R. Hebrus.

HERACLEA, one of many ancient cities so named, perhaps that in Sicily.

HERMOLAUS (BARBARUS, 1454–1493), editor of Aristotle and Dioscorides, author of *Castigationes Plinianae* (Rome, 1492), pointing out many errors in the *Natural History* by Pliny.

HESIOD (8th cent. B.C.), father of Greek didactic poetry, author of *Theogony* and *Works and Days.*

HESPERIA, beloved by Aesacus and fatally bitten by snake.

HIERO I, tyrant of Syracuse 478–467 B.C.

HIPPOCRATES (468–399 B.C.), Greek physician, writings attributed to him in the *Hippocratic Collection.*

HIRCE (Latin Herceus), a surname of Jupiter.

HISPANIOLA or SPAGNIOLA, originally the entire island of Haiti, in the West Indies, now as Santo Domingo it comprises the eastern two-thirds.

HORTENSIUS, QUINTUS HORTALUS (114–50 B.C.), Roman forensic rival of Cicero.

HYPANUS, Hypanis, modern Kuban, river in N. Caucasus area, in S. Russia.

HYPERIPPA, daughter of Munichus, King of Molossa.

IBICUS (6th cent. B.C.), a Greek lyric poet whose murderers were revealed by cranes.

ILLIRIANS, inhabitants of Illyria, formerly a region extending eastward from the Adriatic between Liburnia to the north, Epirus to the south; modern Yugoslavia.

INSULAE FORTUNATAE, CANARIAE, Canary Islands, archipelago off W. Africa.

IRPRANDUS, properly, Ildebrandus (Hildebrand), who succeeded his uncle, Liutprand, as King of Lombardy, and was deposed shortly.

ISIDORE, Isidorus Hispalensis (A.D. 602–636), Bishop of Seville, author of *Originum sive Etymologiarum libri xx*, a major source of the encyclopedia by Bartholomeus.

IUBA, Juba II, King of Mauretania (50 B.C.–A.D. 23), author of historical and scientific writings used by Plutarch and Pliny.

IURA, mountain range between the Rhine and the Rhone separating France and Switzerland.

JACOB, "Athenian bishop," possibly J. of Nisibis, surnamed the Great, Christian bishop, attended Council of Nicaea in A.D. 325. Died *c.* A.D. 340–350.

JAVA MAJOR, the most important island of the Malay Archipelago.

JEROME (ST., *c.* A.D. 340–420), great Christian scholar and translator of Bible, wrote *Chronicle.*

JOVIUS (GIOVIO), PAULUS (1483–1552), Bishop of Nocera, Florentine historian and biographer, author of *Elogia doctorum virorum ab avorum memoria publicatio ingenii monumentis illustrium*, Antwerp, 1557, Basle, 1571, etc.

JULIUS ALEXANDRINUS (1506–1590), Italian physician, author of *libros XXXIII de sanitate tuenda,* Cologne, 1575.

JUNIUS, L. Junius Pullus, Roman consul 249 B.C., referred to by Cicero, in *De Divinatione.*

KILDE, see Galloway.

KIRANIDES, that is, of Kiranus or Cyranus, King of Persia, a title designating the author of a work on virtues of plants and animals, a translation from a Greek translation from Arabic.

LACEDEMON, a name for Greek Laconia.

LAIUS, transformed into a bird, probably the Blue Thrush *Monticola solitarius* (Thompson); see 102r.

LANGIUS, Lange, Johann (1485–1565), German physician, later lived in Italy at Bologna and Pisa, author of many medical tracts.

LEANDER, ALBERTUS, or ALBERTI, LEANDRO (1479–1552), Italian author of a book on famous Dominicans (Bologna, 1517) and of a description of Italy, *Descrittione di tutta Italia . . . et piu gli huomini famosi che l'hanno illustrada . . .*, Bologna, 1550.

LELANTA, wife of Munichus, King of the Molossi.

LEMNOS, island in N. Aegean Sea.

LEONICUS TOMAEUS, see Tomaeus.

LEUCIPPA, see Meneus.

LIBERALIS, ANTONINUS (fl. A.D. 150), author of collection of tales of mythical transformations, *Transformationum congeries,* (Greek) Basle, 1568, (Greek and Latin) Lyons, 1674.

LICAONYANS, natives of Lycaonia, a region of ancient Cilicia, in Asia Minor.

LICIA, ancient district in S. coast of Asia Minor, S.W. Turkey; through it flows the River Xanthus.

LIERE, ancient Liger or LIGIER, modern River Loire.

LIPSIUS, JUSTUS (1547–1606), Flemish humanist, eminent editor of classical texts, author of *De Constantia.*

LIUTPRANDUS, or Liutprand, able King of Lombardy A.D. 712–744.

LOBELIUS, Lobel, de L'Obel, Mathieu (1538–1616), eminent French botanist and physician, at Antwerp, then in England, physician to James I, author with Pena of *Stirpium Adversaria* (1570) and other botanical works.

LONGOLIUS, GYBERTUS, Gilbert of Longueil (1507–1543), author of uncompleted *Dialogus de Avibus,* edited by William Turner, Cologne, 1544.

LORDESTE, a country said to have been visited by Columbus; see 206v.

LUDOVICUS ROMANUS (or PONTANO), Roman writer on India, author of *Singularia Notabilia* (1470), apparently memoirs.

MACHLIN, Flemish Mechelen, modern Malines, Belgian city on the Dyle between Antwerp and Brussels.

MACROBIUS, AMBROSIUS THEODOSIUS (A.D. 395–423), Roman grammarian and philosopher, author of *Saturnalia.*

MAEMACTERION, the Attic month following Boedromion; see ante.

MAGUS, SIMON, a skillful magician of Samaria, founder of the sect of Simonians, a rival of early Christianity.

MANTUAN, Baptista Spagnuoli (1447–1516), Italian and Latin poet known chiefly for Latin pastorals.

MARCELLUS (EMPIRICUS, late 4th cent. A.D.), native of Bordeaux, court physician to Emperor Theodosius, author of *De medicamentis* (1536).

MARCHLAND, ancient Mers (46v), a district of Scotland, also (205r) a central district in Germany, through which runs the River Tanger.

MARE DEL SUR, that is, Sea of the South, here Bay of Bengal.

MARSILIUS (BONON.), Marcellus, Anton Felix, Abbot and Bishop of Perugia, author *Historia naturalis territorii Bononiensis.*

MARTIAL, MARCUS VALERIUS (A.D. 40–104), famous Roman epigrammatist.

MARTYR, PETER, P. M. d'Anghiera (1457–1526), Spanish historian and author of *De Orbe Novo Petri Martyris Anglerii, Decades Octo, . . .* first ed., 1530, and included by Ramusio in his collection of voyages (vol. 3).

MAURITIUS, Flavius Tiberius, fl. 6th cent. A.D., East Roman Emperor, succeeded by Phocas.

MAXENTIUS, a recluse of Poitou, once a French province, named by St. Gregory of Tours, in *Historia Francorum,* Bk. II, ch. 37 (Migne, *Patr. Lat.,* vol. 71).

MAXIMILIAN, probably Maximilian I (1459–1519), Holy Roman emperor who warred in the Netherlands.

MAXIMUS TYRIUS, Sophist of Tyre, *c.* A.D. 125–185.

MEGALETOR, son of Munichus, King of the Molossi.

MEGARIAN, a native of Megara, city on Saronic Gulf and bounded on W. by Geraneian Mts.

MEGASTHENES, Greek emissary to India, *c.* 300 B.C., who left fragmentary account of India, said by Strabo to be full of lies; see Deimachus.

MELICIA, Melitaea, ancient town in Thessaly, situated near River Enepeus.

MELOS, island in the Aegean, at S.W. corner of Cyclades group and E. of Laconian coast.

MENECLES, native of Cyrenaica, author of Athenian history.

MENEUS, properly MINYAS, King of Orchomenus, whose daughters—Leucippe, Aristippe, and Alcithoe—were turned into bats for refusing to share the worship of Dionysus.

MENIS, a mythical kingdom ruled by Oeneus.

MERCURIAL, HIERONYMUS (1530–1606), physician and professor at Padua and at Bologna, author of *Variae Lectiones,* Venice, 1570.

MEROPA, a mountain in Thessaly.

MEROPS, "one of those *Gyaunts* which builded Babell" (86v).

MERULA, GAUDENTIUS (16th cent.), author of *De Gallorum cisalpinorum antiquitate & origine lib. III,* Lyons, 1538.

MINTUS, the River Mincius, or Mincio, which flows near Mantua.

MISNIA, Misna or Misena, a town N.E. of Dresden.

MITHRIDATES (EUPATOR), King of Pontus (1st cent. B.C.), whose legendary feats included a prodigious knowledge of languages.

MIZALDUS (MIZAUD), ANTONIUS (16th cent.), French physician, mathematician, and astrologer, termed the French Aesculapius, author mainly of astrological works. Died in Paris, 1578.

MOLOSSA, Molossia or Epirus, country of the Molossi between Ionian Sea and chain of Pindus (N. Greece and S. Albania), famous for its dogs and other animals.

MOLUCCAS, Spice Islands, properly the Ternate group, in Malay Archipelago, in S. Pacific.

MONSPESSULUM, MONSPESSULUS, Montpellier, town S. France, famous as medical center.

MORIENNA, Maurienne, comté and once a diocese of French Savoy.

MUTINA, modern Modena, commune N. Italy.

MYMICHUS, properly Munichus, mythical King of Molossia.

NAEVIUS (GNAEUS Naevius), Roman epic poet and dramatist, author of *Bellum Punicum,* died *c.* 200 B.C. at Utica. Said by Aldrovandi to be quoted by Festus.

NANZI, properly Manvi, Mansa, or "Mancy" (Hakluyt), once a province, now a town in Burma, due N. of Mandalay.

NARSINGA, modern Narsinghgarh, now a State in Central India.

NAUPLIUS, father of Palamedes, whose death at hands of Greeks he avenged by luring their ships to destruction on cliffs of Caphareus.

NEMESIANUS (3d cent. A.D.), native of Carthage, author of pastoral and didactic poetry, a lost fragment quoted by Longolius; see 204r.

NEOCOMUM, or Comum, modern Como, an Italian town and in ancient times an important city of Cisalpine Gaul, at the southern extremity of Lacus Larius (Lake Como).

NICOSTRATUS, a Greek Middle Comedy poet, supposed son of Aristophanes.

NEPOS, CORNELIUS, Roman historian of time of Julius Caesar, friend of Cicero and Atticus, to whom he dedicated his *Vitae Excellentium Imperatorum.*

NICANDER (2d cent. B.C.), Greek poet, physician, and grammarian, native of Claros, near Colophon, author of *Theriaca* and *Alexipharmaca.*

NINEVEH, ancient capital of Assyrian Empire, on the Tigris.

NONIUS (or NONNIUS), MARCELLUS (early 4th cent. A.D.), legicographer and grammarian, author of *De compendiosa doctrina;* see Perottus.

NOREMBERGA, modern Nuremberg.

OCTAVIAN, unidentified Irishman who informed Turner about Barnacles.

ODORICUS, Odoric of Pordenone (Porta Neonis), Odericus, (fl. *c.* 1286–1331), Franciscan friar and author of *De mirabilibus mundi,* an itinerary, dated 1331, from which much of the voyages of Sir John Mandeville is said to be stolen; included in Ramusio, vol. 2 (1574 and later edd.)

OENEUS, see Menis.

OENOE, or Gerana, Queen of the Pygmies, transformed into a crane.

OLAUS MAGNUS (1490–1558), Swedish ecclesiastic, author of *Historia de Gentibus Septentrionalibus,* Rome, 1555, an encyclopedia of marvels with some factual information.

OPPIAN, (fl. 2d cent. A.D.), native of Corycus, in Cilicia, and author of *Halieutica,* on fishing, *Cynegetica,* on hunting, and *De Aucupio,* of which only notes compiled by Eutecnius are extant.

ORBITELLUS, a town on the Lagoon of Orbitello, coast of Tuscany.

ORCADES, Orkney Islands.

ORUS, Horus Apollo or Horapollo, (fl. *c.* A.D. 40), Greek grammarian and author of *Hieroglyphica.*

PALAMEDES, son of Nauplius, King of Euboea, in post-Homeric legend, and reputed to have invented several letters of Greek alphabet.

PANTHEUS, J. ANTONIUS (15th cent.), physician of Verona, author of *Confabulationes de Thermis calderianis, ubi de ferri, nitri, sulphuris natura vi ac medicina agitur,* Venice, 1488.

M. PAULUS VENETUS, Marco Polo, 1254–1324, a Venetian who traveled to Syria, Persia, India, and China, author of *De regionibus orientalibus,* translated many times and included in Ramusio's *Navigationi & viaggi,* vol. 2.

PAULINUS NOLANUS, or Pontius Meropius, A.D. 353–431), a Neapolitan doctor and Augustinian, Bishop of Nola, author of letters and poems.

PAUSANIAS (2d cent. A.D.), native of Lydia, Greek traveler and geographer. author of *Description of Greece.*

PENTINUM, properly, Peltuinum, Italian town of the Vestini, S.E. of Aquila, on road thence to Popoli.

PETHSLEGE, properly, Pitslego, a coast parish of Buchan, in north Aberdeenshire, Scotland. The castle, begun in 1424, is S.S.E. of adjoining parish of Rosehearty.

PEROTTUS (PEROT), NIC. (d. 1480), a Catholic theologian and learned cleric, author of *Cornucopiae, siue linguae latinae commentarii* (1481), 1532, etc., which includes works of Festus and of Nonius with other miscellaneous matter.

PERSIUS (AULUS PERSIUS FLACCUS, A.D. 34–62), Roman poet and moral satirist.

PETRARCH (1304–1374), the great Italian humanist and poet.

PETILIAN (5th cent. A.D.), Bishop of Cirta, in Africa, author of *De unico baptismo* and *Epistola encyclica,* refuted by St. Augustine.

PHALARIS (*c.*570–554 B.C.), a tyrant of Acragas (Agrigentum) in Sicily, notorious for cruelty.

PHERILLUS, Perillus, Perilaus, of Athens, devised brazen bull in which Phalaris' victims were roasted alive.

PHILO Judaeus, great philosopher of Alexandria, first century A.D.

PHILES (*c.* 1275–1340), a Byzantine poet of Ephesus, author of *On the Nature of Animals,* mostly from Aelian.

PHILAEUS, son of King Munichus.

PHILOSTRATUS (*c.* A.D. 170–245), "the Athenian," author of *Lives of the Sophists* and *Life of Apollonius of Tyana.*

PHIROMACHUS, a glutton named by Posidippus.

PHISION, Phasis, a river in Colchis to the east of the Euxine, rising in Caucasus; see Pliny, 6.4.

PHOCAS, East Roman usurping Emperor, 602–610.

PHOCIS, ancient country in central Greece, the greater part occupied by Parnassus range and famous for its oracle at Delphi.

PHOEMONOE, Phemonoe, mythical Greek poetess of ante-Homeric time, supposed inventor of hexameter, called a "daugher of Apollo."

PIERIUS VALERIANUS, JOH., see Valerianus.

PLACENTINUM, Placentia, modern Piacenza, on the Po, N.E. of Parma, near confluence of the Trebbia and the Po, in Italy.

PLATINA, BAPTISTA (1421–1481), Italian church historian and medical scholar, author of *De Tuenda Valetudine* and, with Apicius* Coelius, *De Re Culinaria libri X.*

POLONIANS, inhabitants of Poland.†

PONTICUS, Aquila of Pontus, who with his wife Priscilla became closely associated with St. Paul while at Corinth.

PORTA, GIAMBATTISTA della (*c.* 1540–1615), eminent Italian natural philosopher and promoter of physical science, inventor of camera obscura, his chief work *Magiae Naturalis Libri XX*, 1589 (begun 1558).

POSIDIPPUS (fl. *c.* 275 B.C.), native of Pella, his poetry contained in *Greek Anthology.*

PROBUS, MARCUS VALERIUS, Roman grammarian and critic, flourished under Nero, known chiefly for commentaries on Virgil's *Bucolics* and *Georgics.*

PUTEOLI, maritime city of Italian Campania, famous trading port, modern Pozzuoli.

RAMUSIO, GIAN BATTISTA (1485–1557), great Italian geographer, of whose *Navigationi e Viaggi* commenced in 1523, two volumes appeared in his lifetime—Vol. I in 1550, Vol. III in 1556, Vol. II not until 1559—the great compilation of travel lore being accomplished with help of many correspondents.

RHAETIA, Raetia, a district in the Swiss Alps.

RHAZES, Rhasis, Razi, Abubecker, Aboo-Bekr-Ibn-Tofail, (fl. 11–12th cent.), Arab doctor, b. in Spain, d. in Morocco, his chief work *El Hhawi* (*Le Contenant*), in the Galenic tradition of medicine.

RHEGINIO, Rhegium, Rheginus, now Reggio di Calabria, important city of Magna Graecia near southern end of Bruttian peninsula, on east side of Sicilian straits.

RHODIGIUM, ancient capital of Polesina, province of the Delta of the Po, upon the Adigetto Canal; modern Rovigo.

* Apicius was a Roman gourmet. This author needs to be distinguished from him.
† Poles were known as Polonians in the age of Topsell.

RONDELIUS, Rondoletius, Rondelet, Guillaume (1507–1566), French physician in his native city of Montpellier and naturalist, famous for his *De Piscibus marinis* (1554) as for several medical tracts.

ST. ANDREWES OF TIRE, Scottish church in parish of Tyrie, adjoining Pitsligo to south, in Aberdeenshire.

ST. JOHN, called "an island in the East Indies," perhaps Chang-Chwen (St. J.), off China coast, S.S.W. of Hongkong; Aldrovandi refers only to authority of Oriental navigators.

SALERNITANS, scholars at the medical school at Salerno, seaport, S.E. of Naples, and through Middle Ages a famous center of medical study, the earliest university in Europe.

SANCTIUS, FRANCISCUS, Francisco Sanchez (fl. 16th cent.), Italian philologist of Salamanca, author of *Commentarii in Andr. Alciati emblemata,* Louvain, 1573.

SAMMONICUS, QUINTUS SERENUS (fl. 15th cent.), Italian physician, author of versified *Liber de Medicina,* Venice, 1488, and *De re medica.*

SANTONES, ancient people of S.W. Gallia, the Celtica of Caesar, modern Saintonge, which is mostly in French Department of Charente Inferieure.

SARDIS, Sardes, ancient capital of Lydian kingdom, at north foot of Mt. Tmolus.

SARMATIA EUROPIA, country in eastern Europe, extending from the Vistula to the Don.

SAUOYE, ancient duchy, now a part of large department in France adjoining the Italian border.

SAXONY, district in N.W. Germany, in 16th cent. much enlarged.

SCALIGER, JOSEPH JUSTUS (1540–1609), 10th son of J. C. Scaliger, scholar, editor, critic of classical learning, chief work *De emendatione temporum* (1583), a study in ancient chronology.

SCALIGER, JULIUS CAESAR, (1484–1558), Spanish soldier under Emperor Maximilian, versatile scholar, poet, humanist, his chief work, *Exotericarum Exercitationum,* 1557 (many editions), an attack upon Cardan's *De Subtilitate;* also author of commentaries on Theophrastus and Aristotle, including the *Historia Animalium.*

SELEUCIA (PIERIA), Seleucis, a city of northern Syria.

SEMIRAMIS (*c.* 800 B.C.), famous Assyrian queen, her legendary history by Diodorus Siculus and others.

SEMONIDES (of Amorgus), fl. in mid-seventh cent. B.C.

SEMPRONIUS (TUDITANUS, GAIUS Sempronius), Roman consul in 129 B.C. and historian, his writings not extant.

SERENUS, see Sammonicus.

SERUIUS Maurus (or Marius) Honoratus, Roman grammarian and commentator on Virgil, fl. end of 4th cent. A.D.

SEVERUS, SULPICIUS (*c.* A.D. 363–425), native of Aquitania, Christian author of a sacred history and a life of St. Martin of Tours, whose influence directed his life of Christian devotion.

SEXTUS PLACITUS, native of Pavia, author of *Liber Medicinae Sexti Placiti Papyriensis ex Animalibus Pecoribus et Bestiis vel Avibus,* Nuremberg, 1538.

SFORTIA, GABRIEL, native of Siena, became Augustinian in 1443, d. 1457. Besides spiritual writings, author of *Comment. in libros physicorum & de anima.*

SILENUS, a native of Chios, in the Aegean, named as compiler of fabulous histories.

SIMEON SETHI (fl. 14th cent.), author of *Symeonis Magistri philosophica et medica,* Basle, 1538.

SILVATICUS, MATTHAEUS, medical author of *Opus Pandectarum Medicinae* (Mantua, 1474, and 9 further edd. by 1541).

(APOLLINARIS) SIDONIUS, CAIUS SOLLIUS (A.D. 430–488), a bishop and Latin poet, author of *Carmina* and *Epistolae.*

(THEOPHYLACTUS) SIMOCATUS (fl. *c.* A.D. 612), native of Egypt, Greek historian, author of *Questiones physicae*, Leyden, 1597.

SOLINUS, GAIUS IULIUS, (fl. 3d cent. A.D.), Latin grammarian and compiler, author of *Collectanea rerum memorabilium,* a description of curiosities.

SOMA, modern River Somme.

SPAGNIOLA, see Hispaniola.

STATIUS, PUBLIUS PAPINIUS, (*c.* A.D. 45–96), Latin poet born at Naples, author of *Silvae,* a collection of occasional verses.

STENELUS, properly Sthenelus, son of Actor, companion of Heracles, father of Comutas, who betrayed Diomedes.

STEPHANUS, Charles (1502–1550), French physician, brother of Robert, the famous lexicographer, his chief works *Praedium Rusticum* (1554), on various aspects of agriculture and medicine, and an edition of Cicero (1555).

STRABO (born *c.* 63 B.C.), Greek geographer of Amasia, in Pontus, author of *Geography,* in 17 Bks., the most important ancient work in that science.

STUMFIUS, probably Johann Stumpf, professor of medicine at Giessen, N. N.W. of Frankfurt, wrote *Dissert. de Affectibus corporis humani,* d. 1640.

STRYMON, second largest river in Macedonia and the ancient boundary of that country towards the East, famous as a haunt of cranes.

SUETONIUS (TRANQUILLUS), GAIUS (fl. *c.* A.D. 100), Roman historian and biographer of the 12 Caesars down to Domitian, in *The Lives of the Caesars.*

SUIDAS (fl. probably end 10th cent. A.D.), Greek lexicographer.

SULPITIUS, Sulpicius, see Severus.

SUSIS, SUSA, chief city in province of Susiana, on east bank of the Choaspes, a winter resort of the Achaemenid Kings and capital of Persia.

SWEUELAND, land of Sueves (Suevi, Suebi), a people of S. Germany; modern Swabia.

TANAGRAEAN, pertaining to Tanagra, town in E. Boetia.

TANGERA, German river, tributary to the Elbe, 30 miles N.E. of Magdeburg.

TAPROBANA, modern Ceylon.

TARSUS, ancient city in Cilicia, the River Cydnus flowing through it.

TARTARIA, a name vaguely designating central Asia, more particularly Turkestan.

TAURUS, a district in Cilicia, in Asia Minor, its northern limit Mt. Taurus.

TENETT, modern Thanet, an isle in N.E. Kent, in England, formed by two branches of River Stour.

THEOPHRASTUS (*c.* 372–287 B.C.), Greek scholar of Lesbos, author of *An Enquiry into Plants, On the Causes of Plants,* and, more widely known, *Ethical Characters.*

THEODORIC (*c.* 454–526), the greatest of the kings of the Ostrogoths, who ruled 475–526.

THORNAX, mountain in Greece near city of Hermione, in Argolis, later called Coccygium, from transformation of Zeus into a Cuckoo; on summit was temple, Zeus Coccygius.

THRANIAS, Tranio, the slave in Plautus' *Mostellaria.*

TOMAEUS, NICOLAUS LEONICUS (1457–1533), Italian humanist, professor at Padua, Greek scholar, translated Aristotle on natural science, wrote *Comment. in Aristotelis parva naturalis,* Basle, 1531.

TRAGUS, Hieronymus Bock, (1498–1554), German theologian and student of plants and medicine, author of *De Stirpium . . . nomenclaturis . . . commentarium libri tres,* translated from German (Strassburg, 1552) and *Dissertationes de herbarum nomenclaturis ad Brunfelsium.*

TRAIAN, MARCUS ULPIUS TRAIANUS (A.D. 52–117), Roman Emperor.

TREMITI, Diomedean Islands, off coast of ancient Apulia, in southern Adriatic, off Italian coast and N. of Mt. Gargano.

TRENT, Italian city, ancient Tridentum, modern Trento, N. of Verona.

TUGIUM, modern Turgi, N.W. of Zurich, on River Limmat.

TURNER, WILLIAM (1508?–1568), Dean of Wells, Somersetshire, England, Protestant Reformer and foremost botanist and ornithologist of the English Renaissance; see Introduction, pp. xvii, xxii–xxv, xxvii.

MAXIMUS TYRIUS, (fl. 2d cent. A.D.), Platonic philosopher, author of *Disputationes Philosophicas,* issued in Latin version by Henri Stephanus and others, 1557.

URETTA, LUIS (16th–17th cent.), Spanish Dominican, author of *Historia ecclesiastica, politica . . . de los . . . reynos de la Etiopia,* Valencia, 1610, whence Topsell drew many strange birds, and *Historia de la Sagrada Orden de Predicatores en los remotos reynos de la Etiopia,* Valencia, 1611.

URSINUS (Orsini), JOHANNES, Italian physician and poet of sixteenth century, author of *Elegiae de Peste* and *Prosopopeia animalium aliquot . . .*, both issued in Vienna, 1541.

VALERIANUS, IOAN PETRUS (1477–1558), author of *Hieroglyphica sive de sacris Aegyptiorum literis commentarii,* Basle, 1556.

VALLA, LORENZO or LAURENTIUS, (*c.* 1406–1456), Italian humanist born in Rome, author of *De Voluptate* and *De Elegantiis Linguae Latinae.*

VALOIS, ancient district of Picardy, now a small area in the departments of the Oise and the Aisne.

VARINUS (PHAVORINUS), or Guarino, learned philologist of early 16th cent., native of Camerino, a city in Italy, later in life a Benedictine Bishop of Nocera. Author of a Greek lexicon. Died 1537.

VARRO, MARCUS TERENTIUS (116–27 B.C.), Roman antiquarian and voluminous writer, author of *Rerum Rusticarum libri tres,* written at age 80.

VERBANUM, Lacus Verbanus, modern Lake Maggiore, N. Italy.

VIVES, JUAN LUIS (1492–1540), Spanish humanist and critic, native of Valencia, friend of Erasmus, author of commentary on Augustine's *De Civitate Dei* (1522).

WOTTON (or WOOTON), EDWARD (1492–1555), English physician and naturalist, attended Oxford and University of Padua, Fellow of College of Physicians, collaborated with Thomas Penny in work on insects, author of *De Differentiis Animalium,* Paris, 1552.

XANTHUS, modern River Eshen-Chai; see Licia.

XENOPHON, a Greek physician, native of Cos, reputed to have been the instrument of Agrippina in the alleged poisoning of the Emperor Claudius in Rome.

ZOROASTER, prehistoric Bactrian or Persian philosopher, founder of the national religion of Iranian people, a mystical and superhuman figure whose authorship of the sayings is not authenticated.

BIBLIOGRAPHY

Bibliography

Primary Sources

Acron, Helenius. *Psevdacronis Scholia in Horativm Vetvstiora.* Ed. Otto Keller. 2 vols. Leipzig, 1902–1904.

Aelian. *On the Nature of Animals.* Ed. A. F. Scholfield. Loeb. 3 vols. 1958–1959.

———. *Aeliani De Natura Animalium, Varia Historia, Epistolae et Fragmenta...* Ed. Rud. Hercher. Paris, 1858.

———. *Ex Aeliani Historia per Petrvm Gyllium Latini Facti . . .* Libri XVI. *De ui & natura animalium.* Lyons, 1535.

———. *Opera omnia.* Ed. Gesner. Zurich, 1556.

Aeschylus. *Tragicorum Graecorum Fragmenta.* Ed. Augustus Nauck. Leipzig, 1889 (2d ed.).

Africanus, Leo. *The History and Description of Africa.* Translated by John Pory, 1600. Ed. Robert Brown. 3 vols. Burt Franklin, n.d., New York.

Alberti, Leandro. *Descrittione di tvtta Italia...* Bologna, 1550.

Albertus. *De Animalibus Libri XXVI.* Ed. H. Stadler. 2 vols. Munster, 1916, 1920.

Alciati. *Emblemata.* Lyons, 1551.

Aldrovandi, Ulysse. *Ornithologia, hoc est de Auibus Historiae libri XII.* Bologna, 1599. Volume 2., Bks. XIII–XVIII, appeared in 1600. Volume 3, Bks. XIX–XXIV, appeared in 1603. Other printings at Frankfurt: Vol. 1, 1610; Vol. 2, 1629; Vol. 3, 1635.

Alexander, of Aphrodisaeus. See Aristotle: *Habentvr...*

———. *Problemata.* Venice, 1488.

Ambrose, Saint. *Hexaemeron.* In *Patrologiae Latinae,* 14. Ed. J. P. Migne. Paris, 1882.

Aretaeus. In *Corpus Medicorum Graecorum.* Ed. F. Hude, 11 vols. Leipzig, 1923. II.

Ariosto. *Orlando Furioso.* Translated by Sir John Harington. London, 1607.

Aristotle. *De Historia Animalium Libri IX. De Partibus Animalium . . . Libri IIII. De Generatione Animalium Libri V. Theod. Gaza interprete.* Venice, 1545.

———. *Works.* Ed. J. A. Smith, W. D. Ross, *et al.* 12 vols. Oxford, Clarendon Press. IV. *Historia Animalium.* Translated by D'Arcy W. Thompson, 1910. V. *De Partibus Animalium.* Translated by William Ogle, 1911, and *De Generatione Animalium.* Translated by Arthur Platt, 1910. VI. *Opuscula, De Mirabilibus Auscultationibus.* Translated by L. D. Dowdall, 1913.

———. *The Problemes of Aristotle.* London, 1595.

———. *Habentvr hoc volumine haec Theodoro Gaza interprete. Aristotelis de natura animalium lib. IX . . . Alexandri Aphrodisiensis problemata duobus libris.* Venice, 1488, 1504–1513.

Aristophanes. Ed. Benjamin B. Rogers. Loeb. 3 vols. 1924.

Athenaeus. *Deipnosophistae.* Ed. C. B. Gulick. Loeb. 7 vols. 1927–1941.

Augustine, Saint. *Contra litteras Pitiliani Donastistae.* In *Patrologiae Latinae,* 43. Ed. J. P. Migne. Paris, 1865.

Ausonius. Ed. H. G. Evelyn White. Loeb. 2 vols. 1919–1921.

Bartholomaeus (Anglicus). *Batman on Bartholome.* Ed. Stephen Batman. London. 1582.

Basil, Saint. *Commentarius in Isaiam Prophetam* and *Homiliae in Hexaemeron.* In *Patrologiae Graecae,* 29–30. Ed. J. P. Migne. Paris, 1886, 1888.

Belon, Pierre. *L'histoire de la Nature des Oyseaux.* Paris, 1555.

———. *Les Observations de plusieurs singularitez . . . trouuées en Grèce, Asie . . . et autres pays estranges.* Paris, 1553.

Boece, Hector. *Scotorum Historiae Prima Gentis Origine . . . Libri XIX.* Paris, 1574.

———. "The Description of Scotland." Translated by Wm. Harrison, in Holinshed, *Chronicles of England and Scotland,* 1577.

Caius, John. *De Rariorum Animalium atque Stirpium Historia.* London, 1570. (Excerpts with translation by Evans, *Turner on Birds,* pp. 192–211.)

Cardan, Girolamo. *De Subtilitate,* 1553.

"Carmen de Philomela." In *Poetae Latini Minores.* Ed. Aemilius Baehrens. 5 vols. Leipzig, 1883. V.

Cassiodorus, Magnus Aurelius. . . . *variarvm libri xii.* Augsburg, 1533.

———. In *Patrologiae Latinae,* 69–70. Ed. J. P. Migne. Paris, 1848.

Cicero. *De Divinatione.* Ed. Arthur S. Pease. University of Illinois, Urbana, 1920.

———. *De natura deorum.* Ed. H. Rackham. Loeb. 1933.

Contile, Luca. *Ragionamento di Luca Contile sopra la Propietà delle Imprese.* Pavia, 1574.

Cooper, Thomas. *Thesavrvs Lingvae Romanae & Britannicae,* . . . London, 1578.

Crotti, Elio Giulio. . . . *Opvscvla. Qvorvm catalogvm sequens pagella continet* . . . Ferrara, 1564.

Diodorus Siculus. *The Library of History.* Ed. C. H. Oldfather *et al.* Loeb. 12 vols. 1933–67.

Dionysius of Halicarnassus. *Roman Antiquities.* Ed. E. Cary. Loeb. 7 vols. 1937–1950.

Encelius, Christophorus. *De re metallica . . . libri III.* Frankfurt, 1551.

Ennius. *Remains of Old Latin.* Ed. E. H. Warmington. Loeb. 4 vols. 1935–1940. I. Ennius and Caecilius.

———. *Ennianae Poesis Reliquiae.* Ed. Iohannes Vahlen. Leipzig, 3d ed., 1928.

Euripides. Ed. A. S. Way. Loeb. 4 vols. 1912.

Eusebius. *Preparation for the Gospel.* Ed. Edwin H. Gifford. Oxford, 1903.

Eustathius. *Eustathii Commentarii ad Homeri Iliadem.* Ed. Georg Olms. 4 vols. Leipzig, 1827–30. Reprint: Hildesheim, 1960.

Festus, Sextus Pompeius. . . . *De Verborum Significatione Libri XX.* 2 vols. London, 1826.

Frederick. *The Art of Falconry: Being the De arte venandi cum avibus of Frederick II of Hohenstaufen.* Translated and edited by Casey A. Wood and F. Marjorie Fyfe. Stanford University Press, Stanford, California, 1943.

Fulgosus (or Fregoso), Battista. *De dictis factisque memorabilibus collectanea a Cammillo Gilino latina facta,* 1509.

———. *Factorum Dictorvmque memorabilium Libri IX.* Paris, 1578.

Gellius. *Attic Nights.* Ed. J. C. Rolfe. Loeb. 3 vols. 1927.

Gerard, John. *The herball.* London, 1597.

Gesner, Conrad. *Historiae Animalium.* Book III. *De avium natura.* Zurich, 1555.

Giovio (Jovius), Paolo. *Elogia Doctorum Virorum.* Translated by Florence A. Gragg, *An Italian Portrait Gallery.* Boston, 1935.

Gregory, Saint, Bishop of Nyssa. *Opera quae reperiri potuerunt omnia.* In *Patrologiae Graecae,* 44–46. Ed. J. P. Migne. Paris, 1863.

Hakluyt, Richard. *The principal navigations, voiages and discoueries of the English nation.* 3 vols. London, 1598–1600.

Hesiod. *Hesiod, Homeric Hymns and Homerica.* Ed. H. G. Evelyn-White. Loeb. 1936.

Homer, *Iliad.* Ed. A. T. Murray. Loeb. 2 vols. 1934–1937.

———. *Odyssey.* Ibid. 2 vols. 1934–1937.

Horace. *Satires, Epistles, Ars Poetica.* Ed. H. R. Fairclough. Loeb. 1926.

Horapollo. *Hori Apollinis Niliaci Hieroglyphica.* Lyons, 1621.

Isidorus Hispalensis. *Etymologiarum Lib. ix.* In *Patrologiae Latinae,* 82. Ed. J. P. Migne. Paris, 1850.

Liberalis, Antoninus. *Transformationum congeries.* Amsterdam, 1674.

Longolius, Gybertus. *Dialogus de auibus et earum nominibus graecis, latinis et germanicis, non minus festivus quam eruditus, et ad intelligendas poetas utilis* . . . Ed. William Turner. Cologne, 1544.

Lucian. Ed. A. M. Harmon *et al.* Loeb. 8 vols. 1913–1967.

Mantuanus, Baptista. *De Calamitatibus Temporum, Libri Tres.* Ed. Wessels. Rome, 1916.

———. *Trophaei Francisci Gonzagae,* in *Opera omnia.* Antwerp, 1576. III.

Martial. *Epigrams.* Ed. W. C. A. Ker. Loeb. 2 vols. 1930.

Martyr, Peter. *De Orbe Novo Petri Martyris Anglerii . . . Decades octo . . . Labore . . . Richardi Haklvyti . . .* Paris, 1587.

———. *De Nouo Orbe, or the Historie of the west Indies . . . Comprised in eight Decades. . . . Whereof three, haue beene formerly translated into English, by R. Eden, whereunto the other fiue, are newly added by . . . M. Lok.* London, 1612.

Moffet, Thomas. *Insectorum . . . theatrum.* London, 1634.

———. *The theater of insects.* Translated by John Rowland. London, 1658. (Topsell on Beasts and on Serpents included.)

Nemesian. In *Minor Latin Poets.* Ed. J. Wight Duff and Arnold M. Duff. Loeb. 1934.

Nicostratus. In *Comicorum atticorum fragmenta.* Ed. T. Kock. 2 vols. Leipzig, 1884. II.

Nonius. *De Compendiosa Doctrina.* Ed. Wallace A. Lindsay. 3 vols. Leipzig, 1903. (Also in N. Perottus, *Cornvcopiae,* Basle, 1532.)

Odoric. "The Journal of Friar Odoric." In *The Travels of Sir John Mandeville.* Ed. A. W. Pollard. London, 1900. (Odoric text from Hakluyt, *The Second Volume of the Principal Navigations,* 1599. Also in Ramusio, II, fols. 245v–253.)

Olaus Magnus. *Historia de gentibus septentrionalibus.* Rome, 1555.

Oppian. *Eutecnii Sophistae Paraphrasis Oppiani vel potius Dionysii Librorum de Aucupio, Interprete Conrado Gesnero.* Zurich, 1776.

———. *De Aucupio.* In *Poetae Bucoli et Didactici.* Ed. F. L. Lehrs, *et al.* Paris, 1862.

———. *Cynegetica* and *Halieutica.* In *Colluthus Tryphiodorus.* Ed. A. W. Mair. Loeb. 1928.

Ovid. *Metamorphoses.* Ed. F. J. Miller. Loeb. 2 vols. 1958–1960.

———. *Tristia and Ex Ponto.* Ed. A. L. Wheeler. Loeb. 1924.

Oviedo, Gonzalo Fernando. *Sommario . . . della sua Historia naturale & generale, dell' India occidentali, . . .* 1526.
———. *Historia general y natural de las Indias.* Salamanca, 1535.

Paulinus, Saint, Bishop of Nola. *Opera omnia.* In *Patrologiae Latinae,* 61. Ed. J. P. Migne. Paris, 1861.
Pausanias. *Description of Greece.* Ed. W. H. S. Jones. Loeb. 5 vols. 1918–1935.
Perottus, N. *Cornvcopiae.* Venice, 1513; Basle, 1532.
Petrarch. *De remediis utriusque Fortunae libri duo.* Bern, 1605.
Philostratus. *Historiae de vita Apollonii Tyanei Octo.* Paris, 1555.
———. *The Life of Apollonius of Tyana.* Ed. F. C. Conybeare. Loeb. 2 vols. 1912.
Pindar. *The Olympian and Pythian Odes.* Ed. Basil L. Gildersleeve. New York, 1885.
Platina, Bartholomaeus. *De re Culinaria Libri Decem.* Lyons, 1541.
Plato. *Scholia Platonica.* Ed. Guilielmus C. Greene. Haverford, Pa., 1938.
———. *Republic.* Ed. Paul Shorey. Loeb. 2 vols. 1930–1935.
Plautus. Ed. Paul Nixon. Loeb. 5 vols. 1916–1938.
Pliny. *Natural History.* Ed. H. Rackham and W. H. S. Jones. Loeb. 10 vols. 1938–62.
Plutarch. *Moralia.* Ed. Frank C. Babbitt. Loeb. 14 vols. 1927.
———. *The Parallel Lives.* Ed. B. Perrin. Loeb. 11 vols. 1914.
Porta, G. B. della. *Phytognomonica . . . octo libris contenta.* Frankfurt, 1591.

Ramusio, Giovanni B. *Navigationi et Viaggi.* 3 vols. Venice. Of relevant authors Vol. I (1550, 1554, 1563, 1587) contains Leo Africanus and Francesco Alvarez, on Africa; Vol. II (1558, 1573, 1583, 1606) the travels of Marco Polo and of Friar Odoric (latter added in 1573); Volume III (1556, 1565, 1606) Peter Martyr and Oviedo on the West Indies and (added to 1606 ed.) de Veer on Nova Zembla, among other lands.
Ray, John. *The Ornithology of Francis Willughby.* London, 1678.
Reusner, Nicolaus. *Emblemata . . . Partim Ethica, et Physica, Partim vero Historica, & Hieroglyphica.* Frankfurt, 1581.

Scaliger, J. C. *Exotericarum Exercitationum.* Frankfurt, 1592.
———. *Ivlii Caesaris Scaligeri viri Clarissimi Poemata in duas partes diuisa.* Heidelberg, 1591.
Serenus. In *Corpus Medicorum Latinorum.* 5 vols. Leipzig. II, 1916. Ed. Fridericus Vollmer.
Sidonius. In *Epigrammatum anthologia palatina . . . veterum ex libris et marmoribus ductorum . . .* Ed. Fred. Dübner. 2 vols. Paris, 1864–1872.
Smyrnaeus, Quintus. *The Fall of Troy.* Ed. Arthur S. Way. Loeb. 1913.
Strabo. *Geography.* Ed. Horace S. Jones. Loeb. 8 vols. 1917–1932.

Strabus, Walafridus. *Glossa Ordinaria*, in Migne, *Patrologiae Latinae*, vols. 113–114. Paris, 1879.
Suidas. *Lexicon*. Ed. F. Bekkerus. Berlin, 1854.
Sylvius, Aeneas (Pius II). *Opera quae extant omnia*. Basle, 1561.

Theocritus. In *The Greek Bucolic Poets*. Ed. J. M. Edmonds. Loeb. 1912.
Theophrastus. *Enquiry into Plants*. Ed. Sir Arthur Hort. Loeb. 2 vols. 1916.
———. *De Causis Plantarum. Book One*. Ed. Robert E. Dengler. University of Pennsylvania, Philadelphia, 1927.
———. *Theophrasti Opera . . . Omnia*. Ed. F. Wimmer. Paris, 1866.
Topsell, Edward. *The historie of fovr-footed beastes* . . . London, 1607.
———. *The historie of serpents* . . . London, 1608 (both also with Moffet on Insects, ed. Rowland. London, 1658. A facsimile of this text is: *The History of Four-Footed Beasts and Serpents and Insects* . . . with a New Introduction by Willy Ley. 3 vols. New York, Da Capo Press, 1967.).
Turner, William. *Avivm Praecipvarvm, apvd Plinivm et Aristotelem mentio est, breuis & succincta historia*. Cologne, 1544.
———. *Turner on Birds*. Translated by A. H. Evans. Cambridge University Press, 1903.

Uretta, Luis de. *Historia Eclesiastica Politica, Natural, y Moral de los Grandes Remotos Reynos de la Etiopia*, . . . Valencia, 1610.
Ursinus, Ioannes. *Prosopopeia Animalivm Aliquot*. Vienna, 1541.

Valerianus. *Ioannis Pierii Valeriani Bellvnensis Hieroglyphica*. Lyons, 1626.
Varro, M. Terentius. *Rervm Rvsticarvm Libri Tres*. Ed. Henricus Keil. Leipzig, 1889.
———. Ed. W. D. Hoope. Revised H. B. Ash. Loeb. 1936.
Veer, Gerrit de. *Diarivm navticum, seu Vera descriptio trium navigationum admirandum*. Amsterdam, 1598. Also in Ramusio, III, 1606.
———. *A True Description of Three Voyages by the Northeast towards Cathay and China*. Hakluyt Soc. Publication XIII (1853), 79–81.
Virgil. Ed. H. R. Fairclough. Loeb. 2 vols. 1916–1918.

Wotton, Edward. . . . *De Differentiis Animalium Libri Decem*. Paris, 1552.

Secondary Sources

Allen, Elsa G. "The History of American Ornithology before Audubon." *Transactions of the American Philosophical Society*, n.s., XLI (1951), 386–591.
Arber, Edward. *A Transcript of the Registers of the Company of Stationers of London*. 5 vols. London, 1875–77.

Birch, Thomas. *An Historical View of the Negotiations between . . . England, France, and Brussels, from . . . 1592 to 1617.* London, 1749.
Byrne, M. St. Clare. *The Elizabethan Zoo.* London, 1926.

Christy, Bayard H. "Topsell's 'Fowles of Heaven.'" *Auk*, n.s., L (1933), 275–283.

Fisher, James. *A History of Birds.* Boston, 1954.

Greg, Walter W. *Licensers for the Press, &c. to 1640.* The Oxford Bibliographical Society, Oxford, 1962.

Harrison, Thomas P. *They Tell of Birds: Chaucer, Spenser, Milton, Drayton.* University of Texas Press, Austin, 1956.
———. *John White and Edward Topsell: The First Water Colors of North American Birds.* University of Texas Press, Austin, 1964. Rev. *Times Literary Supplement,* March 11 and April 1, 1965.
———. "Longolius on Birds," *Annals of Science,* XIV (1958), 257–268.
———. "Phoenix Redivivus," *Isis,* LI (1960), 173–180.
Heltzel, Virgil B. "New Light on Edward Topsell," *Huntington Library Quarterly,* I (1938), 199–202.
Heron-Allen, Edward. *Barnacles in Nature and Myth.* London, 1928.
Hulton, Paul, and Quinn, David B. *The American Drawings of John White.* 2 vols. The Trustees of the British Museum, London, and The University of North Carolina Press, Chapel Hill. I. A. Catalogue Raisonné and a Study of the Artist. II. Plates in Colour Facsimile and Monochrome.

Jackson, William A. *Records of the Court of the Stationers' Company, 1602 to 1640.* The Bibliographical Society, London, 1957.

Lind, M. L. *Aldrovandi on Chickens.* University of Oklahoma Press, Norman, 1963.

Macleod, R. D. *Key to the Names of British Birds.* London, 1954.
Miall, L. C. *The Early Naturalists: Their Lives and Work (1530–1789).* London, 1912.
Murphy, Robert. *The Oceanic Birds of South America.* 2 vols. The Macmillan Company and the American Museum of Natural History. New York, 1936.

Newton, Alfred. *A Dictionary of Birds.* London, 1893–1896.

Peile, John. *Biographical Register of Christ's College, 1505–1905.* 2 vols. Cambridge University Press, 1910–1913.

Quinn, David B. *The Roanoke Voyages, 1584–1590. Documents to Illustrate the English Voyages to North America Under the Patent Granted to Walter Raleigh in 1584.* Hakluyt Society, 2d ser. CIV. 2 vols. London, 1952, 1955.

Raven, Charles E. *English Naturalists from Neckam to Ray.* Cambridge, 1947.
———. *John Ray, Naturalist.* Cambridge University Press, 1950.

Sabin, Joseph. *A Dictionary of Books relating to America.* 29 vols. Amsterdam, 1961–1962.

Sarton, George. *An Appreciation of Ancient and Medieval Science During the Renaissance.* University of Pennsylvania Press, Philadelphia, 1955.

Swainson, Charles. *Provincial Names and Folk Lore of British Birds.* London, 1885.

Swann, H. Kirke. *A Dictionary of English and Folk-Names of British Birds.* London, 1913.

Thompson, D'Arcy W. *A Glossary of Greek Birds.* Oxford, Clarendon Press, 1895.

Thorndike, Lynn. *A History of Magic and Experimental Science.* 8 vols. New York, 1923–1941.

Tilley, M. P. *A Dictionary of the Proverbs in England in the Sixteenth and Seventeenth Centuries.* University of Michigan Press, Ann Arbor, 1950.

Venn, J. A. *Alumni Cantabrigiensis.* Cambridge, 1927.

Wightman, W. P. D. *Science and the Renaissance.* 2 vols. Edinburgh and London, 1962.

Witherby, H. F., et al. *The Handbook of British Birds.* 5 vols. London, 1952 (7th edition).